HEALTH
for Christian Schools®

Anna Turner
David Rhodes

BOB JONES UNIVERSITY PRESS
Greenville, South Carolina 29614

NOTE:
The fact that materials produced by other publishers are referred to in this volume does not constitute an endorsement by Bob Jones University Press of the content or theological position of materials produced by such publishers. The position of Bob Jones University Press, and the University itself, is well known. Any references and ancillary materials are listed as an aid to the student or the teacher and in an attempt to maintain the accepted academic standards of the publishing industry.

HEALTH for Christian Schools®

Anna Sumabat Turner
David Rhodes

Produced in cooperation with the Bob Jones University College of Arts and Science, the School of Religion, and Bob Jones Academy.

ISBN 0-89084-756-8

15   14   13   12   11   10   9   8   7   6   5   4   3   2

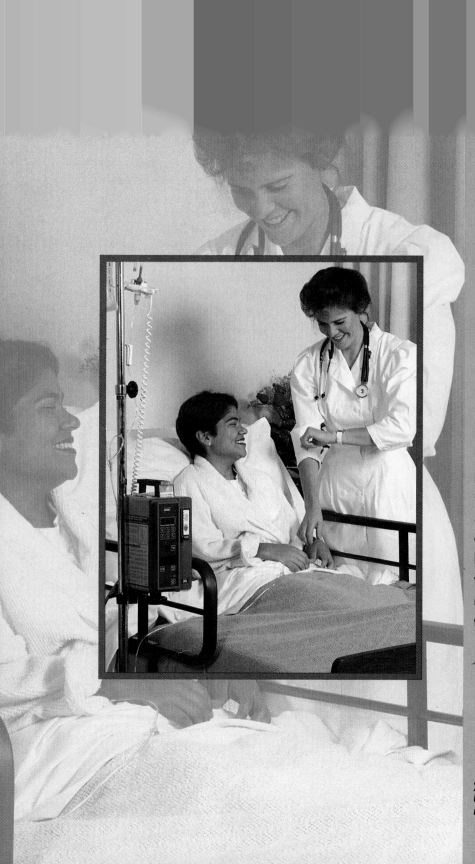

When you hear the word *temple*, you may think of Solomon's temple or picture a large building where people worship and sacrifice. However, a temple is any place where God chooses to dwell. If you are a Christian, God the Holy Spirit dwells in your body, making you a living, breathing temple. Christians have the unique opportunity to serve God by being caretakers of their bodies. A Bible-based view of health care makes the Christian a fit servant.

"What? know ye not that your body is the temple of the Holy Ghost . . . , and ye are not your own?"
I Corinthians 6:19

THE BODY, A TEMPLE OF GOD

Once King Solomon began building the temple it took seven years to complete. During this time God was concerned with every aspect of its construction. A detailed record in the Old Testament includes everything from the exact dimensions to the building materials and the furnishings. The maintenance of the temple was also important to God. He set aside an entire tribe, the tribe of Levi, to minister as priests and to maintain the temple.

God is just as concerned with your temple today as He was with the temple Solomon built. He has given you the responsibility to build and maintain it. Unfortunately, some Christians do not take this responsibility very seriously. Some abuse their temples by establishing bad habits, and others simply neglect their temples, assuming that everything will keep working properly. The practice of good health habits is not a major value to many Christians. **Values** are those things you believe to be important. They are the basis for your actions and your goals.

Some Christians, however, are discovering that building up and caring for their temples is an exciting and challenging activity. They are selecting better foods, avoiding bad habits, and beginning regular exercise programs. As their temples improve, they find that they look better, feel better, work better, and are able to serve God better.

The choice is yours. What type of temple do you want? You are the only one who can make that decision. For instance, your parents may try to help you by insisting that you brush your teeth. But few parents have the time to supervise how you brush or the patience to remind you to brush. If you want clean, healthy teeth, you must cultivate the habit of brushing them regularly and correctly on your own. You must set your own **standards** or levels of attainment. Your standards will be based on your values. If you think that something is important (of value), you act upon it. Your limits of acceptability (standards) determine how much action or the quality of action you are willing to exert.

Your teacher and this textbook can also help you to improve your temple by giving you useful ideas for staying healthy. However, knowing the best information available on health will not make you any healthier. To be healthier you must take the information and use it to develop good health practices. If you follow good health practices, you will be the one who benefits. But if you choose to ignore good health practices, you will be the one who suffers.

There is one other important fact that you must remember about your temple. Your temple does not belong to you; it belongs to God. God allows you to use and care for it, but it is His. First Corinthians 4:1 states that we are stewards. A steward is a trusted servant. **Stewardship** means that you have the responsibility to manage your master's goods. Not only will you reap the results of how you treat your temple, but you will also answer to God for the way you take care of it.

This may sound like an awesome responsibility, but it is also an exciting opportunity. Just as Solomon had the unique opportunity to construct and furnish the magnificent Old Testament temple, you have a chance to build and care for an even more magnificent temple. Determine today that your temple will be one that you and your Lord can be proud of.

Section Review

1. What is meant by the word *temple* as it is used in the Bible and in this chapter?

2. Who was to maintain the Old Testament temple? Who is responsible to take care of the New Testament's temple of the Holy Spirit?

3. Does God's concern for His temple have any implications for us today?

4. According to the Scripture passage at the beginning of this lesson, in what two ways are you to glorify God?

A CHRISTIAN VIEW OF HEALTH

Almost everyone is interested in health. There are hundreds of books and magazines that give all kinds of health information. Since many of these sources are not written by Christians, it is important to know the difference between how a non-Christian views health and how a Christian should view health. The next few sections will discuss some of these differences.

Health Should Glorify God

Everything a Christian does should be glorifying to God. Of course, this includes efforts to be healthy. It has been established that if you are a Christian, your body is the temple of the Holy Spirit. Because of this you should do your best to keep your temple in good condition.

Many people in the world do not believe that the purpose of man is to glorify God. Instead, they believe that man's purpose is to promote and glorify himself. This religion, which worships man, is called **humanism.** Because humanists worship man, they see health as a way to make man more godlike. To the humanist, health is far more important than any preparation for life after death.

In contrast, the Christian views health as a means of glorifying God and is more concerned about eternal than temporal matters. At times, he may glorify God through a willingness to risk his health. For example, God may lead a missionary to go to a country that does not have good health

Serving God as Patch the Pirate: A Profile of Ron Hamilton

Ron Hamilton grew up in a family that loved to sing at home, in church, or in the car while traveling. Even as a child Ron loved music and later studied it at Bob Jones University.

Ron was saved at the age of five and surrendered his life for God's use during the summer of 1970 when he was sixteen years old. The Lord used Ron's talents to produce Bible-based music such as "It Is Finished," and the cantatas *Born to Die, The Centurion,* and *The Greatest Gift.* In 1977 God opened new areas for service as Ron traveled with a preaching, lecture, and music program called the Symphony of Life Seminars.

During a routine eye examination, a doctor found a small spot in Ron's left eye. Ron was sent to a surgeon who told him that the problem might be minor or that it might be cancer. Ron went into surgery content for God's will to be done. He later said, "When I woke up, I realized that my left eye was gone, but I also was very aware that God's peace had come to take its place." The seeming tragedy was turned into a blessing. Ron soon wrote his inspiring song " O Rejoice in the Lord." He began another phase of musical ministry by becoming Patch the

Ron Hamilton as Patch the Pirate

Pirate. His children's music, recordings, and Patch the Pirate clubs have been a blessing to children and adults around the world. Ron was able to take adversity and turn it into an opportunity to serve and glorify the Lord.

O Rejoice in the Lord *by Ron Hamilton*
© 1978 Majesty Music. Used by permission.

God never moves without purpose or plan
When trying His servant and molding a man.
Give thanks to the Lord though your testing
    seems long;
In darkness He giveth a song.

I could not see through the shadows ahead;
So I looked at the cross of my Savior instead.
I bowed to the will of the Master that day
Then peace came and tears fled away.

Now I can see testing comes from above;
God strengthens His children and purges in love.
My Father knows best, and I trust in His care;
Through purging, more fruit I will bear.

O rejoice in the Lord,
He makes no mistake.
He knoweth the end of each path that I take.
For when I am tried and purified,
I shall come forth as gold.

conditions. In spite of the danger to his health, he accepts the poor conditions because he wants to obey and glorify God. Although a missionary may face a greater risk of death and disease than other Christians, he is still responsible to God for his health. He must do his best to protect the temple of God within the circumstances in which God has placed him.

God can use even poor health to glorify Himself. There are several examples of this in the Bible. In the Old Testament we read of Job, a servant of God, who enjoyed many blessings. Yet God allowed Job to experience poor health to bring glory to Himself. Then in John 9, the Scriptures tell us of Jesus meeting a man who had been born blind. When the disciples saw him, they became judgmental and asked, "Who did sin, this man, or his parents, that he was born blind?" (v. 2). However, Christ responded, "Neither hath this man sinned, nor his parents: but that the works of God should be made manifest in him" (v. 3). As Christians we

need to be careful not to judge other people's health problems. Only God knows whether the problems they face are the result of sin or occur to bring Him glory.

Sin's Effect on Health

Many people in the world do not recognize sin or its consequences. This perception contradicts what the Bible says. There are at least two ways that poor health can be the direct result of sin. First, poor health can be the natural result of a lifestyle that does not glorify Christ. If a Christian chooses to smoke, certain effects will follow naturally. Health experts tell us that smoking is the single most preventable cause of death and disease in the United States today. When a Christian smokes, he is subjecting himself to the harmful effects of smoking. The same can be said of the Christian who drinks alcohol, uses harmful drugs, chooses not to exercise, or overeats habitually.

Second, poor health can be the result of God's judgment and not the result of poor health habits. An example of this is given in I Corinthians 11. This chapter tells how some of the Corinthian believers were abusing the Lord's Supper (Communion). "For this cause many are weak and sickly among you, and many sleep" (v. 30). God sent poor health as a judgment for their sin. Although not all sickness is caused by sin, it is clear that sickness and death may be sent from God as a punishment for sin.

Health in God's Hands

Although the things you do can have a great effect on your health, in the end your health is in God's hands. You can do everything humanly possible to protect your health and still get sick. God can also protect you and even heal you, if that is His will.

Most Christians take their health for granted. Since God gives you your health, you should thank Him for it. First Thessalonians 5:18 says, "In everything give thanks: for this is the will of God in Christ Jesus concerning you."

How long has it been since you thanked God for your health? If God gives you good health, you should thank Him for a healthy mind and body. If God allows you to experience poor health, you should thank Him for it (Rom. 8:28) and seek to know what God is trying to accomplish through your illness.

THE IMPORTANCE OF A CHRISTIAN VIEW

As you learn about health and practice good health habits, it is essential to keep these Christian perspectives in mind. Health is important, but it must not be the most important thing in your life. A proper balance must be maintained. You cannot let health become the focus of your life, nor can you choose to ignore or abuse it. Good health can be one of your greatest assets for serving God.

There are many areas of health that a Christian will view differently from the world. You will learn more about these as you continue through this book. Do your best to see these health areas as God sees them.

Section Review

1. What is humanism?

2. What are some characteristics that distinguish a Christian view of health from a non-Christian view?

3. What are two ways that sin can cause poor health?

CHAPTER REVIEW

Terms

temple	stewardship
values	humanism
standards	

Content Questions

1. Explain what the concept of stewardship has to do with health.

2. Is humanism acceptable to a Christian? Give a scriptural reason for your answer.

3. Why is attaining and maintaining optimum health your responsibility?

Application Questions

1. To what extent do your parents' values affect your health? Give two examples.

2. List at least six of your health values. Analyze whether your motives are to promote self or God.

3. Examine your health standards. What are your levels of acceptability in the following dimensions of health: physical health—nutrition, weight, fitness; spiritual health—devotions, church attendance, witnessing?

Monday April 25 2005

IN SERVICE

Medical Missionaries

Job Description: Medical missionaries are doctors, dentists, nurses, technicians, physiotherapists, and other paramedical people who are called by God to provide health care and spiritual guidance to their patients and community. Although all Christian physicians, nurses, and technicians may have opportunities to witness and minister to the spiritual needs of their patients, medical missionaries serve with the distinct goal of using their expertise to open opportunities for witnessing.

After all, medical missions obeys the commands of Christ (Matthew 10:7-8) and follows the example that the Lord set while He was here on earth. Priorities should be kept in the right order—the spiritual before the physical.

Job Location: Medical missionaries usually serve in poor, underdeveloped areas with inadequate or no medical facilities. Many hazards face health care workers (back injury, exposure to radiation and chemicals, hazards from compressed

gases, shock from electrical equipment). However, the medical missionary must also face the dangers of unstable political climates, lack of resources, loneliness, and spiritual attacks. Physical, emotional, and spiritual stamina are mandatory for medical missionaries. Medical missionaries must have the special calling and provision of God in order to succeed in their work. However, God never calls His servant without making provision for him.

Training Required: A candidate must graduate from an approved medical school or approved training program for nurses or technicians, pass national examinations, and obtain a license in his field. He should have training in biblical studies, theology, counseling, and teaching methods. He may need additional work in foreign language, cultural and social studies, and tropical medicine.

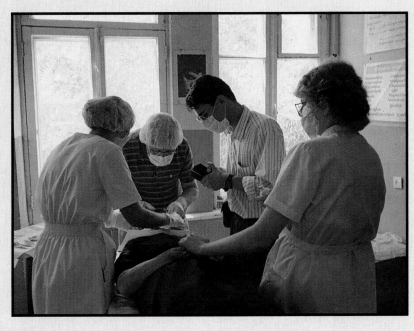

UNIT

1

Protecting
Your
Temple

Unit I Objectives

Introduction
- Determine personal health values and evaluate whether they are self-promoting or God-honoring.
- Distinguish between biblical views and unbiblical views of health.

Chapter 1—Basic Health Facts
- Differentiate between the five components of health.
- Describe how to improve health through wise management in the four major health factors.
- Evaluate health information in terms of reliability.
- Explain the importance of self-discipline in upholding values, standards, and goals.
- Establish health goals and begin working on them.

Chapter 2—Body Basics
- Differentiate between the anatomical components: cells, tissues, organs, and body systems.
- Identify the major functions and locations of the components of each of the main body systems.
- Recognize the characteristics of the major components within the main body systems.
- Describe how the various systems work together.
- Trace the routes of oxygen through the respiratory system, blood through the circulatory system, and food through the digestive and excretory systems.

Chapter 3—Mental and Emotional Health
- Discuss how the mind and will affect emotions.
- Explain why it is more important for a Christian to have a godly self-concept than a good self-concept.
- Follow a defined thinking process when making decisions.
- Identify how to handle stressors and to deal with anxiety biblically.
- Differentiate between the common definition of maturity and a Christian's definition of maturity.

Chapter 4—Social Health
- Identify the three obligations you have in your relationship with your parents.
- Define *sibling rivalry* and identify causes and the best solution for it.
- Determine standards for choosing friends.
- Explain how cliques and prejudice are unhealthy for a Christian.
- Establish dating standards within guidelines established by God, parents, school, and government.

Chapter 5—Nutrition
- Explain why people with abundant food resources can still suffer malnutrition.
- Identify the functions of water, carbohydrates, protein, fat, vitamins, and minerals in the body.
- Give a proper recommendation for daily water intake.
- List the recommended servings of each basic food group that a teen-ager should consume per day.
- Promote six guidelines for good eating habits.

Chapter 6—Exercise
- Explain the importance of specificity, intensity, duration, and frequency in a successful exercise program.
- Describe how to measure cardiorespiratory fitness, recognize the importance of target heart rate, and describe how to figure your own target heart rate.
- List five components of physical fitness.
- Identify ways to rest the body while continuing activity.
- Discuss benefits of exercise.

BASIC HEALTH FACTS

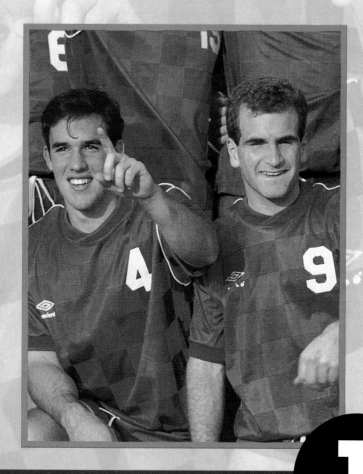

When asked, "How are you today?" you probably respond automatically with, "Fine, thank you!" But are you really fine? You might have a headache, be angry with your best friend, and not have had your devotions for over a month. Can you be considered fine with all these problems? It depends on your definition of *fine*. If you mean that you feel fine, your answer may be correct. But if you mean you are in fine health, your answer may be very wrong.

CHAPTER 1

"Beloved, I wish above all things that thou mayest prosper and be in health, even as thy soul prospereth."
III John 2

After Spring Break ☺

What is health? Some people think of health as the absence of disease. Others think of health as living a long time. While both of these ideas are included in a definition of health, health is more than not being sick or living a long time. **Health** is the process of attaining spiritual, physical, mental, emotional, and social well-being.

COMPONENTS OF HEALTH

Health is divided into at least five components: spiritual, physical, mental, emotional, and social. While it is useful to study these areas separately, it is important to remember that they cannot be separated completely.

Spiritual Health

Yielding Yourself to God—The most important part of your health is your spiritual health. "For what shall it profit a man, if he shall gain the whole world, and lose his own soul?" (Mark 8:36). There is nothing in this world as important as yielding yourself to God. Everything else lasts only for the short time you live on this earth. Your spiritual health affects you for eternity.

Spiritual health begins when you receive Jesus Christ as your personal Savior. Nicodemus, a wealthy and influential Jew, came to Christ by night to inquire about his own spiritual health. Christ told Nicodemus that there was only one solution to his problem: "Ye must be born again" (John 3:7). What Christ told Nicodemus applies to everyone today. There is no remedy for those who are spiritually dead except to be born again.

Once you have been born again, you can progress to greater spiritual health. Studying God's Word, applying its principles to your life, fellowshipping with God in prayer, and uniting with other believers in worship are examples of things you should do. As you incorporate these practices into your life, you will become a stronger, more mature Christian. To be spiritually mature and holy should be the goal for spiritual health.

Physical Health

Maintaining Your Body—Physical health deals with your overall physical condition. It includes such things as the ability of your body to resist infection, to complete daily tasks, and to participate in strenuous activities. By establishing habits that improve your physical health, you can increase your energy level, sharpen your alertness, improve your muscle tone, resist infection, and reduce extra body fat. Because you are the steward, God's trusted servant, you should want to do what is best to maintain your temple.

Physical fitness takes work. A Christian's goal should reflect the concept of being fit to serve.

Mental Health

Evaluating Information—Many people today are mentally lazy. They would rather watch a worthless television program than read a good book. Thinking is a labor that many avoid because it is difficult. It takes effort and work to learn to analyze and develop creative ideas. In II Corinthians 10:5 the Apostle Paul admonishes, "Cast . . . down imaginations, and every high thing that exalteth itself against the knowledge of God, and bring . . . into captivity every thought to the obedience of Christ." You cannot reason or evaluate accurately without learning and understanding what God's Word teaches. Mental health requires discipline in the things you think about.

Emotional Health

Controlling Reactions—Your emotional health deals with your responses. It includes feelings such as anger, hate, love, and joy. To be emotionally healthy you should be satisfied with the life and conditions the Lord has given you. A Christian realizes that God is in control of the circumstances and looks past the situation to see what God is accomplishing. Good spiritual and emotional health will produce satisfaction and peace.

Social Health

Getting Along with Others—It is a Christian's responsibility to develop sound relationships. A sound relationship is one that is free from moral defect and worthy of confidence. Social health does not focus merely on a few friendships. Social health includes getting along with parents, **siblings** (SIB lings; brothers and sisters), **peers** (people of equal standing in age, class, or rank), friends, and acquaintances.

Components Work Together

Each component of health (spiritual, physical, mental, emotional, and social) has a great influence on your body's total health. Much of this influence results from the fact that each component can affect every other component. For example, if you break an arm (physical), you might become frustrated and

angry (emotional) because you cannot play your clarinet and will have to miss the upcoming band trip. As the day of the band's departure approaches, your frustration may continue to build and you may become argumentative (social). Finally, you may be so upset that you blame God and find that you cannot pray effectively (spiritual). It is easy to see how problems or benefits in one area of health often affect another. In all areas of life, keep your focus on Christ and not on people, situations, or circumstances.

Section Review

1. Is the best definition of health "not getting sick"? Support your answer.
2. What are the five components of health and how do they differ?
3. What is the difference between siblings and peers?

Pictures of Health: Caleb and Moses

Both Caleb and Moses are examples of men who enjoyed full and healthy lives in God's service. When Caleb was forty years old, he was already a leader among his people and was chosen to be one of the twelve spies who searched the Promised Land. The Israelites refused to believe Caleb's report of faith and would not enter the land God had promised them. Caleb wandered with the Israelites in the wilderness for the next forty years. He was among the Israelites who fought for five years to conquer the land of Canaan. When the time came to divide the land, Caleb was eighty-five years old. He was still a strong and healthy warrior. In Joshua 14 Caleb said that he was just as strong at eighty-five as he had been at forty years of age. Instead of retiring to a life of rest and safety, Caleb volunteered to fight against some of the most feared enemies of Israel. God used Caleb throughout his life. He was an example of fitness for service.

Moses was about eighty years old when God called him to deliver the children of Israel from Egypt. Moses was greatly used of God in opposing Pharaoh and leading God's people. Because of a sin, Moses was not permitted to enter the Promised Land and died when he was 120 years old. Deuteronomy 34:7 says that "his eye was not dim, nor his natural force abated."

LEVELS OF HEALTH

Your health is constantly changing. You may be in good health today and be in poor health tomorrow. You may be thirty pounds too heavy today yet be exactly the right weight by next year.

You can compare your health to an elevator. Inside the "health elevator," you can control not only which direction you want to travel but also how far you want to go. Remember that wherever you are now, you can be on a different level tomorrow.

Whether your health changes for better or for worse depends on what you do today. Sometimes these changes can occur quickly. For example, if you are in a serious automobile accident your health may change instantly. However, most changes in health occur slowly. If you make a decision today to improve your physical condition, you will not wake up totally fit tomorrow. It will take several months of hard work and a lot of determination to reach a higher level.

FACTORS THAT DETERMINE YOUR HEALTH

There are many things that play an important role in your health. What you eat, the air you breathe, the thoughts you think, and thousands of other things are all factors in determining how healthy you are. Most of these factors can be placed into four basic categories: your lifestyle, your environment, your heredity, and the health care you receive.

Lifestyle

God has placed in your control an important factor affecting your health. Your **lifestyle,** the way you live, will influence your health more than any other factor. Since it includes such areas as your habits and attitudes, it is your responsibility to make choices that will fortify your body as the temple of the Holy Spirit. Unfortunately, many people do not have lifestyles that will make them healthier. They allow poor health habits such as too little exercise, poor nutrition, too much stress, and the use of alcoholic beverages and tobacco products to come into their lives and rob them of their health. These five poor health habits alone cause about eighty percent of the disease and disability in the United States today.

Environment

Environment is the combination of conditions that surround an individual. Your environment is made up of such things as the air you breathe, the water you drink, and the home you live in. As a young person you have very little control over your environment. For instance, you probably have little say about the kind of house you live in. But there are some things (such as cleaning your room or sitting in a nonsmoking section at a restaurant) that you can do to improve your surroundings. As you get older and become more independent, you will have more control over your environment, but some aspects of your environment you may never be able to change.

Heredity

Heredity is the set of characteristics transmitted to an individual from his parents. These characteristics are determined by your genes. There is little you can do about the genes that you inherited from your parents. However, you can be aware of disorders that may be common to your family and do your best to reduce their effects on your health. Some problems are inherited directly (muscular dystrophy, colorblindness, hemophilia, etc.); you can do little to reduce their effects. In these cases you must learn to be content with the way God has made you and do your best with what you have.

Other disorders may not be directly inherited from your parents, but you may inherit a predisposition for them. A **predisposition** (PREE dis poh

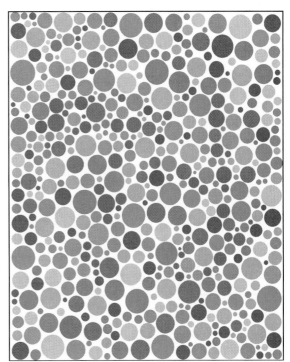

People with red-green colorblindness would not be able to see the number in this box. Most colorblind people can still see some colors. Only one person in 40,000 views the world in black and white.

ZISH ehn) is a tendency or inclination toward a certain condition. Heart disease, diabetes, and obesity are disorders for which you may inherit a predisposition. If you have a predisposition for a certain disease, you may prevent it from developing if you can control other factors, such as a lifestyle, that contribute to the development of that disease. Therefore, it is important to know diseases that are common to your family and to take steps to prevent them from occurring.

Health Care *Tuesday April 26 2005*

Health care is the final factor that helps determine your health. It is the quality and variety of services available to treat illnesses and promote health. The hospitals, doctors, dentists, and ambulance services available are some of the factors of your health care. Most of the health care services in the country do more to treat illness than to promote health.

Although the treatment of disease is important, there is a need to do more to prevent problems from occurring in the first place.

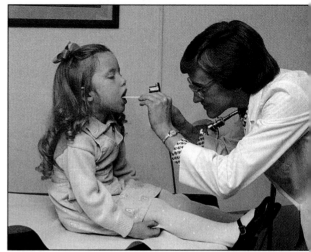

From the look of it, this doctor could be in which practice? (Che the chart on the left.)

Doctor! Doctor!

Allergist–allergies
Anesthesiologist–anesthetics
Cardiologist–heart
Dentist–teeth
Dermatologist–skin
Endocrinologist–internal secretion glands
Family practitioner–general health
Gastroenterologist–digestive system
Geriatrician–elderly
Gynecologist–female reproductive system
Hematologist–blood
Internist–nonsurgical diseases
Nephrologist–kidneys
Neurologist–nervous system
Obstetrician–childbirth
Oncologist–cancer
Ophthalmologist–eyes
Orthopedist–skeletal system
Otolaryngologist–ear, throat
Otorhinolaryngologist–ear, nose, and throat
Pathologist–disease in tissues
Pediatrician–children
Podiatrist–feet
Pulmonologist–lungs
Radiologist–x-rays
Surgeon–operative procedures
Urologist–urinary tract

IMPORTANCE OF HEALTH CARE

You may be thinking, "Why worry about my health now? I am still young. Health is something for old people to worry about." While it may be true that the elderly are concerned about their health, health should be important to everyone. Some of your health problems may have already begun. For example, if you have a mouth full of cavities, you cannot restore the tissue that has been destroyed. Fillings and good oral hygiene may prevent your cavities from getting worse, but the damage has already been done.

You do not have to be in your forties to have some serious **health risks.** A health risk is any factor (habits, traits, or conditions) that increases the chance of having a health problem. Many young people already have at least one factor that could contribute to heart disease, a stroke, or cancer. Even though a health risk does not always result in poor health, it is important to reduce health risks whenever possible and avoid creating habits which may lead to health risks.

Section Review

1. What are four factors that affect your health?
2. Define *lifestyle* and explain how it affects your health.
3. What is a *predisposition,* and why should you take notice of it?
4. Five poor health habits contribute to eighty percent of disease and disability in the United States today. List three of these habits.

wed April 27 2005

AN OUNCE OF PREVENTION

There is a saying that "an ounce of prevention is worth a pound of cure." This means that it is often easier to stop something before it happens than to try to repair the damage done afterwards. For example, a car owner should habitually check his car's oil level. Checking the oil and maintaining the right level may take a little extra effort and time, but it is better than having to replace the engine due to a lack of proper maintenance. This principle of prevention also holds true for health. It is much better to practice good health habits than to ignore them and become ill.

According to Philippians 3:21, Christ will one day change the Christian's vile body to one like His glorious body. Your new body will never grow old or sick. Until that change takes place, you will occasionally get sick no matter how healthy you are. But there are several things you can do to prevent frequent and serious illness. Eating the right foods, exercising regularly, becoming well informed about health, and avoiding destructive habits such as smoking cigarettes or drinking alcohol can help you avoid many illnesses. Modern science also helps to fight disease by developing new medicines. By applying many of these small preventive measures, you can avoid having to use a "pound" of cure.

Learn About Health

In order to stay healthy, you should learn all you can about good health practices and then adopt them. During this course you will learn a great deal about health, but learning once is not enough. Health information is constantly changing; you must stay informed. Each year there are thousands of studies that produce new information about health. Most of these studies improve current ideas of health, and some even prove present information to be false.

New information has changed the way people think about dieting. Health experts used to believe that overweight people could easily trim extra pounds off by simply eating less. However, today

Quick Quack Qualifiers

Do the advertisements use testimonials or anecdotes rather than scientific studies to support claims?

Does the cure promise dramatic, immediate, effortless, or miraculous results?

Does the remedy suggest that most diseases can be cured by nutritional methods?

Is the treatment promoted as a cure-all for an illogically wide range of diseases?

Are credentials obscure or suspect?

Do the advertisements ridicule orthodox doctors and medical practices for rejecting "alternative" medicine?

Do they cite popular-medicine books rather than respected medical journals as proof that a treatment is sound?

Is the treatment promoted only in the back pages of magazines, over the phone, by mail order, in newspaper ads in the format of news stories, or by biased or invalid sources?

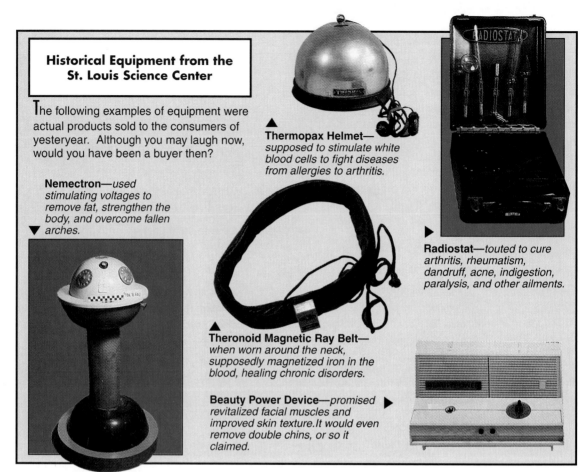

it is known that losing weight is not that simple; improper dieting may actually make the problem worse.

Unfortunately, there is a great deal of misinformation concerning health. This wrong information comes from all kinds of sources. It may come from a friend who tells you that chewing tobacco really does not hurt you. Or it may come from a book written by an "expert" who is marketing a quick way to lose weight. Because your health is often influenced by the advice you take, it is important that you use reliable sources for your health information.

Learn About Yourself

Most of the time people wait until they are sick to go to the doctor, but it is important to visit the doctor for a routine health check when you are well. During this visit the doctor will give you a **physical examination** (also called a physical), a thorough medical exam to determine a person's physical condition. During a physical, the doctor is not looking for a specific illness but surveys the person's overall health.

Everyone should have physical exams regularly. Just how often a person needs to have a physical exam depends on such factors as his age, health condition, current activities, and family background. For example, a fifty-year-old man who is overweight, has a family history of heart disease, and possesses a high-pressure job should probably have a physical examination every year. For a teen-ager, a physical about every three years should be adequate, unless he has special health problems or is competing in strenuous sports.

Another way of finding out about your health is to participate in a **health screening** program. Health screening tests groups of people for health problems. Some tests that are usually included are height, weight, blood pressure, vision, health habits, and blood chemistry. These tests are conducted by qualified health personnel and are usually free or very inexpensive.

A health fair or school screening can often help find potential problems.

You have probably already benefited from some type of health screening. Your school may have conducted vision tests for all the students, or perhaps you have participated in a health fair at a local shopping mall. No matter where it takes place, health screening can be useful in teaching you more about yourself and can aid in finding potential problems even when you do not feel ill.

Use What You Learn

You can know all about sickness and ways to prevent it; you can learn all about your body and how it functions. But all this knowledge will not help you if you do not apply it properly. You must use what you know about good health to develop good health habits. Many teen-agers know that they should exercise; some even wish that they exercised regularly. As long as they choose to sit in front of

the television instead of going swimming or jogging, they will not get the exercise they need. Many times the problem is not knowing what to do, but doing it.

When a person finally decides to do something about poor health habits, time often becomes the enemy. Instead of making changes right away, many wait for a more convenient time. Procrastination is a common obstacle to good physical health. Exercise programs and diets are two areas people frequently put off until tomorrow. Procrastination also affects spiritual health. Many Christians know they need to have regular devotions or tithe their income, but they keep waiting for a better time to begin.

Once a person gets caught in the "time trap," he usually fails. For example, a Christian who has neglected his devotions may decide to compensate by reading the entire New Testament in a few days. Reading in haste, he gets little benefit from his Bible study. He finds it more and more difficult to keep up with his reading. Completely frustrated, he concludes that devotions are just not "right" for him.

Many exercise programs fail in the same way. Suppose a person who has not exercised for years decides to run five miles a day. After two days, every muscle in his body aches. Instead of feeling healthier, he feels worse than he has ever felt in his life. He soon decides that, although exercise may be beneficial for some people, it does not work for him.

You do not have to become a victim of these "time traps." As you learn of health habits that require change, set reasonable goals and start working on them without delay. **Goals** are those things you desire to accomplish. A Christian's goals should reflect his godly values and standards. What should be accomplished, how it is to be done, and when it should be finished are questions a Christian should seek God's leading in. Goals must be specific and realistic. If you cannot discern which goals are reasonable, ask for help. Godly parents, teachers,

The prize comes only after goals are set and work is applied.

would be to do well in daily schoolwork in high school in order to insure acceptance into college. An immediate goal may be an end in itself. A student who is pressed for time and working on a book report may only desire to see the report finished. The goal of an athlete after a race might be to get a drink of water. No matter how mundane the task may be, goals will help to get the job done. With God's help, wise counsel, and determination, you can accomplish your goals.

Good intentions accomplish nothing without action. **Self-discipline** means controlling your conduct. The effort made to accomplish your goals displays your self-discipline. You must learn to control yourself in order to fulfill your quests. It is not easy. For example, you may intend to eat a nutritious meal before going to school. However, getting up earlier in order to eat a good breakfast takes self-discipline. You must determine to do what you know to be right. Dr. Bob Jones, Sr., often said, "The test of your character is what it takes to stop you." James 4:13-17 deals with committing plans to God and ends with this admonition: "Therefore to him that knoweth to do good, and doeth it not, to him it is sin."

pastors, and youth leaders are excellent sources for advice.

Not all goals are immediately attainable. There are three types of goals: long-range, intermediate, and immediate. Immediate and intermediate goals aid in attaining long-range goals.

For instance, if the long-range goal is to become a teacher, the intermediate goal would be to attend college, graduate with a degree in education, and obtain teacher certification; the immediate goal

It Is Up to You

When you have finished this book, you will know some facts that you did not know before. You will be more aware of your personal responsibility for your own health. You will not be healthier, however, unless you make needed changes. Your temple is in your hands to build up or to tear down. There is no better time to begin than today.

Section Review

1. List two different ways to evaluate your present health status as discussed in the chapter.

2. Define *goals* and *self-discipline*.

3. List the three types of goals.

4. What are two qualities that goals should have?

CHAPTER REVIEW

Terms

health

siblings

peers

lifestyle

environment

heredity

predisposition

health care

health risk

physical examination

health screening

goals

self-discipline

Content Questions

1. What is health?

2. What is the difference between spiritual health, physical health, mental health, emotional health, and social health?

3. Name four factors that affect your health. Which of these is most important? Which factor do you have the most control over, and which factor do you have the least control over?

4. What are two medical methods of assessing your current health status?

5. What is the difference between immediate and intermediate goals?

6. In order to make your goals more attainable, be sure they are _____ and _____.

7. How does self-discipline affect goals?

Application Questions

1. What is self-discipline? Why is self-discipline in each component of health required of a Christian? List each of the five components of health and explain how self-discipline is needed in each component.

2. Why do you think health is defined as "a process of attaining" rather than "having" spiritual, physical, mental, emotional, and social well-being?

3. What is the difference between health and holistic health?

4. How can a Christian make sure that his goals are what God wants? Support your answer with verses.

Medical Assistants

Job Description: The work of medical assistants varies from office to office. The major responsibility of a medical assistant is to keep the doctor's office running smoothly. In some practices, the medical assistant is responsible for maintaining neat and orderly waiting, consulting, and examination rooms, greeting the patient; telephoning prescriptions to the pharmacy; scheduling appointments; recording and filing medical information; and handling insurance, billing, and bookkeeping. The medical assistant may also be trained to help in routine clinical tasks (recording vital signs and medical histories, explaining treatments to patients, preparing the patient for examination, collecting laboratory specimens, and sterilizing and arranging instruments).

Job Location: Medical assistants usually work in clean, well-kept offices. Most have a forty-hour workweek (which may include evening or weekend hours, depending on the doctor they work for

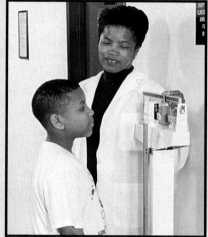

and their individual responsibilities).

Training Required: Many assistants have no formal training. However, some course work in health, biology, mathematics, typing, bookkeeping, computers, and office practices is preferred. Some states require a one- or two-year degree before medical assistants can do certain tasks (give injections, draw blood, apply dressings).

BODY BASICS

God's great majesty and power shine throughout His creation. Although the universe is vast and the earth is filled with many amazing things, you are one of God's greatest creations. He has intricately designed your body to carry on millions of functions automatically. The human body is more efficient and complex than any machine designed by man. It is a living miracle!

CHAPTER 2

"I will praise thee; for I am fearfully and wonderfully made: marvellous are thy works."

Psalm 139:14

Men have intensely studied the human body for thousands of years, but there is much they still do not know about it. Physicians often study for years to specialize in one small aspect of treating the body. Fortunately, you do not have to be an expert in anatomy to practice good health. Some basic knowledge about the body will help you to understand the reasons for certain health practices. This chapter is designed to acquaint you with some basic information about the human body.

BODY SYSTEMS

You already know some facts about the body. For instance, you probably know that your stomach helps to digest food. You may also know where your heart is located and understand that it pumps blood. However, knowing a little bit about many body parts may give you some wrong ideas about your body. Understanding body systems can give a more accurate idea of what each body part does.

Before you learn about body systems, you need to know about the basic body parts. The most basic living part of your body is the **cell.** These structural units of living things are usually so small that they can be seen only with a microscope. Your body consists of approximately forty trillion cells.

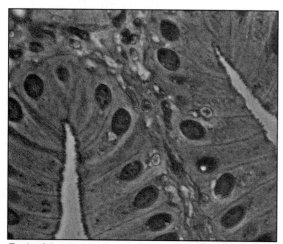

Each of the dark oval areas in the photograph is the nucleus of an individual human epithelial cell. Cells are the structural and functional units of life.

Similar cells in your body are often grouped together to perform certain functions. These groups of cells are called **tissues.**

For example, muscle cells group together to form muscle tissue. There are four major types of tissue in the human body: connective, epithelial (EP uh THEE lee ul), muscular, and nervous.

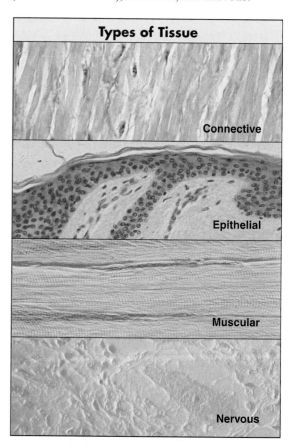

Types of Tissue

Connective

Epithelial

Muscular

Nervous

Organs are formed from various tissues that are grouped together to perform a specific function. Your stomach, lungs, heart, liver, and kidneys are examples of organs. Often different organs work together to perform certain vital functions. When organs that perform vital functions are grouped together, they form a **body system.** In the following pages you will learn about eight different body systems. Although each body system is presented

Back Pact: Treating Your Back with TLC

Tender loving care (TLC) is the best way to avoid back strain and pain. Good posture is one of the best ways of preventing back problems. Correct posture means positioning your body in a way that requires the least strain on muscles and bones. Skillful sitting, standing, bending, lifting, and working techniques can aid in proper back care.

When sitting, sit up straight, keep your feet flat on the floor, and shift positions frequently to relieve pressure on the spine. Whether you are in a car or on a chair, a little cushion placed behind the small of your back can supply any needed support. During long periods of sitting, relax by shrugging your shoulders and moving your head and neck.

When standing, "stand tall." Keep your head aligned over your shoulders. Keep your knees relaxed, not stiff,

incorrect posture

and your feet slightly apart. Shoe heels that are over two inches high can force the body's weight forward, causing the back to arch in order to maintain balance. Avoid prolonged standing in one position by moving around or shifting your body weight occasionally.

Bending for prolonged periods of time can produce back strain. If you are working at a desk, make sure that all of the equipment (typewriter, books, paints, papers, computer, etc.) is at waist level. Use a tilted desk or board to prevent the strain of bending forward. Avoid movements that are repetitious by changing chores or positions frequently.

Be sure to use your larger muscles instead of back muscles when lifting. Bend your knees and squat (using leg and thigh muscles) when

correct posture

you pick things up off the floor rather than stoop from the waist, possibly straining your back. This is especially essential when you lift anything heavy. Keep your movements slow and smooth.

If you are mopping, vacuuming, or shoveling snow, use the arm muscles in a left-to-right motion rather than a push-and-pull manner. Use short strokes and keep the tool used close to your body. Kneel or sit when possible in order to keep from bending and stretching the back when doing tasks such as planting, tucking in sheets, or tying shoes. Be sure to keep from twisting your body while pulling with back muscles. Try to keep your shoulders and pelvis facing the same direction.

Except for degenerative changes in the spine, most backache problems can be traced to physical strain. Correct posture is the main ingredient to good back care. Make it a habit to treat your back right; make a back pact.

separately, it is important to remember that body systems interconnect and work together. God made you as an organized body with all of its parts "fitly joined together" (Eph. 4:16).

The Skeletal System

When you look at your classmates, it is easy to note their differences. Some are tall and others are short; some have black hair and others have blond hair. Because of the variety of characteristics, it is usually not difficult to tell them apart.

But think for a minute how your classmates are alike. They all have a head, arms, legs, feet, knees, ears, and hundreds of other similar characteristics. Although everyone's head looks different, you have no difficulty distinguishing someone's head from any other part of his body. This is because God has designed all men with the same basic framework. This framework is called your *skeletal system.*

There are about 206 bones that form the skeletal system. More than half of the 206 bones of the body are found in the feet and hands. The skeleton weighs

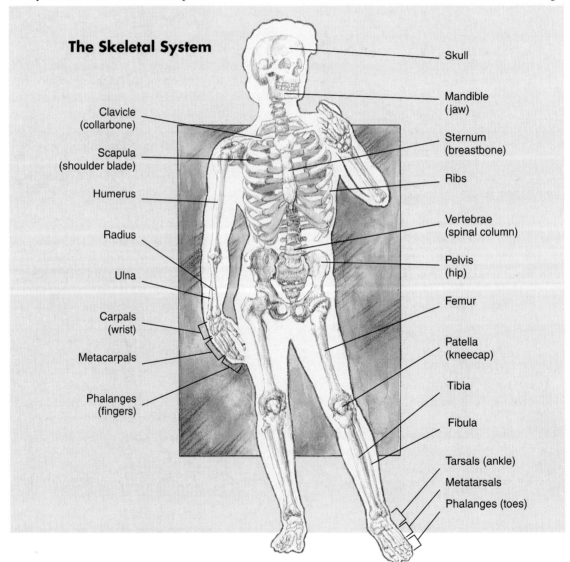

The Skeletal System

Skull

Mandible (jaw)

Clavicle (collarbone)

Sternum (breastbone)

Scapula (shoulder blade)

Ribs

Humerus

Vertebrae (spinal column)

Radius

Pelvis (hip)

Ulna

Femur

Carpals (wrist)

Patella (kneecap)

Metacarpals

Tibia

Phalanges (fingers)

Fibula

Tarsals (ankle)

Metatarsals

Phalanges (toes)

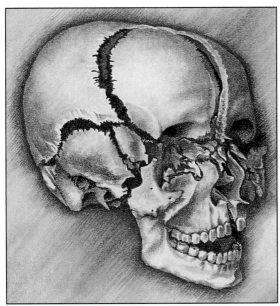

The skull is composed of not one bone but twenty-nine bones.

Bones do more than just give your body shape; they allow you to move. The bones of the skeleton serve as a support for the body and aid in movement through the contraction of muscles attached at the joints. Walking, jumping, running, lifting, and throwing are just a few examples of body movements that are produced by muscles pulling on bones. Most body movement occurs when a bone moves within a specific **joint.** A joint is the place where two or more bones join. Some joints, such as your shoulder joint, allow for a great variety of movement. Other joints, such as some of those in your skull, do not allow any movement. The type of joint determines the amount of movement that is possible.

Bones also shield many of your vital organs. Your brain is protected by your skull. Your heart and lungs are protected by your ribs and your breastbone (sternum). Without bones to protect these organs, even a little bump could cause serious injury. The bones also produce blood cells and function as a storage reservoir for calcium, phosphorus, and other minerals.

about twenty pounds or fourteen percent of your body weight, yet it is about four times stronger than concrete. Ounce for ounce, bone is stronger than steel.

Section Review

1. What is a cell? How does it differ from tissue?
2. What are the four major types of tissue in the human body?
3. List five functions of the skeletal system.
4. In the skeletal system, what is a joint?

The Muscular System

Another of the body systems that greatly determines your appearance is the *muscular system.* Since many people desire to enhance their appearance, interest in fitness has increased. Certainly a fit, muscular body can be attractive, but appearance is not the main function of the muscular system. The primary function is to provide movement. Unlike other tissue, muscle tissue can **contract** (shorten). This ability results in movement.

Many muscles are under conscious control (controlled by thinking). These muscles are called **voluntary muscles.** When you throw a ball, iron a shirt, or lift a weight, you are using voluntary muscles. **Involuntary muscles** are not controlled through conscious thinking. Your heart is an example of an involuntary muscle. It beats without your having to think about it. God also created the muscles that form the walls of many internal organs and

The Muscular System

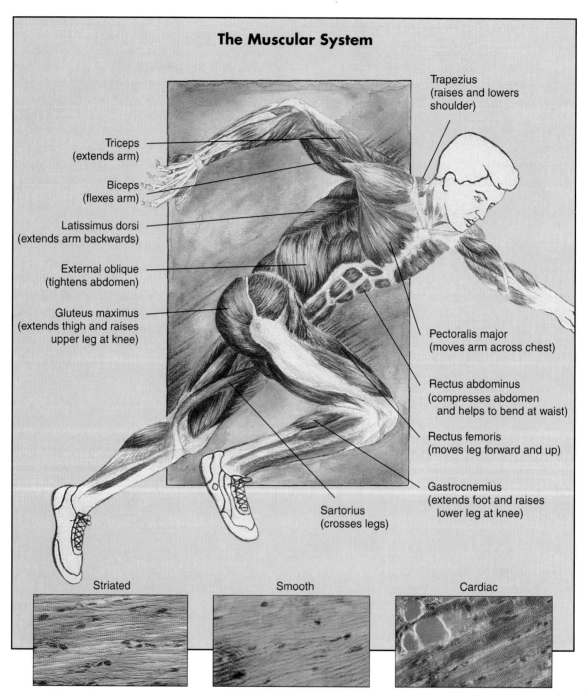

Trapezius
(raises and lowers
shoulder)

Triceps
(extends arm)

Biceps
(flexes arm)

Latissimus dorsi
(extends arm backwards)

External oblique
(tightens abdomen)

Gluteus maximus
(extends thigh and raises
upper leg at knee)

Pectoralis major
(moves arm across chest)

Rectus abdominus
(compresses abdomen
and helps to bend at waist)

Rectus femoris
(moves leg forward and up)

Gastrocnemius
(extends foot and raises
lower leg at knee)

Sartorius
(crosses legs)

Striated

Smooth

Cardiac

Striated (skeletal) muscle tissue is striped (striated) and is voluntary. Smooth muscle tissue is not striated and is involuntary. Cardiac muscle is striated and is involuntary.

the walls of blood vessels to function without your having to think about them.

Voluntary muscles that are used to move the skeletal system are sometimes called *skeletal muscles*. When skeletal muscle is observed under a microscope, bands or striations are observed in the tissue; thus, skeletal muscle is also referred to as *striated* (STRY ay tid) *muscle*. Most involuntary muscle does not have these striations and hence is called *smooth muscle*. Although there are striations in heart muscle tissue, the striations are not always as distinct as in skeletal muscle. This type of muscle tissue is found only in the wall of the heart and, therefore, is called *cardiac muscle*.

Muscles also help maintain body heat. Because they are so numerous and almost continually engaged in action, muscles produce a large amount of body heat. If your body is chilled and you are inactive, you might experience the muscle contractions known as shivering. These contrac[...] increase the body temperature slightl[...]

Another function of muscles is to p[...] port and maintain posture. Back and le[...] support the spine in an upright positio[...] muscles protect and hold certain organs i[...] place. Your stomach or abdominal muscles are an example of muscles that work in this manner. They help protect and hold in your stomach and intestines. The potbelly that many Americans develop during middle age is partially caused by abdominal muscles that are not kept in good condition.

You have more direct influence over the condition of your muscular system than you have over most of your other body systems. Through exercise you can greatly improve the condition of your muscular system. You will learn more about muscles and how they respond to exercise in a later chapter.

Section Review

1. What is the difference between voluntary and involuntary muscles?

2. List three functions of the muscular system.

3. What are the three major types of muscle tissue?

The Circulatory System

Earlier in this chapter you learned that cells are the most basic living parts of the body. Because cells are alive, they must be constantly supplied with certain substances such as oxygen and food. There must also be a way for cells to get rid of the waste products that they produce. If these requirements are not met, the cells will die. Can you imagine what a task it would be to take care of the needs of forty trillion cells? God has designed your circulatory system to perform this seemingly impossible job.

The *circulatory system* is your body's internal transportation system. It is designed to carry vital materials to cells and remove waste materials from cells. Any interruption in the work of this system is serious; a lapse as short as ten minutes or less is often fatal. The primary organs responsible for performing this job are your heart and blood vessels. One of the most critical jobs of the circulatory system is the delivery of oxygen to the brain. Brain damage may begin if the brain is deprived of oxygen for four to six minutes.

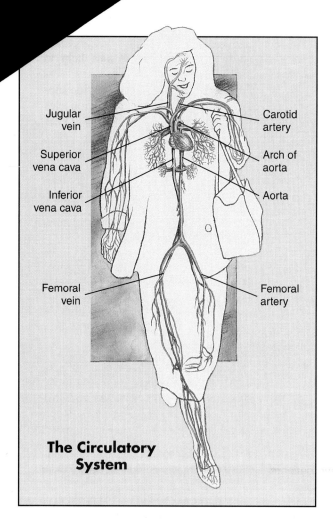

The Circulatory System

Jugular vein

Superior vena cava

Inferior vena cava

Femoral vein

Carotid artery

Arch of aorta

Aorta

Femoral artery

Blood Vessels—**Blood vessels** are the passageways for blood in the body. They are the "roads" that allow pick-up and delivery service to every cell. There are three primary types of blood vessels in your body: arteries, veins, and capillaries.

Arteries are blood vessels that carry blood away from the heart. As the blood leaves the heart, it is under a great amount of pressure. The thick, muscular walls of the arteries help keep them from rupturing from the pressure. Blood in arteries is usually bright red because it is rich in oxygen.

Blood is returned to the heart by **veins.** Because the returning blood is under little pressure, the walls of veins are not as thick or muscular as those of arteries. The blood in veins is dark red because it usually contains less oxygen than the blood found in arteries. Most of the blood vessels you can see just under the surface of your skin are veins.

The Heart—Your heart is the most important organ of your circulatory system. A muscular organ about the size of a man's fist, the heart is composed of two separate pumps. The right side receives blood from the body and pumps it to the lungs. The left side receives blood from the lungs and pumps it to the body. The heart beats about seventy times every minute, or about thirty-five million times per year.

Because your heart is a muscle, you can strengthen it by exercising regularly. A strong heart can help you live a longer and better life. Unfortunately, the lifestyle of many Americans weakens rather than strengthens their hearts. As a result, heart disease is a very serious problem in the United States today.

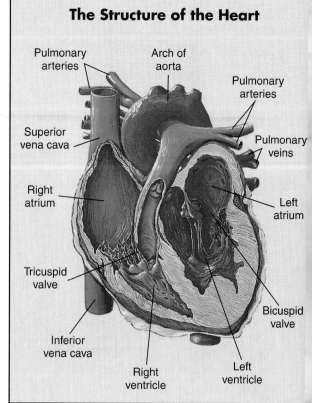

The Structure of the Heart

Pulmonary arteries

Arch of aorta

Pulmonary arteries

Superior vena cava

Pulmonary veins

Right atrium

Left atrium

Tricuspid valve

Inferior vena cava

Bicuspid valve

Right ventricle

Left ventricle

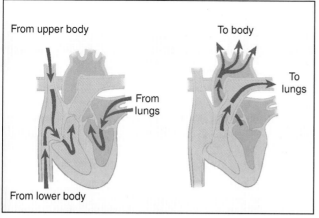

Diagram of blood flow through the heart

Erythrocytes are biconcaved disks. Leukocytes are white blood cells of varying shapes. Platelets appear to be round or oval discs.

The tiny blood vessels that connect arteries to veins are called **capillaries.** These vessels are just large enough for single blood cells to pass through. During circulation the thin walls of the capillaries allow vital substances to pass from the blood to the cells nearby and certain waste products to pass from the cells into the blood.

The life-giving substance that travels through-out all the passageways of the circulatory system is blood. The largest component of blood consists of a straw-colored liquid called **plasma**. Although plasma contains different substances, it is ninety per-cent water. Blood also contains a variety of cells that are designed for specific purposes. These include red

Leeches and Barbers: Strange Bedfellows

Bloodletting is the deliberate removal of small amounts of blood from the body. Thought to be a method for curing a variety of illnesses, bloodletting was practiced by the ancient Egyptians. To bleed a patient, doctors would make small incisions or apply leeches (bloodsucking annelid worms). In fact, early physicians were often called leeches.

Medieval doctors often relied on astrological charts or religious sanctions to get "better results." Rooms were often set aside in medieval churches for bloodletting. Because monks of the Middle Ages were required under ecclesiastic law to be bled from time to time, barbers began to perform bloodletting as well as clipping and shaving the monks' heads. In order to advertise the best times for bleeding, barbers would often hang white cloths with red blood stains outside their doors. The red and white barber pole is still a symbol for barbers today, although bloodletting is not practiced.

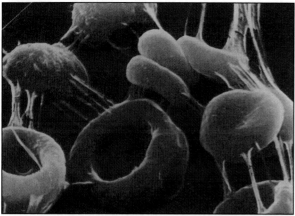

The process of blood clotting is also called coagulation. An injury initiates the formation of a fibrin clot.

cells) fight infection, and **platelets** help blood to clot at cuts or wounds.

Life Is in the Blood—Blood is a precious fluid. For many years medical science did not recognize the importance of blood. Doctors thought that certain illnesses were caused by too much blood and treated patients by draining blood from them. In contrast, the Bible has long testified to the importance of blood. Leviticus 17:11 says, "The life of the flesh is in the blood."

Blood is vital not only for physical life but also for spiritual life. In the ninth chapter of Hebrews we learn that the shedding of blood is necessary for the remission of sins. Christ's blood was shed to cleanse us from our sin. Just as there is no physical life without blood, there is no spiritual life without the blood of Christ.

blood cells, white blood cells, and platelets. **Erythrocytes** (ih RITH ruh SITES; red blood cells) carry oxygen, **leukocytes** (LOO kuh SITES; white blood

Section Review

1. What are the three major types of blood vessels in the circulatory system?

2. What are the four major components of blood?

3. Besides their color, what is the difference between erythrocytes and leukocytes?

4. What verse in the Bible specifies the physical importance of blood?

The Respiratory System

The circulatory system is responsible for transporting oxygen to the many cells of your body. However, your circulatory system cannot make the oxygen it must transport. This oxygen must come from some other place. Fortunately, God placed an abundant supply of oxygen in the air that surrounds the earth.

The circulatory system is not designed to take oxygen directly from air that is outside the body. This is the job of the *respiratory system.* Your respiratory system takes oxygen from air and delivers it to your circulatory system. It also takes carbon dioxide from your circulatory system and returns it to the air around you. This is what happens when

you breathe. You usually breathe about sixteen to twenty times each minute.

Your respiratory system consists primarily of a series of passageways that lead from outside your body into your lungs. Some of the more important organs included in this system are the mouth and nose, pharynx, larynx, trachea, and lungs.

Mouth and Nose—Your mouth and nose are the primary passageways from the outer environment to the inside of your body. Your nose warms and moistens the air you breathe and also filters many impurities out of the air.

Pharynx—The **pharynx** (FAIHR ingks) is a muscular tube that is about five inches long. You

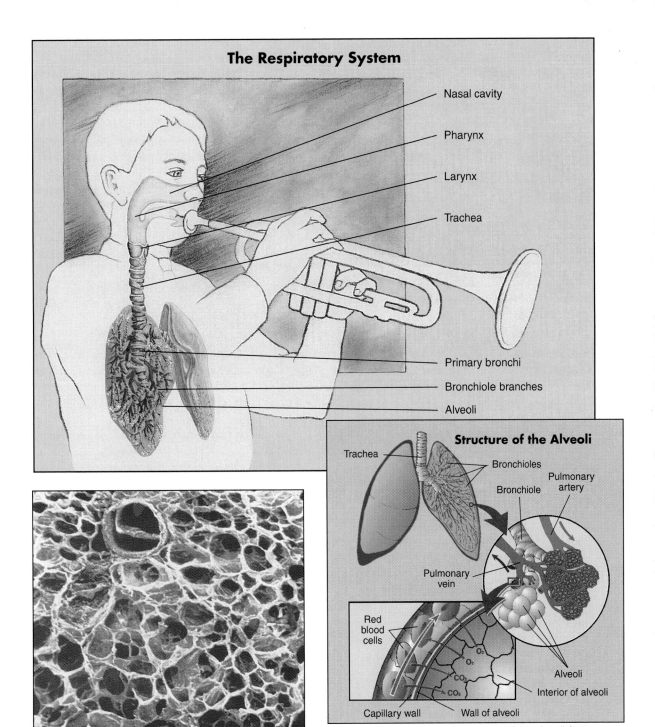

The Respiratory System

- Nasal cavity
- Pharynx
- Larynx
- Trachea
- Primary bronchi
- Bronchiole branches
- Alveoli

Structure of the Alveoli

- Trachea
- Bronchioles
- Bronchiole
- Pulmonary artery
- Pulmonary vein
- Red blood cells
- O_2
- CO_2
- CO_2
- Alveoli
- Interior of alveoli
- Capillary wall
- Wall of alveoli

The small cavities in this electron micrograph are cross sections of alveoli. It has been estimated that the lungs contain about 300 million alveoli.

Through the thin membranous walls of the alveoli (0.5 μm thick), oxygen from the lungs diffuses into the red blood cells, and carbon dioxide from the red blood cells diffuses into the lungs.

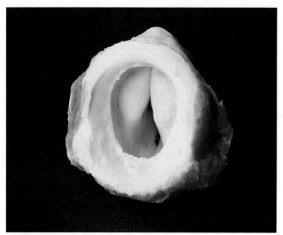

These cow vocal cords are similar to human vocal cords, except they do not possess the fine elastic ligaments (true vocal cords; vocal folds) that God made in man.

thickness and length of the vocal folds: the thicker and longer the folds, the fewer the vibrations and the lower the pitch. The quality of the voice is also determined by the shape and size of the nose, mouth, pharynx, and sinuses in your skull.

Trachea—Sometimes called the windpipe, the **trachea** (TRAY kee uh) is a tube about four or five inches long. It is a passageway that leads from the pharynx to the two tubes that enter the lungs. Although it functions primarily as a passageway for air, the inside walls of the trachea are designed to trap and expel substances such as dust, smoke, and bacteria.

Lungs—The lungs are the largest organs of the respiratory system. Before reaching your lungs, the trachea divides into two large tubes. These tubes are called **bronchi** (BRAHNG kye). Inside the lungs the bronchi divide into smaller and smaller tubes called *bronchioles* (BRAHNG kee oles). Eventually the tubes lead to thin-walled air sacs called **alveoli** (al VEE uh LYE). The alveoli are the connection between the respiratory system and the circulatory system. Oxygen and carbon dioxide are exchanged between the alveoli of the respiratory system and the capillaries of the circulatory system.

probably call it your throat. Because it is a passageway for both air and food, the pharynx is part of the digestive system as well as the respiratory system.

Larynx—Although people refer to it as the voice box, the **larynx** (LAIHR ingks) warms and filters incoming air and keeps food and liquids from entering the respiratory system. The vibration of the vocal cords within the larynx produces your voice. The pitch of the voice is determined by the

Section Review

1. How is oxygen transferred from the outer environment to the cells of the body through the respiratory system?

2. How are the pharynx and larynx different? In what way are they similar?

3. What are the differences between bronchi, bronchioles, and alveoli?

The Digestive System

You learned earlier that cells need oxygen and nutrients from food to stay alive. Just as the respiratory system is designed to take air from the outside and transfer it to the circulatory system, the digestive system is designed to take food from the outside and transfer it to the circulatory system. Before food

can be absorbed into the circulatory system, it must be broken down into simple substances. The process of changing food in the body from complex substances to simple substances is called **digestion.**

Most of the digestive system is simply a long tube inside the body. Some sections of this tube are wide

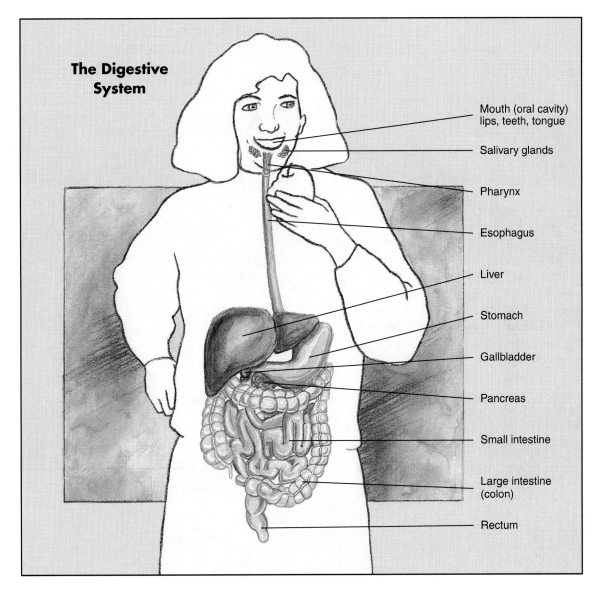

The Digestive System

Mouth (oral cavity) lips, teeth, tongue

Salivary glands

Pharynx

Esophagus

Liver

Stomach

Gallbladder

Pancreas

Small intestine

Large intestine (colon)

Rectum

(such as the stomach or large intestine), and other sections (such as the esophagus or small intestine) are narrow. A few organs that are not actually part of this tube are also included in the digestive system. They are included because they secrete substances that help break down food. After food enters your mouth, it is transported along the tubular digestive system and broken down as it moves along. Useful substances are absorbed into the circulatory system, and waste products are excreted.

Mouth—Have you ever seen someone "wolf down" his food? He seems to swallow his food the second it hits his mouth. This is an unhealthful and impolite practice. The teeth, tongue, and salivary glands start the process of digestion, and a person needs to take time to let them do their job completely.

Teeth are designed to tear and crush food into smaller pieces. These smaller pieces of food not only make food easier to digest but also help prevent choking. As you chew your food, the *salivary glands* secrete **saliva.** Saliva moistens food so that it will move through the digestive system easily and begins to break down some of the large molecules of food. Your tongue helps position food in your mouth for chewing and swallowing.

Pharynx and Esophagus—From your mouth, food is pushed into your pharynx as you swallow. You learned earlier that the pharynx is also a passageway for air going to the lungs. Because food entering the lungs is very dangerous, God has designed a special flap (the epiglottis [EHP ih GLOHT is]) to close the entrance to your lungs when you swallow. This is why you cannot swallow and breathe at the same time.

From the pharynx, food moves into your **esophagus** (ih SAHF uh gus). Your esophagus leads from your pharynx to your stomach. It is a relatively straight tube that is about ten inches (25 cm) long. There are muscles in the wall of the esophagus that contract to move the food along. Usually the trip from mouth to stomach takes only a few seconds.

Stomach—The widest portion of your digestive tract is your stomach. Your stomach has muscular walls that churn food and mix it with fluids that continue to break down food until it is in an almost liquid state called **chyme** (KYME). Then it gradually releases the food into the small intestine. Your stomach can hold about two quarts of food at a time.

Small Intestine—The **small intestine** is ten to thirteen feet (3-4 m) long and is the workhorse of the digestive system. It is here that food is finally broken down into the form that can be used by the rest of the body. The small intestine is also the place where food is absorbed into the blood stream for transportation throughout the body.

Large Intestine—The **large intestine** is shorter (about five feet [1.5 m] long) and has a greater diameter than the small intestine. After the small

Microscopic view of villi in the small intestine

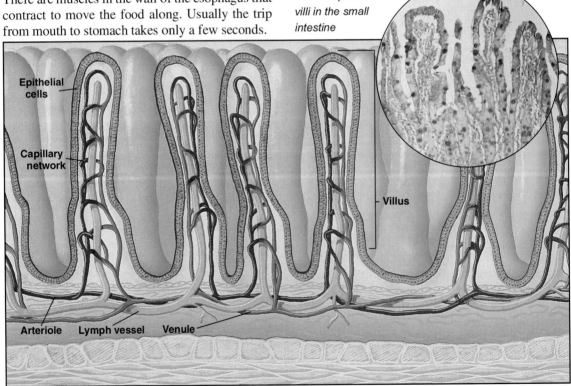

Epithelial cells

Capillary network

Villus

Arteriole   Lymph vessel   Venule

The walls of the intestines are lined with projections called villi (VIL EYE). The villi absorb digested food products and transfer the dissolved materials to the blood and circulatory systems.

intestine has finished its job, there is little left (except water) that your body can use. It is the job of the large intestine to reabsorb most of the water and certain minerals and vitamins. The waste products are transported to the end of the digestive system, where they can be expelled.

Liver, Gallbladder, and Pancreas—Your digestive system also includes organs that are not part of the digestive tube. These organs belong to the digestive system because they secrete substances into the digestive tract that are necessary for breaking down certain food substances. Your liver, pancreas, and gallbladder are such organs.

These organs are sometimes called **accessory organs.** The liver is one of the most complex organs in the body and performs a great variety of functions. Its most important digestive function is the secretion of **bile.** The bile produced by the liver is stored and concentrated in the **gallbladder.** When food moves from the stomach into the small intestine, bile flows from the gallbladder into the small intestine. Bile is needed to break down fatty substances.

Like the pharynx, the **pancreas** (PANG kree us) is included in two different body systems. As a part of the digestive system, the pancreas secretes digestive juices that break down a variety of food substances. Later in this chapter, you will learn how the pancreas also functions as part of the endocrine system.

Section Review

1. List the organs that make up the digestive tract. Beside each organ, write a brief explanation about its contribution to the digestive process.

2. What are the accessory organs? What do they do?

3. What is chyme? Where is it produced?

The Excretory System

As cells carry out their various functions, they produce a variety of waste products. These waste products must be removed or cells will die. You learned that the pick-up service for these substances is supplied by your circulatory system. Waste products from cells pass through the thin walls of capillaries into the blood stream.

Although this may sound like the end of the problem, it is not. If wastes are not removed from the blood stream, they will accumulate and the blood will become a poisonous stream rather than a life-giving fountain. The job of removing waste products from the blood stream is performed primarily by the *excretory system.* It removes waste products from the blood and *excretes* or discharges them from the body. Although sweating, respiration, and elimination are methods of removing

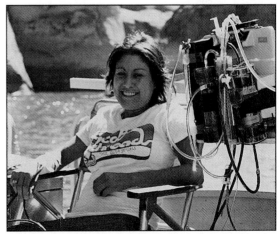

A kidney machine filters nitrogen waste from the blood and regulates the pH and electrolyte balance of the plasma. The filtering of the blood is called hemodialysis or simply dialysis.

waste from the body, the kidneys and urinary bladder are the primary organs in this system.

Kidneys—The kidneys are located near the inside surface of the back below the ribs. Their important function is to remove waste products from the blood. Most people have two kidneys which work separately but perform the same functions. However, God in His providence has designed the body so that it can function even if only one kidney is working properly.

Urinary Bladder—The waste removed from the blood by the kidneys is called urine. After urine is removed by the kidneys, it travels down two long tubes (ureters) to the urinary bladder. The **urinary bladder** collects and holds urine until it is removed from the body during urination.

Section Review

1. List the parts of the excretory system and describe the function of each part.

2. Why is the excretory system important?

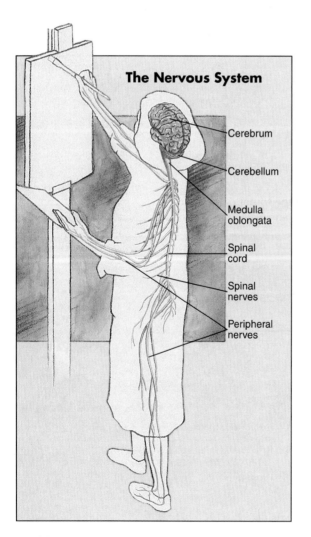

The Nervous System

Cerebrum

Cerebellum

Medulla oblongata

Spinal cord

Spinal nerves

Peripheral nerves

The Nervous System

The *nervous system* is the body's communication center. It is composed of nerve cells called **neurons** (NOOR AHNZ). Similar to the telephone wires that cross the country, nerve cells are threaded throughout the body. They keep you in contact with the environment outside the body and with many things that are happening within the body. The various factors that cause the body to respond are called **stimuli** (STIM yuh lye). Neurons are designed to receive and interpret stimuli.

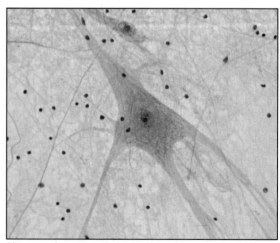

Neurons do not touch each other. Messages are transmitted between them through chemical reactions.

The Structure of the Brain

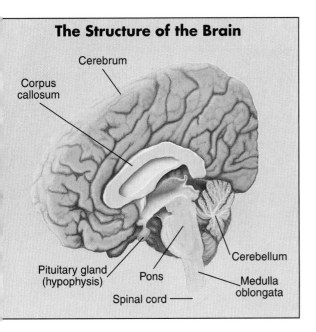

Cerebrum

Corpus callosum

Pituitary gland (hypophysis)

Pons

Spinal cord

Cerebellum

Medulla oblongata

is called **paralysis.** Paralysis is often a sign of damage to the nervous system.

Brain—The most remarkable organ in the human body is the brain. It contains billions of nerve cells and is the control center of the body. It is where your thoughts originate, and it controls vital body functions (such as telling the heart to beat) without your even thinking about them. More than any other organ in your body, your brain is you. Your heart, liver, or kidney can be replaced, but your brain is irreplaceable. It is a computer more complex than any designed by man.

Spinal Cord—In order to control the various areas of the body, the brain must be connected to them. The **spinal cord** consists of bundles of nerves and serves as a connection between the millions of nerves spread throughout the body and the brain. Located along the center of the back, the spinal cord is protected by a series of bones called the backbone or *vertebral column.* If the spinal cord is damaged, the use of all the nerves below the injured area may be lost.

The spinal cord has two major functions. It transmits nerve impulses to and from the brain, and it is a reflex center. Although the primary function of the spinal cord is to connect nerves to the brain, it also allows you to react to some stimuli before the message has been transmitted to the brain. These reactions are called **reflexes.** Reflexes allow you to react to dangerous stimuli quickly. For instance, if

Your phone is useful only if it is connected to the millions of other phones in the phone system. If you cut the wire from the telephone cable to your phone, the phone will be useless. If a major telephone cable is cut, many phones will not work. The nervous system is similar to this; it works only when everything is properly connected. If you cut a nerve to an area of your body, you may not be able to feel or use that part. Injury to certain vital parts of the nervous system can cause a loss of use and of feeling in most of the body. This loss of function

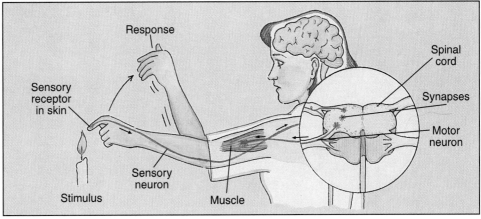

A simple reflex arc occurs when a receptor senses a stimulus (a flame or a prick), a sensory neuron passes this message to the spinal cord, and a motor neuron sends a message from the spinal cord to the effector (the muscle or gland), which carries out the actual response.

Response

Sensory receptor in skin

Stimulus

Sensory neuron

Muscle

Spinal cord

Synapses

Motor neuron

you place your hand on a hot burner, you will probably move your hand before your brain even realizes that the burner is hot. The quickness of this reaction may save you from serious injury.

Section Review

1. Explain what neurons are and describe their major function.

2. Define the word *stimuli.*

3. What is the major function of the brain?

4. List the major functions of the spinal cord.

The Endocrine System

The nervous system controls many of the body's actions. However, the *endocrine* (EN duh krin) *system* also controls functions, communicates changes, and maintains stability within the body.

The effects of the endocrine system can be more subtle than those of the nervous system. The nervous system conducts impulses through neurons, but the endocrine system accomplishes its functions through the use of chemical messengers called **hormones.** Hormones affect the functions of various body organs when they are released into the blood stream. These minute amounts of chemicals are produced by a variety of endocrine **glands.** Glands are organs that make and secrete substances into the body. Because endocrine glands secrete hormones directly into the blood stream and not through a duct or tube, they are sometimes called *ductless glands.*

The complex actions of the endocrine system are especially important to a maturing young person. Many of the physical and emotional changes experienced by teen-agers are influenced by the endocrine system. This chapter will acquaint you with some of these organs and the important roles they play in your body.

Pituitary Gland—The **pituitary** (pih TOO ih TEHR ee) **gland** is a small gland at the base of the brain that releases several different hormones. It is occasionally called the "master gland" because many of

Dwarfism and giantism are two examples of disorders that are often caused either by an underproduction or overproduction of growth hormone.

these hormones help regulate the activity of other endocrine glands. In addition to these hormones, the pituitary gland also produces a hormone that regulates growth. If the pituitary gland produces too much or too little of this hormone, it can greatly affect a person's size.

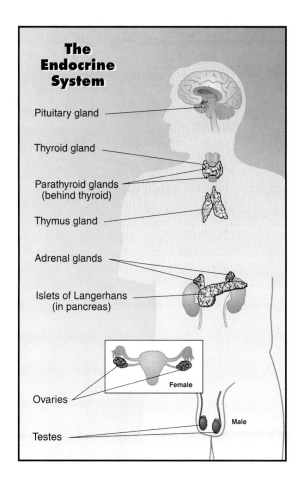

The Endocrine System

- Pituitary gland
- Thyroid gland
- Parathyroid glands (behind thyroid)
- Thymus gland
- Adrenal glands
- Islets of Langerhans (in pancreas)
- Ovaries
- Testes

Female

Male

Thyroid Gland—The **thyroid** (THY ROID) **gland** is located in front of the trachea and just below the voice box. It secretes a hormone that affects growth and the amount of energy the body uses. If too much of this hormone is released, a person may become nervous and overactive and lose weight. If too little is released, a person may become sluggish and overweight.

Pancreas—Earlier you learned that the *pancreas* was part of the digestive system. It is also a part of the endocrine system. The pancreas is located behind and below the stomach. Scattered throughout the pancreas are specialized groups of cells that secrete a hormone called **insulin.** Insulin regulates the amount of sugar in the blood.

Adrenal Glands—The **adrenal** (uh DREE nul) **glands** are small glands located at the top of each kidney. They secrete several hormones that produce a variety of effects on the body. One of the most well known of these hormones is epinephrine ([EP uh NEF rin], sometimes called adrenaline [uh DREHN uh lihn]). Epinephrine prepares the body for action. Some of the ways the body reacts to an increase in epinephrine include breathing faster, increasing the heart rate, and preparing muscles for a maximum effort. Some superhuman feats have been accomplished when these hormones have been released. Men and women have lifted cars off loved ones, ripped doors off hinges, and fought off attackers who were much larger and stronger.

Reproductive Glands—Both males and females have glands in the pelvic region that influence appearance and development. In the female, these glands are the **ovaries** (O vuh rees); in the male these glands are the **testes** (TES TEEZ). Ovaries produce female hormones, and testes produce male hormones. It is the secretion of these hormones during the teen-age years that changes boys into young men and girls into young women.

FOR BETTER OR FOR WORSE

After reading this chapter you may think that your body is very complex. It is! This chapter has barely introduced you to the information available. But even with this limited discussion, you should realize that your body is one of your most valuable possessions and must be protected. If you care for your body properly, you will work better, feel better, and maybe look better. However, if you abuse it, you may have to live with the consequences for the rest of your life. It is your decision—for better or for worse.

Section Review

1. How does the endocrine system communicate with the rest of the body?
2. Make a chart of the major endocrine glands. List their locations and their major functions.

CHAPTER REVIEW

Terms

cell	pharynx	kidneys
tissues	larynx	urinary bladder
organs	trachea	neurons
body system	bronchi	stimuli
joint	alveoli	paralysis
contract	digestion	spinal cord
voluntary muscles	saliva	reflexes
involuntary muscles	esophagus	hormones
blood vessels	chyme	glands
arteries	small intestine	pituitary gland
veins	large intestine	thyroid gland
capillaries	accessory organs	insulin
plasma	bile	adrenal glands
erythrocytes	gallbladder	ovaries
leukocytes	pancreas	testes
platelets		

Content Questions

1. List two common functions of the skeletal system and of the muscular system.

2. Besides the joint that enables you to move your jaw, does the skull have any other joints?

3. Give an example of striated muscle and smooth muscle by specifying where they can be found in the body.

4. Match the following terms concerning the circulatory system.

   1. artery
   2. vein
   3. capillary
   4. plasma
   5. erythrocyte
   6. leukocyte
   7. platelets

   a. blood vessels that connect a vein to an artery
   b. carries oxygen
   c. helps blood to clot
   d. vessel that carries blood away from the heart
   e. vessel that carries blood to the heart
   f. fights infection
   g. ninety percent water

5. Which cells are designed to receive and interpret stimuli?

6. A paraplegic has complete paralysis of the lower half of the body (including both legs). This is often caused by injury or disease of the _____.

7. Endocrine glands are also called _____ glands since they secrete hormones directly into the blood stream.

Application Questions

1. Do most skeletal muscles that move joints have a matching muscle of opposite action?

2. Are bones solid masses of nonliving minerals? Explain.

3. Johnny and Jarrod are playing. Johnny startles Jarrod, who reacts with a reflex action and strikes Johnny. Of course, Jarrod apologizes profusely, but was he really consciously responsible for hitting Johnny?

Surgical Technologists

Job Description: Surgical technologists work under the supervision of the surgical nurses to ready the operating room and the patient for surgery. The technologists make sure that the room is prepared with linens, equipment, surgical instruments, and fluids (saline, glucose, etc.) that will be needed. They also help by transporting, washing and disinfecting, draping and positioning the patient on the operating table. It is also the surgical technologist who helps in passing instruments and supplies to the surgeon; counting the sponges, needles, and instruments used; preparing specimens for laboratory analysis; and holding retractors and cutting sutures during the operation. After the operation, it is usually the surgical technologist who transports the patient to the recovery room and helps the nurses to sterilize and restock the operating room.

Job Location: The working conditions are normally cool, clean, and well-lit. Work hours are usually during the day. However, the surgical technologist may be placed on a rotating schedule or be on call in order to be available for emergency surgery.

Training Required: Surgical technologists must complete their formal instruction (usually in a technical institute or a hospital) and pass a national certification examination in order to obtain professional credentials. Because surgical technologists must stand on their feet for the hours of an operation, they need stamina. They also must be able to think clearly, be strong emotionally, be orderly, and react quickly since there is little room for error.

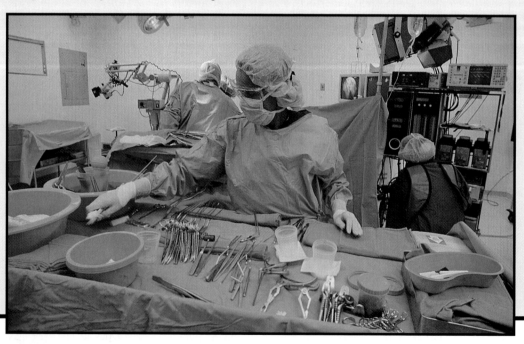

MENTAL AND EMOTIONAL HEALTH

Have you ever wondered why people enjoy riding on roller coasters? The ride is fast, confusing, and scary. At times you may feel that your life is similar to a roller coaster. Sometimes you may be at the peak of happiness; other times you may plummet into a valley of depression or get caught in a spin of confusing circumstances. In order to avoid a "roller coaster" life, you must learn to make wise choices and to respond to circumstances correctly.

CHAPTER 3

"A merry heart doeth good like a medicine: but a broken spirit drieth the bones."

Proverbs 17:22

This chapter explores the concepts involved in maintaining good mental and emotional health. Mental and emotional health affect what the Bible calls the *inner man.* The inner man consists of the mind, the will, and the emotions. These all work together when responding to circumstances. According to Romans 12:2, you should be striving to be "transformed by the renewing of your mind, that ye may prove what is that good, and acceptable, and perfect, will of God."

PUTTING IT TOGETHER

Mental health and *emotional health* are terms that describe the condition of the inner man (the mind, the will, and the emotions). In order to understand how

the inner man works, the following analogy may be used.

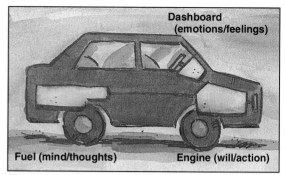

Dashboard (emotions/feelings)

Fuel (mind/thoughts) **Engine (will/action)**

This diagram illustrates the important principle that most of the emotions experienced are a direct result of how you think and what you choose.

A Case Study—Bad News for Ted!

The inner man is constantly involved with the process of thinking, choosing, and feeling. If Ted takes a test at school and fails it, the process of his inner man may function like this:

1. Ted gets a test back from his teacher and looks at the grade. His MIND *evaluates* the score (68%) with what it knows about percentages (anything below 70% is a failing grade in this class). His MIND also *reminds* him that if he gets poor grades he cannot play sports. He has, some time ago, chosen to believe that the most important thing at this time of his life is being admired as a competent athlete. His MIND *reminds* him that he cannot let anything interfere with that goal.

2. Using the thoughts that his MIND has provided, his WILL *decides* that the teacher made the test too hard. He *chooses* to blame someone else.

3. His EMOTIONS register *anger* at his teacher, *fear* toward his parents and his coach, and an increasing *emptiness* and *loneliness* within himself because he knows he is moving further and further away from God and others (his teacher, parents, and coach) as he pursues his own goals in life.

As you can see, what a person thinks and how he chooses ultimately determine his emotions. If Ted continues to think in a carnal (self-centered) fashion and to choose selfishly, his emotions will become more and more of a problem for him. He

may try to ignore his emotions and let the anger burn inside. He may try to express his emotions sinfully by complaining about his teacher, driving recklessly, or yelling at his little brother. He may try to compensate for unpleasant emotions by pursuing some activity that brings him pleasure (sports, drugs, sex, friends, pornography, shopping, work, eating, etc.).

Ted an Addict?

Any activity that Ted engages in to alter his moods (feelings or emotions) has the potential of becoming addictive. Drugs can become addictive in themselves because of the chemical dependency they create in the body. Other activities (pornography, work, music, etc.) become addictive as the person

Every automobile has a dashboard that displays indicator lights and gauges. They alert the driver to the internal condition of the engine (oil pressure and water temperature) as well as the external progress of the vehicle (speed and distance traveled). Emotions are best understood as indicators of the condition of other parts of the inner man (the mind and will) as well as indicators of the progress made toward Christ-likeness (loving God and others).

THINKING THINGS THROUGH

Have you ever been around people who "put their mouths into action without putting their brains into gear"? It can be frustrating and embarrassing. How many times do you just react rather than think and then act? In order to control the inner man, you should be sure to think things through.

As shown in the car analogy, thoughts are the fuel that the will translates into action. If the will uses "high-grade fuel" to make all of its decisions, the will can perform in a way that is pleasing to God. James says that a man's "conversation" (his lifestyle) will reveal the quality of the "wisdom" he has been giving attention to (3:13-18).

Man was created a dependent creature. Although Adam was the highest form of man that has ever existed, he still had to be told who he was and what he was supposed to do on the earth. He did not know all the information. He was dependent on some outside source to give him knowledge.

becomes hooked on the pleasurable mood the activity momentarily provides.

Ted Responds Correctly

God says that you can be "transformed by the renewing of your mind" (Rom. 12:2). How could the situation be different if Ted would react with a renewed mind? With a renewed mind, Ted would be looking at life and its problems from God's perspective.

1. Ted gets a test back from his teacher and looks at the grade. His MIND *evaluates* the score (68%) with what it knows about percentages (anything below 70% is a failing grade in this class). His MIND also *reminds* him that if he gets poor grades he cannot play sports. He has, some time ago, chosen to

believe that the most important thing in his life is pleasing God. He *knows* that his poor grade reflects misplaced priorities. He had not felt like studying because he was discouraged when he was cut from the first string of the soccer team and because he lost his girlfriend to a starting soccer player. He had been living as if God did not even exist. He has not taken time to talk to God or allowed God to talk to him for several weeks. His MIND *reminds* him that God is too loving to be unkind to him and is too wise to make a mistake. He recognizes the crossroad God has brought him to at this time. He must start thinking and acting in ways that reflect a desire to

please God instead of himself.

2. Using the thoughts that his MIND has provided, his WILL *decides* that it is time for him to humble himself and *repent* of his recent independence from God. He *chooses* to thank God for the unsettling grade that made him stop and think. He *chooses* to see his teacher, coach, and parents to let them know what God has been doing to get his attention.

3. His EMOTIONS register *sorrow* and *shame* over his failure, but because he chose to look at his situation from God's perspective, he also experiences *peace* and *joy* because he made the right choices.

There are two sources to which man can turn for data about himself and his purpose. He can turn to God (James calls this "wisdom that is from above" in 3:17) or he can turn to Satan (James calls this wisdom that "descendeth not from above" in 3:15). This means that you are either continually depending on God to tell you how to live or you are depending on Satan to tell you how to live. In the Bible, information from God is called *wisdom;* information from Satan is called *foolishness.* The source of the information with which you feed your mind will affect the choices you make in your will. You cannot get high-grade performance out of a car that is burning low-grade fuel.

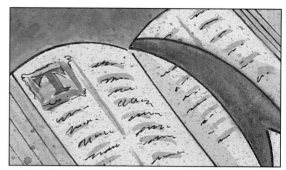

Everyone is born a fool (Prov. 22:15) and remains a fool unless he submits himself to wisdom's teaching methods—doctrine, reproof, correction, and instruction in righteousness (II Tim. 3:16-17). The result of meditating on God's perspective will be stability and usability (Psalm 1). The right fuel for your mind must include right thoughts about God and man.

1. You must think rightly about God (God-concept). This is more important than man's concept of himself (Ps. 50:16-23; especially note v. 21). Man always acts consistently with his view of God; consider Pharaoh, King Saul, Pilate, and the disciples.

2. You must think rightly about man (self-concept). The right concept of self is possible only if man has the right concept of God for "in him we live, and move, and have our being" (Acts 17:28). You cannot define man apart from a proper understanding of God. The Bible does not present man as having inestimable worth, intrinsic value, or unlimited potential. In order for the will to make the proper choices, the mind must understand that man is—

    a. A sinner—although unworthy, he is loved by God.

    b. A son—once saved, he has been granted privileges and responsibilities.

    c. A servant—out of gratitude for his salvation, man should respond with grateful service (Rom. 12:1-2).

The process through which fallen but redeemed man can begin to think like God is called meditation. For the Christian, **meditation** is concentration

Giovanni Andrea Sirani, Michael Overcoming Satan, *Bob Jones University Collection of Religious Art*

(rational, intensive thought) on a specific content (the Word of God) that leads to reflective inner conversation and positive biblical change in action. Through meditation on God's Word a Christian obtains a renewed mind. In Colossians 3:10, Christians are instructed to "put on the new man, which is renewed in knowledge after the image of him that created him."

Section Review

1. What does the term *inner man* mean?

2. List two basic sources from which man can learn about himself and his purpose.

3. What two things affect the emotions?

4. For a Christian, what is meditation?

LOOKING AT SELF-CONCEPT

Too much emphasis is placed on external appearances in today's society. People want to have the perfect body, a magnetic personality, and all the right clothes. Because you are human, you want other people to like you and to make you feel accepted. The way you think and feel about yourself is called your **self-concept.**

If you have what is called a **negative self-concept,** you might think that you can never do anything

right and that no one likes you. Your thoughts might always focus on the things you do wrong. A negative self-concept will eat away at your happiness and, if left unchecked, will result in self-consciousness and depression.

A **positive self-concept** indicates that you have accepted yourself and feel at ease with who you are in relation to your peers.

As a Christian teen-ager, you can combat a negative self-concept by focusing on the Word of God and the person of Jesus Christ. You can find a more balanced perspective of yourself by realizing that you belong to God. The Scripture very clearly teaches that your focus should not be on yourself; it should be on Christ.

When you consider what your self-concept should be, you must avoid extremes. First, guard against the sin of pride. Many people have a more exalted view of themselves than they should have. If you are a Christian, you are a sinner saved by grace and kept by the mercy of God. The Bible repeatedly warns against the dangers of pride. Pride brings contention and destruction.

Because of added involvement, responsibility, and honor in school activities, some may think they are a little better than others around them. A conceited person (someone who has too high an opinion of himself) does not glorify God but seeks his own glory.

If you are attractive, be thankful, but do not focus on your looks; emphasize spiritual growth. If you are a gifted athlete, seek ways of using your abilities to serve God. If you are smart and have an easy time earning good grades, thank God for the intelligence He gave you and use it to glorify Christ. An attitude of *gratitude* and *servitude* will help you guard against pride.

While pride is a great danger to a proper Christian attitude, a failure to realize your uniqueness and potential can be just as dangerous. Many young people have such a poor self-concept that they do not feel confident about anything. These people are often so self-conscious they refuse to try any new task because they do not want to risk failing. The idea of worthlessness can rob you of your greatest opportunities.

It is important to remember that you do have talents and abilities. To be used of God, you must recognize your abilities and have the courage to use them for the Lord. There are jobs that God has planned for you that no one else can do. You were "custom-made" by the greatest craftsman in the

Italian Mannerist 16th c., Saint Paul, *Bob Jones University Collection of Religious Art*

universe and were actually made in His image to complete these tasks.

What should your opinion of yourself be? For the answer to this, go to the Scriptures. Philippians 2:3 says, "Let nothing be done through strife or vainglory; but in lowliness of mind let each esteem other better than themselves." The Apostle Paul referred to himself as the chief of sinners. He said he was not worthy to be called an apostle, yet he realized that he could do all things through Christ. He magnified the office and ministry that God had given him and exhibited an emphasis on God, not on himself.

Probably the best indication of Paul's self-concept is given in I Corinthians 15:10, where Paul says, "But by the grace of God I am what I am." You must recognize that everything you are is due only to God's grace. To be the best you can be for God's service should be your goal as a Christian.

Rather than emphasizing *who* you are, stress *whose* you are.

Intellectual Comprehension

Why do you come to school? Because it is required? In order to have fun with friends? The wise student attends school for the main purpose of learning and expanding his intellect. The wise Christian student does his best not only to benefit himself but also to honor and glorify God.

Be careful to use the opportunities God has given you to learn. Following are some study tips that may be of help to you.

- Listen in class.
- Take accurate notes.
- Do not try to write every word the teacher says; note the major facts.
- Record information in outline form for ease in studying and review.
- Ask questions if you do not understand a concept.
- If you still do not understand, make arrangements to speak with the teacher after school for help.
- Keep up with homework assignments, projects, and readings.
- Be sure to have your work turned in on time.
- Review your notes daily as if you were going to have a quiz (or test) the next day.
- Do not wait until the end of the unit to cram the information into your mind.

Do the best you can with the abilities and time that God has given you. He will reward your efforts.

Thinking takes discipline. Just as an athlete works at building up his muscles, you should be exercising your mind to develop it to its fullest potential for God's glory. Seek after knowledge; work at learning. You are accountable not only to your parents and yourself for your diligence (or lack of it) but also to God.

Evaluating Information

In Columbus's day, many of his peers assumed that the world was flat and his voyage would result in disaster. Today, no one questions whether the earth is flat or round. Science and technology have proved that the earth is a sphere. However, not all information given is necessarily true. In reading, hearing, and thinking, it is vital to consider and evaluate information in comparison to biblical truths.

There are many philosophies and beliefs that you will confront in your lifetime. God has given man the ability to **reason,** or understand, to organize, and to use information. However, a Christian must be sure to exercise **discernment,** or judgment, and evaluate information in the light of God's Word. Of course this makes it imperative for you to know what God's Word says. You must check the accuracy of the information you read and hear.

If you do not evaluate information, bad consequences can occur. For example, humanism has exerted a great influence on society today. If you begin to truly believe the philosophy that man is the center of all, and that you are the ruler of your own destiny, pride enters and a sense of invulnerability to rules can influence your thinking. You may begin to assume that the boundaries set by laws and regulations do not apply to you. You need to evaluate the philosophies around you in order to protect yourself from believing a lie and to guard against hurting yourself and others around you. It is your responsibility to evaluate information correctly; think it through.

Learning More

"*Free Pizza*—all you can eat!" If you were to read this advertisement, would you be at the pizzeria? Most students would be. However, if you were to read "*Free Learning*—all you can hold!" would you be rushing to attend? Somehow it seems much easier to indulge in almost anything other than thinking. Perhaps you have not discovered the excitement and fun that learning can be.

In order to become better informed and more well-rounded in a variety of subjects, consider studying a topic or developing a hobby during vacation or during each school year. Many astronomers and geologists started out with a simple telescope or rock collection.

- Choose a subject that is of interest to you (skiing, insects, weather, spelling, literature, computers, rockets, electricity, carpentry, etc.).
- Go to the library and read about the subject.
- Talk to people who are in that field of study or are interested in it.
- Begin to collect, participate, or proceed in the subject chosen.

It will amaze you how interesting learning can be. After you have mastered the subject or hobby, add another field of study.

How many times have you sung the song "More About Jesus"? Do you really want to learn more about Jesus, God, and the Bible? If so, read the Bible, meditate on it, and memorize it. Bible memorization not only increases mental acuity but also strengthens the Christian. Paul wrote in Colossians 1:9-11, "that ye might be filled with the knowledge of his will in all wisdom and spiritual understanding; that ye might walk worthy of the Lord unto all pleasing, being fruitful in every good work, and increasing in the knowledge of God; strengthened with all might, according to his glorious power." Hiding God's Word in the portals of the mind and heart is one of the best ways to increase in godly wisdom and knowledge.

Section Review

1. What is an excessively high opinion of yourself called?

2. Describe how the Apostle Paul viewed himself.

3. Explain how one can increase knowledge and become more well-rounded in various topics.

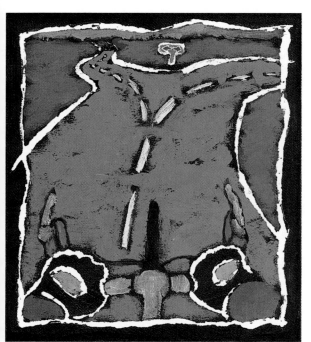

God has given man the ability and responsibility to make choices. A seemingly small decision may make a world of difference as to where your path ends.

MAKING CHOICES

The purpose for filling the mind with God's thoughts is to promote choices that are pleasing to God instead of seeking things pleasing to self. Look in Psalm 119 to see how many times David asks God to show him His way so that he might choose rightly. Joshua states that the purpose of meditation is "that thou mayest observe to do according to all that is written therein" (1:8).

As a Christian, you are to "gird up the loins of your mind" that you may walk as "obedient children" (I Pet. 1:13-14). The knowledge of God and of your relationship with Him is to be the basis for your choices (Rom. 12:1-2). If the mind is not renewed with this knowledge, it will not be transformed to become like Christ and, therefore, not be useful to Him.

It does not matter how much a person knows; it is what he does with what he knows that counts. A medical technician knows how to administer CPR,

but unless he applies it to the victim, his knowledge is useless. A student may know how to complete his homework; however, unless he does it, he will not get credit for it. By the same token, a Christian who knows to cast his cares upon the Lord will not know peace until he places his burdens in the hands of God (I Pet. 5:7). A person must chose to do what is right or wrong. Making correct choices is vital to the development of the inner man.

Not My Will

Decisions! Decisions! You make decisions all the time. Some are relatively simple (what to wear), while others are more difficult (where to go to college). How does one go about making the *right* decision?

Before you make any decisions, you must first answer the most important question of who is in control of your life. Is Christ supreme in your life? Do you want His will or your own? Many decisions are already made for you if you submit your will to Christ and the directions given in His Word.

When you make a decision, identify your values. Do you value the eternal or the temporal? Do you value family more than friends? Get down to the roots of each dilemma. What other areas of your life will be affected by your decision? Identify whether your choice will help or hinder others. Examine your options. Consider your goals. What is important to you? Or better yet, what is important to Christ?

Decision making is a thinking process. For a Christian, it should also be a praying process. Take time to think things through; evaluate your decisions. It is also wise to refrain from making decisions when you are emotionally upset. Many foolish decisions result from angry, bitter, rash reactions or from overjoyed, ecstatic reactions. Seek godly wisdom. Proverbs 3:5-7 says, "Trust in the Lord with all thine heart; and lean not unto thine own understanding. In all thy ways acknowledge him, and he shall direct thy paths. Be not wise in thine own eyes: fear the Lord, and depart from evil."

The Decision-making Process

When making a decision, it is helpful to follow specific steps of decision making.

1. State the problem.
2. Seek solutions.
3. Think through the alternatives.
4. Make a choice.
5. Take action and accept responsibility for your decision.

The first priority is identifying the problem. It often helps to write the problem out. Make sure that your statement is specific and true. For instance, the problem may seem to be "Should I go to the party?" In truth, the problem might be that you know that a movie will be shown and music will be played that neither of which your parents or you approve. Therefore, the true problem is "Should I go to the party even though they are watching a movie and listening to music that is unacceptable?"

The second step of decision making is to seek solutions to the problem. When seeking solutions, list as many options as you can think of. Do not rule out any ideas yet; they may prove to be a springboard for a solution. For major decisions, it would be wise to seek godly counsel. Talk it over with your parents, pastor, or youth pastor.

The third step is to think through the alternatives. Take time to evaluate all your possible solutions in light of your goals, values, and the future consequences. This is the time to pray for guidance and wisdom. Take into consideration the advice given by counsel. Determine whether the mediocre solutions could be improved upon. If the idea is hopeless, delete it from your list.

After you have looked at many different solutions and thought through the alternatives, it is time to make your decision. If you were prayerful and careful in the first three steps, the wisest decision should be fairly obvious. God does not want His will to be obscure to you. He will point the way, if you are willing to follow it.

The final step, and possibly the most difficult, is taking action and accepting the consequences for the decision, good or bad. Many people stop at the decision stage without realizing that they need to activate their decision and take responsibility for it. You must follow through and act upon your choice. If you procrastinate to the point that your decision is no longer feasible, then you have made the decision not to decide. When God opens doors for you or shows you something you ought to do, it is a sin to avoid or ignore His leading. James 4:17 is very clear in stating, "Therefore to him that knoweth to do good, and doeth it not, to him it is sin."

Section Review

1. Before any other decisions are made, what needs to be decided first?

2. List in order the five steps of decision making.

3. Why is it unwise to make a decision when emotionally upset?

4. At which step of the decision-making process is action actually taken to implement the decision?

CONTROLLING YOUR REACTIONS

Emotional health is often described as the absence of emotional disorder. Others define it as the ability to cope with daily routine and problems. Another definition is that emotional health is a positive outlook on life. All these views are true. Emotional health deals with your ability to control your reactions to circumstances.

Traits of Emotional Health

The Christian realizes that the foundation for good emotional health is a proper relationship with God. When a person obediently chooses to please God and trusts God to control all the situations that confront him in life, he finds peace, contentment, and joy.

Peace—In the midst of national crisis or personal struggles, people search for peace. Unfortunately, people seek peace everywhere except where true peace is found. As a Christian you have a source of peace that no psychological technique can come close to duplicating. When you are confronted with troubles or problems, you can turn to Christ for strength and guidance.

However, according to Isaiah 48:22, there is no true peace for the unsaved person. That is because true peace is not something you can produce for yourself. Peace is a gift from God to those who trust Him.

Biblical peace of mind does not come because God protects the Christian from conflict. In fact, Scripture promises that the Christian will face difficulties. A person should expect persecution when taking a stand for Christ. The world hated Christ; therefore, they will hate His followers for standing in His name. Looking to the Lord gives a stronghold in life when circumstances seem confusing and constantly changing. Only the Lord can give peace in the midst of many problems.

Contentment—In this society of greed and materialism, dissatisfaction with circumstances is common. "The-grass-is-greener-on-the-other-side-of-the-fence" philosophy can easily creep into the thoughts and gain a stronghold. A student can quickly fall into the trap of always wanting the physical appearance or attributes of peers.

Even in the midst of a national or personal crisis, a Christian can have the peace of God. "Peace I leave with you, my peace I give unto you: not as the world giveth, give I unto you. Let not your heart be troubled, neither let it be afraid" (John 14:27).

Pressures from Events in Life

Specific events that occur in life can act as stressors. How many stressful events have you faced in the past year? The following chart shows some major stressors or pressures you may face in life. As a Christian, you can rest in the knowledge that your life is in the loving hands of God. Do not focus on the stressors, but examine these as opportunities to experience God's strength and grace. No matter how difficult the circumstance, Philippians 4:13 stands true: "I can do all things through Christ which strengtheneth me."

EXTREME PRESSURE
Death of a close family member
Diagnosis of serious illness
Divorce of parents
Expulsion from school
Broken engagement
Getting married
Loss of job
Change in health of a family member
Death of a close friend

MODERATE PRESSURE
Reduced harmony in a dating relationship
Outstanding personal achievement
Relocation of family
Change in personal habits
Conflict with a teacher
Scheduling conflicts
Change in church activities
Transfer to new school
Change in social involvement

SLIGHT PRESSURE
Change in sleeping patterns
Being at home for the holidays
Vacation
Change in eating habits

Because discontentment often produces such problems as envy and bitterness, it can have disastrous results in a Christian's life. Being discontent can affect your emotional and physical health, rob you of peace, and affect your relationship with God. There is much to lose by allowing discontentment into your life. Begin right now to cultivate an attitude of contentment.

Joy—Many of the wealthiest and most famous people in the world have also been the most unhappy. Suicide, divorce, drug use, and depression are common among the rich and famous. Do material possessions and fame guarantee happiness? Definitely not.

The distinction between joy and happiness is not always clear. The two words are often used interchangeably, and there is certainly some overlap between the terms. In this context, joy is an enduring state of peace and acceptance that transcends circumstances, and happiness is fleeting feelings of excitement and rejoicing. Whatever it is

called, the emphasis should be in seeking a life that is marked by consistent fulfillment in the will of God rather than living from one artificial and temporary high point to the next.

The world seeks for happiness, but the Christian has joy through Christ. Matthew 6 says that unbelievers seek for *things* such as food and raiment. But the Christian is commanded to "seek . . . first the kingdom of God, and his righteousness; and all these things shall be added unto you" (v. 33). Joy for the Christian comes from finding God's will and doing it.

In John 15:11 Christ says, "These things have I spoken unto you, that my joy may remain in you, and that your joy might be full." Circumstances can rob you of your happiness, but you can have joy even in the worst of circumstances. The disciples rejoiced even when they were beaten and persecuted (Acts 5:40-41). Happiness is often temporary, but the joy that Christ gives lasts forever.

Facial expressions for emotions are the same around the world. Even people who are born blind use the universal expressions for happiness (smiling).

Unpleasant Emotions

Everyone is subject to sorrow, fear, anger, jealousy, shame, disgust, hurt, and loneliness. These are unpleasant emotions that God made man capable of feeling. God understands and is "touched with the feeling of our infirmities" because he experienced them while on earth. Christ felt unpleasant emotions, "yet without sin" (Heb. 4:15).

All unpleasant emotions must be examined by the mind as soon as they are recognized as unpleasant. They must be evaluated according to wisdom and not foolishness. The right choices of the will, based on godly wisdom in the mind, will then result in the ability to respond correctly to the unpleasant emotions. Peace, contentment, and joy will either replace the unpleasant emotions or at least coexist with and dominate the unpleasant emotions. "Wherein ye greatly rejoice, though now for a season, if need be, ye are in heaviness through manifold temptations: that the trial of your faith, being much more precious than of gold that perisheth, though it be tried with fire, might be found unto praise and honour and glory at the appearing of Jesus Christ" (I Pet. 1:6-7).

It is important to understand that God made man capable of experiencing pleasant and unpleasant emotions at the same time. For example, a friend loses a parent in death. He may hurt but at the same time experience peace and joy from God. First Peter 1:6 testifies that he can "rejoice" at the same time he experiences "heaviness." As his mind considers the loss of his loved one, your friend's will decides that he misses his parent. His emotions are sorrowful. This is a legitimate emotion but unpleasant. If he chooses (exercise of the will) to meditate (exercise of the mind) on God's goodness and omnipotence, he will experience peace, contentment, and joy in his sorrow. However, if his mind is determined that he does not like unpleasant feelings and must avoid them at all costs, he may choose to avoid any thought or reminder of the deceased. The resulting emotions may be hardness and bitterness.

Stress

An important influence on mental and emotional health is stress. **Stress** is the body's reaction to any demand placed on it. It is the *strain* on the body that occurs when pressures are not handled biblically. **Stressors** are things that cause stress; they are the *pressures* of living, the demands placed on a person. Jogging a mile, fighting with your sister, giving a speech, or meeting a friend's parents are stressors. Notice that stressors are not always caused by *bad* things happening (death of a loved one, expulsion, fear). Sometimes wonderful things can cause stress (graduation, winning a game, getting engaged). Stress can be caused by pleasant as well as unpleasant situations. You must learn to handle both pleasant and unpleasant pressure biblically in order to reduce strain on your body.

When you are faced with strong stressors, your body prepares for action. Have you ever felt your heart beating rapidly before a big game or an important test? That is one of the changes that occurs when you are faced with pressure. Your heart beats faster and you breathe more rapidly. Once you begin the test or competition, your body's reactions usually settle down. However, if you find many questions you cannot answer or you make several errors in the ball game, these reactions may continue and even increase.

Your response to the demands placed on you can affect your body's response so that your heart and lungs continue to work faster and faster. When you respond incorrectly to the stressors, harmful effects can result. Incorrect responses can affect your performance and eventually result in a variety of medical problems such as stomach ulcers, high blood pressure, headaches, and even a heart attack. Although stress is a normal part of life, if it is not handled properly, it can kill you.

A disciplined body and a renewed mind will help you to cope with life's pressures. Physical health can

---

Fight or Flight Response

When you are faced with strong stressors, your body prepares for emergency action. The "fight or flight" response is usually signaled by rapid heartbeat and breathing, sweaty palms, dry mouth, and a "knot" in the stomach. The following body changes also occur:

- Pupils dilate.
- Blood pressure rises.
- Blood supply to the skeletal muscles increases.
- Blood sugar level increases.
- Epinephrine is secreted.
- Digestion slows down.
- Arrector pili muscles in the skin contract so that hair stands on end.

Can I Cry Now?

Crying is, in physiological terms, "inspiration followed by a series of short spasmodic expirations, the glottis being freely open during the whole time and the vocal folds being thrown into characteristic vibrations. Accompanying facial expressions are also part of this action. Laughing consists essentially of the same movements as in crying, but the rhythm and the accompany-

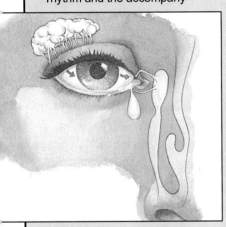

ing facial expressions are different. Laughing and crying frequently become indistinguishable" (Sigmund Grollman, *The Human Body: Its Structure and Physiology,* 3rd ed., New York: Macmillan Publishing Co., Inc., 1974).

Tears are usually produced to moisten the eye, protect it from infection, and wash away irritants. However, tears are also produced when you cry. Chemical analysis has been done on emotion-

shed tears and functional tears (such as tears caused by exposure to onion vapors, wind, or irritants). The findings indicate that emotion-caused tears have more protein in them. Some researchers believe that crying helps to eliminate harmful chemicals or proteins from the body. Whether this is the case or not, crying has proved an effective way to reduce tension.

Tears are formed in the lachrymal glands located above each eye in a depression of the frontal bone. The tears drain from a dozen small tear ducts in the upper and outer corners of each eye. The fluid then flows across the eye and empties through two small dots (punctae) at the inner corner of the eye. (These lead to the lachrymal sac.) Because tears empty into ducts leading to the nasal cavities, you often have to blow your nose when you cry.

Crying will not solve problems or remove pressures. However, crying does help to relax a person and to clear his mind so that he can proceed to cope with the stressors surrounding him.

Many Christians see crying as a sign of spiritual immaturity or failure to trust in the Lord. However, God created man with the ability to cry in response to strong emotion. In fact, the Bible records that "Jesus wept" (John 11:35).

You should not be ashamed of shedding legitimate tears. There should be no guilt from crying to dissolve emotional tensions. However, as in everything, there is a time and place for crying. Crying to get attention, sway a decision, or interrupt is inappropriate and immature. Romans 12:15 says to "rejoice with them that do rejoice, and weep with them that weep." Can you cry now? Laugh if you can, but cry if you have to. "We may discover that we can see farther through a tear than through a telescope. Weeping can be appropriate, noble, and majestic. Our tears can be crystallized into lenses through which we can better see God's purpose for us" (Stanley P. Cornils, *Managing Grief Wisely,* Grand Rapids: Baker Book House, 1967, p. 29).

Although all animals living in air produce tears to keep their eyes moist, man is the only creature that weeps.

Stress Reduction Tips

1. Reduce polyphasic thinking (thinking about several things and projects at one time).

2. Reduce time urgency (go slowly, relax, do not push so hard and fast).

3. Get good nutrition and rest.

4. See the humorous side of things (laugh, enjoy friends, read a funny story or comic strip).

5. Seek things to be thankful for; be optimistic.

6. Provide support for others; indulge in a hobby; stay busy, but do not add stressors.

7. Listen to quiet music and sing hymns.

8. Exercise

   a. Aerobic exercises or walking

   b. Back stretches

   c. Jaw relaxers and facial exercises

   d. Good posture

   e. Progressive relaxation (tensing and relaxing groups of muscles)

Note: Beware of using the following stress management techniques: transcendental meditation, Imagery or Visualization, REST (Restricted Environmental Stimulus Therapy–sensory deprivation or sensory isolation by using flotation tanks or isolation tanks), yoga, tai chi (tai chi chuan), or biofeedback. These methods are based on Eastern mystical religion and philosophy. They can leave the mind open to demonic influence and attack. Most of these practices are presented as being scientific; they are not.

The majority of the destructive results of stress do not come from the stressor but from the way one reacts to it. As a Christian, you are equipped with the power of God to overcome stress. You can rest in His promise "that all things work together for good to them that love God" (Rom. 8:28). Godly control of the inner man makes it possible to control your reactions when stressful situations arise.

affect your reactions. For instance, sickness and medications may alter one's thinking and reaction patterns. A regular program of exercise has been found to help relieve some of the **symptoms** of stress. (A symptom is an evidence or sign of a condition.) A nutritious diet is also necessary to combat stressors. Unfortunately, many people skip meals or snack only on junk food when they are facing stressors such as exams, deadlines, or important events. A disciplined body also needs adequate rest. A lack of sleep can hinder you from thinking clearly and from making wise choices. Regular exercise, a nutritious diet, and adequate rest will do much to help you meet stressors calmly.

However, the best way to cope with stress is to react to the cause of stress properly. When first confronted with a stressor, the mind should evaluate the problem. What is the problem? What are possible solutions? How does this affect other facets or people in your life? Think it through, but think with a renewed mind and not a carnal mind. A carnal mind evaluates pressures from a human perspective. A mind that is renewed by God will seek God's perspective. The biblical way to handle stressors is to see pressures with a renewed mind and to determine to react in ways that glorify God rather than self.

Section Review

1. What is the foundation for good emotional health?
2. What is the difference between stress and stressors?
3. What three things help to promote a disciplined body?
4. What is the biblical way to handle stressors?

GETTING HELP

You may face problems or situations that seem to get beyond your control, and you want to talk to someone or get advice. In these times, many people are available to talk with you and are more than willing to spend any amount of time necessary to help you through your problems.

Christ—The Christian always has someone he can go to when he needs help. Christ cares for him and has said in His Word to cast all cares on Him. Christ knows every problem you will ever face, and He has every solution. Nothing is too difficult for the Lord.

Hebrews 4:15-16 says, "For we have not an high priest which cannot be touched with the feeling of our infirmities; but was in all points tempted like as we are, yet without sin. Let us therefore come boldly unto the throne of grace, that we may obtain mercy, and find grace to help in time of need." A child of God has the privilege of having a Counselor who is all knowing and who is always available.

Parents—Though times have changed, life's problems are similar for every generation. Godly parents love their children more than anyone else in the world does. Your parents may not always give the advice that you want to hear, but they have the advantage of having already passed through many of the problems you are facing now. You may be surprised how much your parents know if you would only consult them. The Bible commands children to listen to and to obey their parents. By getting scriptural advice from parents, you can avoid some bad consequences.

Pastors and Teachers—Pastors and godly teachers are also good sources of counsel. Because they work with many young people, they often have a good understanding of the problems teen-agers face. Do not feel that your pastor or teacher is too busy for your problems. Most pastors and teachers feel it is an honor to help direct the lives of young people and consider it a special part of their ministry.

Psychologists and Psychiatrists—The study of the mind and its processes is fascinating and complex. There are people who have dedicated their lives to this study. A medical doctor who specializes in the study of emotional health and disease is called a psychiatrist. A psychologist is an individual who specializes in emotional health but has not completed training as a medical doctor.

There are Christian professionals in this field; however, most psychiatrists and psychologists are trained from a worldly, secular perspective and use humanistic theories to guide their practices. These men and women cannot be trusted to give godly guidance. "But the natural man receiveth not the things of the Spirit of God: for they are foolishness unto him: neither can he know them, because they are spiritually discerned" (I Cor. 2:14). Believers should seek help from Christians who are qualified to give wise, scriptural counsel.

"The way of a fool is right in his own eyes: but he that hearkeneth unto counsel is wise."
Proverbs 12:15

"Hear counsel, and receive instruction, that thou mayest be wise in thy latter end. There are many devices in a man's heart; nevertheless the counsel of the Lord, that shall stand." Proverbs 19:20-21

"There is no wisdom nor understanding nor counsel against the Lord." Proverbs 21:30

Emotional Disorders

"You are crazy!" This phrase is often used in conversation. For the most part, it is used as a jest indicating that a person is acting recklessly or expecting the impossible. Rarely is this phrase used in pointing out a person with an illness.

Alzheimer's disease causes the destruction of brain tissue. The patient progressively deteriorates in his ability to think. In the early stages, short-term memory is lost. As the brain degenerates, personality changes and disorientation increase.

There are people, however, who suffer from physical disorders (such as Alzheimer's, hardening of the arteries, hormone imbalance, brain damage) that affect the mind. A physical problem can cause a person to think or act abnormally. Some symptoms are very mild but keep one from doing his best.

Mental disorders as well as physical disorders can affect a person. Much that is called *mental illness* today is actually the result of sin—brought on by such things as guilt, bitterness, resentment, rebellion, and pride. In these cases, spiritual corrections must be applied rather than psychological. Sufferers need to get their hearts right with God before they can experience good emotional health.

Many severe disorders do not begin as tremendous problems. They are often the result of smaller problems that were never handled properly. A small problem such as anxiety can lead to a more serious problem such as depression. The following section will look at some common emotional problems.

Anxiety—**Anxiety** is the fear or dread of threats; these threats may be real or imagined. There are many things that make teen-agers anxious. Not doing well in your classes, not being accepted by your peers, and not having friends are some of the things that may make you anxious. Worrying accomplishes nothing helpful. Instead of worrying, follow the biblical instructions given in Ephesians 4:22-24.

- Identify specific problems and unfulfilled responsibilities and repent of your neglect or self-centeredness ("put off the old man").

  Specific problems—*"I must plan the big school banquet, and I am afraid of forgetting something."* (Lack of trust or organization); *"I must speak in front of the class, and I am afraid of looking foolish."* (Self-protection or pride)

Unfulfilled responsibilities toward God—*"I have not sought God's guidance."* (Lack of personal devotions or prayer); *"I have*

not been willing to trust God for help." (Lack of faith or trust)

Unfulfilled responsibilities toward others— *"I did not do my chores."* (Lack of obedience or planning); *"I am not ready for my test."* (Lack of discipline to listen in class or to study)

- Identify unbiblical reasoning and motives, and then replace them with biblical thinking ("and be renewed in the spirit of your mind").

  Unbiblical thinking—*"I am afraid that I am becoming afraid."* (Fear spiral); *"I will do anything to get rid of this problem!"* (Rash vow); *"I cannot help it; this fear just overpowers me."* (Victim theme)

  Biblical thinking—*"God will help me to do the things He has given me to do."* (Isa. 41:10, 13; Phil. 4:13); *"If I must suffer or go through unpleasant experiences, God is still in control and will help me."* (I and II Peter, James 1 and 5)

- Develop a biblical plan of action ("put on the new man" [Phil. 4]).

  Thank God for your situation (vv. 4-6).

  Ask God for help (vv. 6-7).

  Do not allow sinful and fearful thoughts to occupy your mind (v. 8).

  Do the loving thing (toward God or others) that the fear would keep you from doing whether you feel like it or not (vv. 9, 11-13).

When anxiety rather than God controls a Christian, fear is a sin. God has not given believers the "spirit of fear" (II Tim. 1:7), and He says in Philippians 4:6 that you should "be careful [anxious] for nothing." By putting your trust in Him, you can overcome anxiety.

Why worry about the past? You cannot change it. If there is sin in your past, then you must confess it and forsake it. Christ's blood is able to cleanse you from all unrighteousness. If you are anxious about the past even though you have done your best to correct your sins and mistakes, you should follow the example of Paul and forget those things which are behind (Phil. 3:13).

Why worry about the present? God has given you this day to do those things He has called you to do. God has promised never to leave you (Heb. 13:5). When you take a test, play ball for your team, or stand against your friends who are doing wrong, God is with you. Is there any task or problem that is too big for you and God?

Why worry about the future? The future is in the hands of God. God knows the end from the beginning. He knows what you will face tomorrow, and He will make sure that you are prepared for what lies ahead. You should prepare for the future, remembering to "take therefore no thought for the morrow: for the morrow shall take thought for the things of itself. Sufficient unto the day is the evil thereof" (Matt. 6:34).

Depression—Sometimes called the "common cold" of emotional disorders, depression is becoming more and more prevalent every day. In fact, a little less than one-fourth of all women and about one-tenth of all men have suffered from serious depression at some time. **Depression** is a deep feeling of sadness, discouragement, or helplessness that can affect every area of life. Normally these feelings last only a few minutes or a few hours; however, some people stay depressed much longer.

Although most Christians agree that sin can cause depression, depression is not always a result of sin. Other factors, such as a chemical imbalance or a reaction to a medication, can cause depression. Physical stress caused by illness or a lack of sleep can also be a cause of depression.

If depression results from sin, repentance of sin and replacement with biblical attitudes are essential. A positive perspective of counting blessings and finding verses of reassurance can help produce biblical responses.

Getting plenty of rest, whether well or sick, provides many benefits. A person's outlook on life will be more positive, making decisions will be easier, and his attention span will be longer if he

Unlike depression, sadness is short term and does not pervade one's personality, perceptions, or actions.

gets the amount of sleep his body needs. Sleep is extremely important when it comes to controlling emotions and fighting depression.

Another precaution to take in the fight against depression is getting plenty of exercise. Exercising can give a break from the pressures of a schedule and supply time to think over problems rather than allow worry to enter into the picture.

Eating properly can also help combat depression. Some people tend to binge and eat and eat and eat when they are depressed. Others respond by refusing to eat. A balanced, nutritious diet is important to keep the body chemistry balanced and to keep the mind in peak condition. Notice the response of Paul and his companions at sea when they finally ate after fourteen days of fasting in Acts 27:35-36. "And when he had thus spoken, he took bread, and gave thanks to God in presence of them all: and when he had broken it, he began to eat. Then were they all of good cheer, and they also took some meat."

Phobia: Exaggerated and Illogical Fear

Phobias can result from bad experiences that caused terror in the past. People with phobias are overcome with anxiety when faced with the presence of whatever they fear. This behavior is usually exaggerated and illogical. These unreasonable fears often intensify to the point that they interfere with normal activity. Christians can overcome fear through Christ. Second Timothy 1:7 says, "For God hath not given us the spirit of fear; but of power, and of love, and of a sound mind."

Phobia	Fear of
Acrophobia	Heights
Aerophobia	Air or flying
Agoraphobia	Open spaces
Androphobia	Men
Anthropophobia	People
Apiphobia	Bees
Astraphobia	Storms, lightning, and thunder
Claustrophobia	Enclosed spaces
Decidophobia	Making decisions
Entomophobia	Insects
Ergophobia	Work
Gynephobia	Women
Hemophobia	Blood
Hydrophobia	Water
Microphobia	Bacteria
Monophobia	Being alone
Necrophobia	Death or corpses
Nyctophobia	Darkness
Ochlophobia	Crowds
Ophidiophobia	Snakes
Phonophobia	Speaking aloud
Sophophobia	Learning
Triskaidekaphobia	Number 13
Xenophobia	Strangers
Zoophobia	Animals

Suicide—**Suicide** is the act of voluntarily taking one's life. When a person becomes very depressed, he often begins to think that life is no longer worth living. But even when circumstances are very bad, they are seldom as hopeless as the suicidal person believes they are. No matter how badly a person has sinned, the Bible teaches that Christ died for that sin and gives a way back to a right relationship with God. First John 1:9 states, "If we confess our sins, he is faithful and just to forgive us our sins, and to cleanse us from all unrighteousness."

Suicide has become a major cause of death among teen-agers. Christian homes are not exempt from this problem. Love, discipline, and communication are factors that help to prevent suicide, and certainly these should be evident in Christian homes. However, many Christian homes are not good examples in these areas. The higher expectations for children from Christian homes may actually make the problem worse. Even if surrounding circumstances are difficult, God expects His children to display an attitude of faith and trust in Him.

Most people who commit suicide give several clues ahead of time. They may talk about suicide, give prized possessions away, or act as though they do not care what happens to them. Be watchful for these danger signals. Many suicides can be prevented by finding help for this type of person. An important step toward preventing suicide is recognizing the potential casualty. Most people considering suicide give some indication of their intentions. Listed below are some of the warning signals of suicide.

- Feelings of worthlessness or hopelessness
- Withdrawal and isolation
- Alcohol or drug abuse
- Preoccupation with death and morbidity
- Apathy and lethargy or restlessness and hyperactivity
- Giving away prized possessions
- Moodiness, loneliness, depression
- Failed love relationship
- Neglect of personal hygiene
- Big change in eating or sleeping habits
- Suicidal talk
- Making a suicide plan
- Writing a suicide note

Every threat of suicide should be taken seriously. Not everyone who talks about suicide actually commits suicide, but each one is a potential casualty. It is important to get qualified help for these people. Do not attempt to deal with the problem by yourself. You may find out too late that you were not qualified to do so.

It Is All in Your Mind

Have you ever noticed how your state of mind influences the way you feel? For example, have you ever felt great and then bumped into a friend who is sick or discouraged? As you talked with him, did the day seem to lose the rosiness it had earlier? As a sick person discusses his illness, have you ever started aching or coughing too? Your mind influences how you feel.

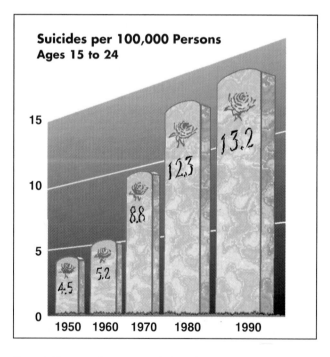

Suicides per 100,000 Persons Ages 15 to 24

The suicide rate of young people has risen 193% in the past 40 years. SOURCE: American Association of Suicidology.

Some of the physical illnesses for which people go to the doctor are related to their state of mind. As mentioned earlier, stress that is not handled properly can result in actual physical changes in the body that can produce illness. Illnesses that are caused by one's state of mind are called **psychosomatic** (SIE kuh so MAT ik) **illnesses.**

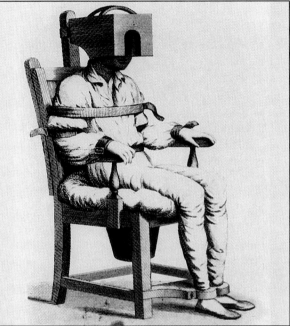

Benjamin Rush, an American physician and also signer of the Declaration of Independence, sought an independence of sorts for the mentally disturbed. He designed this "tranquilising chair" to treat what he believed to be "diseases of the mind." His concept of physical causes for mental disorders varied greatly from the standard belief that all mental problems stemmed from demon possession.

The same mind that can make you sick can also help make you well. Researchers know that recovery from many serious illnesses may depend as much on the patient's state of mind as on any medication the patient may take. The individual who has a strong will to live and whose goal is to overcome his illness is much more likely to recover quickly from health problems. God sets forth this principle in Proverbs 17:22: "A merry heart doeth good like a medicine: but a broken spirit drieth the bones."

Psychoses and Neuroses

Emotional illness is often divided into two major categories: psychoses and neuroses. Severe emotional disorders in which a person loses his ability to deal with real life are called **psychoses** (sie KOH SEEZ; singular, psychosis [sie KOH sis]). A person who suffers from such a disorder is *psychotic* (sie KAHT ik). The psychotic may have moods that change drastically for no apparent reason. He may be elated one minute and severely depressed the next. Another characteristic of psychosis is that the person has trouble thinking clearly and may be unable to distinguish between reality and fantasy. Psychoses are often seen as some of the most severe emotional problems. However, a person can have the symptoms of psychosis as a result of not getting enough sleep or as a side effect of certain drugs. **Neuroses** (noo ROH SEEZ; singular, neurosis, [new ROH sis]) are emotional disorders less severe than psychoses. A person who suffers from a neurosis is called *neurotic* (noo RAHT ik). Anxiety and depression are common in neurotics. The neurotic may also have difficulty sleeping and suffer from a variety of fears. Although a neurotic does not lose touch with reality like a psychotic does, he may have great difficulty completing his daily routine.

The English artist William Hogarth made this engraving portraying the interior of Bethlehem Hospital in London. "The Rake's Progress: Scene in Bedlam" was the eighth engraving in a moral series showing the end of a sinful life.

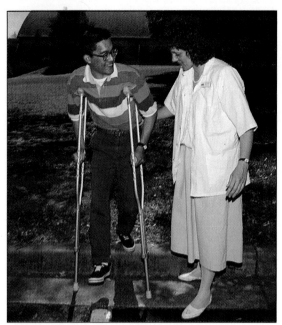
Physical therapy after an injury is not easy. Many times, having a good attitude can bring about a faster recovery.

Promoting Emotional Health

What can you do to promote emotional health? The foundation for emotional health is a proper relationship with God. You must have a renewed mind in order to correctly evaluate problems and make wise decisions. Only God's ability to forgive and change a person's thinking and will can result in healthy emotions. In addition, there are some practical steps that you can take to help you progress toward good emotional health.

Direct Your Thoughts—The attitude of your heart and the choices that you make will greatly influence your life. Proverbs 12:5 says, "The thoughts of the righteous are right: but the counsels of the wicked are deceit." If your mind dwells on wickedness, it will lead to wicked actions. How can you avoid evil thoughts? Every day you are surrounded by temptations for evil thinking. A good way to avoid wrong thoughts is to replace them with right thoughts. Philippians 4:8 instructs Christians to think on things that are true, honest, just, pure, lovely, of good report, virtuous, and worthy of praise. If you flood your mind with these thoughts, you will not find it as difficult to avoid evil thoughts.

The way a person views things will affect his emotional health also. Some people will usually see the worst side of any situation. People who see the problems rather than the opportunities are often called **pessimists. Optimists,** on the other hand, are people who look for positive aspects of life even in the midst of problems. These people see solutions rather than problems.

Work Toward Goals—Home*work,* house*work,* yard *work;* the list could go on and on. Most people do not like to work. You may think of work as something that should be avoided as much as possible. However, God created man with a need to work. Working can give a feeling of accomplishment. It is this feeling of accomplishment that is "sweet to the soul" (Prov. 13:19). As a Christian, you can also have peace and joy by doing the work to which God has called you. Your work helps give more meaning to your life.

One way to help you work better is to form goals. As discussed at the end of Chapter 1, a goal is an end or purpose toward which you work. Goals give you something to strive for and often inspire you to work harder. As you achieve your goals, you will gain a sense of satisfaction.

Avoid Procrastination—Waiting until later to do something you should do now is called **procrastination.** Many times when there is something you do not want to do, you put it off until a later time. Writing reports, practicing a musical instrument, studying for tests, and cleaning the room are some tasks that teen-agers often procrastinate doing.

Remember that procrastination does not eliminate a job; it only causes you to wait until the last minute. Instead of working to complete a task, you may waste energy worrying about it. Many times people end up doing a sloppy or poor job because they put it off and run out of time, energy, or resources.

Procrastination usually leads to poor work, anxiety, and dissatisfaction. The way to conquer procrastination is to start jobs early and to work on them steadily. Most jobs are not that hard once you get started. Think the job through, make plans, and carry out your plans.

Focus on Others—You have probably heard the statement that the way to spell joy is **J**esus first, **O**thers second, and **Y**ourself last. This simple idea contains much truth. As previously stated, the foundation for mental health is to be right with God. If you are right with God, you will also be concerned for other people (I John 4:7-8).

When you are discouraged or depressed, try thinking about others who have worse problems than you have. Then do your best to help them and to show them that you care. Soon you may find that your problems are not as big as you once thought they were. Some of the happiest people in the world are those who have learned to spend their lives helping others.

STRIVING FOR MATURITY

Many a child has asked his parent, "When will I be grown up?" Physically, people usually mature during their teen years. However, mentally, emotionally, and spiritually, some people never "grow up." **Maturity** is sometimes defined as the state of being fully grown. However, there are many more pieces to the maturation puzzle. For a Christian, maturity encompasses becoming more Christ-like and using what you know to the glory of God.

The key to maturing in Christ is learning and applying Scripture to your life. Not even the Apostle Paul claimed to have attained spiritual maturity. He was compelled to press on in pursuit of being conformed to Christ. He states in Philippians 3:12-14, "Not as though I had already attained, either were already perfect: but I follow after, if that I may apprehend that for which also I am apprehended of Christ Jesus. Brethren, I count not myself to have apprehended: but this one thing I do, forgetting those things which are behind, and reaching forth unto those things which are before, I press toward the mark for the prize of the high calling of God in Christ Jesus."

A Christian young person should likewise strive for maturity in Christ-likeness. When you develop your inner man for Christ, you grow spiritually. In addition, your mind, your emotions, and your will are brought into conformity to Christ. A mature Christian strives to develop his mind to its fullest capacity for the glory of God. He uses his knowledge to edify others. Wise evaluation of information is also evident in a mentally mature person.

An emotionally mature person has control of his reactions. The mature Christian replies to circumstances with biblical responses. He can be used of God to encourage others. No matter what the situation, he is secure in Christ.

Lend a Hand

Teen-agers, such as this girl helping with the Special Olympics, can exhibit Christian love as they help in the community. Seek for ways that God can use you to reflect His love. Being a servant requires action. "Thou shalt love thy neighbor as thyself" (Mark 12:31).

A mature Christian not only *knows* that God is in ultimate control but also *allows* God to control his life. He finds completeness in surrendering his will to his Savior. He accepts responsibility for his decisions because he strives to make decisions with God's will in view.

Maturity is often said to be unattainable. However, you can, like Paul, strive to mature in Christ. "But grow in grace, and in the knowledge of our Lord and Saviour Jesus Christ. To him be glory both now and for ever. Amen" (II Pet. 3:18).

Section Review

1. When emotional turmoil confronts you, what are four sources of help to which you can turn? What are some qualifications that should be considered before seeking help from these sources?

2. Is there any difference between a psychologist and a psychiatrist? If so, what?

3. List four emotional disorders that can be caused by stress.

4. What are four steps that could help you to maintain good emotional health?

5. What is the difference between how the world views maturity and how a Christian views maturity?

CHAPTER REVIEW

Terms

meditation	stressors	neuroses
self-concept	symptoms	suicide
negative self-concept	psychiatrist	psychosomatic illnesses
positive self-concept	psychologist	pessimists
reason	anxiety	optimists
discernment	depression	procrastination
stress	psychoses	maturity

Content Questions

1. What does the *inner man* have to do with mental and emotional health?

2. Give a brief explanation of what a Christian's self-concept should be.

3. What are at least six suggestions for improving study methods?

4. Why should a Christian concern himself with correctly evaluating information given to him?

5. What are the steps one initiates in overcoming unpleasant emotions?

6. What three pleasant and three unpleasant situations can produce stress?

7. What are at least two medical problems that may be caused or aggravated by stress?

8. Should a Christian cry because of emotions? Why or why not?

9. When stressful situations occur, what makes it possible to exhibit good emotional reactions?

10. What are three biblical steps that will help you deal with anxiety, fear, and worry?

11. Why should surrendering to God's will be the primary decision made before all other decisions?

Application Questions

1. What does wisdom have to do with mental health? Be sure to support your explanation with Scripture.

2. How can Scripture memorization help one's mental and emotional health?

3. Consider the statement "Making no decision is actually a decision in itself." Explain what this statement means and find a scriptural example of this principle.

4. Construct a diagram that illustrates the components of the inner man and how the inner man is related to maturity.

5. List and explain reasons a teen-ager should determine to expand his intellect and interests during his free time. List at least five areas of interest that you could pursue this summer that would increase learning.

Counselors

Job Description: The field of counseling is diverse and offers many opportunities for service. People in this field can be found working as guidance counselors, camp counselors, social workers, adoption agents, and counselors to abused wives, abused children, unwed mothers, runaways, drug addicts, and alcoholics. Counselors who work in an educational setting work with the students to evaluate, guide, and advise them. Christian counselors in other areas of human services do less formal evaluation than guidance counselors but often serve to promote spiritual, emotional, and mental development.

Job Location: Because privacy is usually necessary in counseling, most counselors have private offices. The environment and comfort of the counselor's office depends greatly on whom and where he is called to serve. Hours vary depending on the type of counseling done. Guidance counselors work during school hours and often enjoy the same vacations as students and teachers. Counselors in residential settings (halfway houses, group homes) usually work in shifts since the homes must be supervised seven days a week, twenty-four hours a day. The work of a counselor is rewarding but usually very draining. Many counselors, like teachers and pastors, will probably agree that their work by no means ends at the office.

Training Required: A college degree in counseling, sociology, or psychology is helpful but usually not adequate for licensing or certification. A master's degree in a specific type of counseling is generally recommended. Because of radical differences in philosophy, it is imperative for a Christian counselor to receive training from a fundamental Christian school rather than from a secular school.

SOCIAL HEALTH

"Nobody loves me, everybody hates me, I think I'll go eat worms." Do you remember this childhood chant? Many times your relationships make you feel as though eating worms is appropriate behavior. After all, have you ever had a misunderstanding with your parents or a falling-out with a friend? The way you respond to problems reflects your emotional health; how you interact with others, in a crowd or one-on-one, reveals the condition of your social health.

CHAPTER 4

"A man that hath friends must shew himself friendly."
Proverbs 18:24

YOUR SOCIAL HEALTH

Social health is one of the five components of total health. Your social health is determined by how you get along with other people. Do you feel comfortable around others? Can you carry on a conversation with a new acquaintance without being at a loss for words? Do you have many friends? All of these questions may help indicate your present level of social health.

Importance

God created man (Adam) and provided a bountiful environment for him. Adam seemed to have everything he needed to be happy. However, God saw that Adam was alone and created Eve. It is evident that God saw that it was not good for man to live in isolation. Scientists have observed that people who become isolated are often unhealthy and may even die prematurely. God made you with a need to fellowship with other people.

Just being with people or in the center of a mass of people does not indicate good social health. Loneliness can occur in a crowd. Many people want friends but do not know how to make or keep friends. Some people turn to work and busyness as a substitute for friendship or strong family relationships. The empty *heart* can find adequate filling in fellowshiping with God, but an empty *life* can find fullness only in fellowship with man.

Being alone does not necessarily indicate loneliness; it can give one an opportunity to think or to pray.

It is important to note, however, that although people need fellowship, there is nothing wrong with moments of quiet solitude. People need a balance between being alone and being with other people. The need for moments of reflection and solitude must not be overlooked. In fact, it is in the refreshing moments alone that God can best speak to the heart and that a Christian can enjoy the richness of communion with God.

Your social health during the teen-age years may have a greater effect on your total health than at any other time in your life. Teen-agers need friends. When you are a teen-ager, friends have a tremendous influence on your life. To a great extent, you will be like the people you choose as friends.

Not only is your total health affected by your social health, but your social health can have a great effect on your spiritual health. God has given every Christian the ministry of witnessing to others who do not know Christ as their Savior. If you are not comfortable around other people and cannot talk to them, it will be difficult for you to be an effective witness for Jesus Christ. Do not be discouraged. The power of God can overcome any weakness you may have in this area. After all, look at the example of Moses. When God called Moses to go to Egypt and lead the Israelites to the Promised Land, Moses claimed he was slow of speech. Through the power of God, Moses became one of Israel's greatest leaders. God can work in your life just as He did in Moses' life.

Introvert or Extrovert

Have you ever had a complete stranger start talking to you as if you were old friends? Depending on the comments made, the time taken, and your personality, you may have found yourself feeling rather amused or embarrassed. People who seem to know everyone they meet are called **extroverts.** An extrovert is a person who often directs his attention outside himself to people and things.

Other people seem to be withdrawn and shy. They may spend much of their time alone and are often uncomfortable around others. People who seem to direct their attention to more private matters are called **introverts.**

Even though there is probably no one who is completely introverted or completely extroverted, most people have a tendency to be either one or the other. Do you tend to be an introvert or an extrovert? Which would you prefer to be? A good goal for a Christian might be to use the strengths of both in order to be most effective for God.

The friendly nature of an extrovert is necessary when welcoming visitors to your church, and the outgoing nature of an extrovert helps when delivering a scripture lesson or giving a testimony. But being an extrovert is not a virtue in itself. Extroverts may develop very shallow relationships and fail to cultivate any real interest in other people.

The quiet nature of an introvert is an encouragement when it is time to study the Bible and meditate on the Word of God. It is often the introvert that becomes the patient listener or the silent prayer warrior. However, many introverts can retreat into their own world to the point that they seem to be aloof or unwilling to help others. The main point to remember is that to be socially healthy you should have the ability and desire to communicate effectively with others.

You will not become more outgoing or more serene by just wanting it to happen. You must work at it. Most things of value take work to accomplish, and building your social health is no exception.

Politicians must cultivate extroverted lifestyles to communicate their concern and viewpoints to their constituents.

Section Review

1. True or False—To a great extent you will be like those you choose as friends.
2. What is the difference between an introvert and an extrovert?
3. Name four people in your class who you think are extroverts. Do you tend to be introverted or extroverted?

YOUR SOCIAL SKILLS

Many people are uncomfortable around others because they lack confidence. As a Christian, you have no excuse. Psalm 118:8 says, "It is better to trust in the Lord than to put confidence in man." *Self-confidence* can never equal confidence in God. Do not focus on your abilities or lack of them; instead, consider what God can do for you and through you.

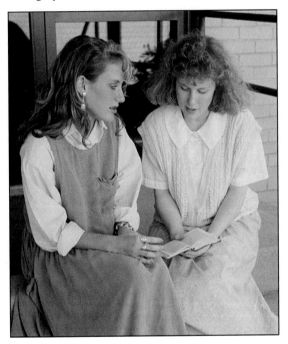

Because God is your helper, it does not mean that you can resort to reckless abandon. If you have never gone mountain climbing, you *might* lack confidence in scaling a cliff. However, you can be confident that God will enable you to do any task that He gives you to do.

You can increase your usefulness by building your social skills. **Social skills** are the tools or characteristics that enable you to interact with other people. Have you ever been unable to finish a job because you did not have the right equipment? Your dad would not be able to fix the car if he did not have the right tools; your mother could not wash the laundry without detergent. In order to accomplish tasks effectively and efficiently, you must have the proper equipment. Likewise, you can achieve better social health by improving your social skills.

Polish Your Personality

Your **personality** is the combination of personal qualities that influence your attitudes and behavior. A sense of humor, loyalty, dependability, and tact are examples of personality traits. As you mature, your personality changes. You can improve your personality by allowing God to modify your personality traits.

Sense of humor—A sense of humor is a valuable personality trait to possess. The ability to laugh even during times of stress will help you and those around you feel more relaxed. Laughter makes people feel good. Learn to appreciate the funny things in life, even when they are about you. Most people enjoy being around someone with a good sense of humor.

While people enjoy the company of those who have a sense of humor, no one likes to be made fun of. You should never laugh at those things that make other people uncomfortable. There is nothing humorous about teasing or laughing at the expense of another person's feelings. Laughing at others is a good way to lose friends and make enemies.

Risibility (RIZ uh BIL ih tee) is the ability or tendency to laugh. Man is the only creature on earth that can tell a joke or understand one, and laugh about it.

Funny or What?

There are many meanings for the word *funny*. A person can be said to be funny because he can tell humorous stories or laugh easily. The "funnies" (comic strips) or a funny play can produce laughter or amuse the viewer. These meanings all denote funny as a positive trait.

However, *funny* can also mean strange or odd. A student seen crawling around under a table may be perceived as odd until he produces the escaped hamster he was chasing, at which time he would seem humorous.

Part of being socially healthy is having the ability to be funny without seeming weird. There is nothing funny about a person who laughs at an inappropriate time or in an inappropriate manner. Ecclesiastes 3:4 says that there is "a time to weep, and a time to laugh." It takes discernment to know the best way to approach some situations.

Many Christians appear odd to the unsaved because they lack the social skills of communication or tact. Some believers can become so obnoxious in their presentation of biblical truth that no one will seriously listen to them. Romans 10:14 asks, "How then shall they call on him in whom they have not believed? and how shall they believe in him of whom they have not heard? and how shall they hear without a preacher?" This verse serves two purposes. It reminds you to be sure that your actions do not drown out the message of your words. The unsaved cannot hear if they are unwilling to listen due to the strange behavior of the believer. However, one must be sure not to be so concerned about appearing odd that he does not witness to the unsaved. God expects you to be a living testimony for Him, and He holds you responsible for your actions.

> Laughing at your own expense costs you nothing.

A person who exhibits discernment in hilarity must have strength of morals and character. Mirth must be tailored with love, understanding, and respect in order not to seem sarcastic. Jokes should be above reproach and not demeaning to others. Even if told to only your closest friends, indecent jokes or innuendoes hurt your testimony and reputation. "Proving what is acceptable unto the Lord. And have no fellowship with the unfruitful works of darkness, but rather reprove them. For it is a shame even to speak of those things which are done of them in secret. See then that ye walk circumspectly, not as fools, but as wise, redeeming the time, because the days are evil" (Eph. 5:10-12, 15-16).

Loyalty—Have you ever heard the expression "a fair-weather friend"? A fair-weather friend is someone who seems to be your friend when everything is going fine, but when trouble approaches, he deserts you. A true friend is a friend during good times and bad. Loyalty is alluded to in Proverbs 17:17, "A friend loveth at all times." **Loyalty** is faithfulness or allegiance to a person or a cause.

It is important to note that loyalty does not imply a blindness to faults. In fact, a loyal friend is often one who has the courage to tell you when you are wrong. This idea is brought out in Proverbs 27:6, which says, "Faithful are the wounds of a friend; but the kisses of an enemy are deceitful."

When it comes to loyalty, silence is not always the best choice. Loyalty is characterized by standing up in spite of opposition. It is tempting to stand silent when criticism is brandished. However, a loyal person will speak up in defense of his friend or cause. Again, loyalty does not mean defending a friend or a cause that is wrong.

Team spirit is an opportunity to display your loyalty.

You probably say the pledge of allegiance regularly. By taking this pledge you are promising loyalty to the United States. Loyalty is an essential personality trait if you want others to trust you. No one wants to be around someone who may betray him. There are many areas in your life that require your loyalty. You should be loyal to your family, your church, your school, your country, and your friends, but, as a Christian, your first loyalty should be to God.

Dependability—Have you ever gotten ready to drive to an important meeting only to find that the car would not start? How frustrating! It is refreshing to be able to trust upon dependable machinery, but it is even more important to be able to rely upon dependable people. **Dependability** is the character trait of being reliable.

It has been said that the greatest ability is dependability. When a dependable person is given a job, he will do his utmost to get the job done. Dependability does not imply that just because someone says he will do something that he will always be able to comply. Sometimes circumstances make it impossible to fulfill commitments. However, the dependable person will try to make amends or take responsible action when he cannot keep his promise.

If you tell someone that you will meet him at a certain time in a certain place, make plans to be there on time. If he is not there, wait. It is better for you to keep your word. However, be sure to consider your obligations, abilities, and resources before you commit yourself in the first place. Many people have lost friends, opportunities, or their reputations by promising everything to everyone without stopping to think things through. If you want people to rely on you, you must prove to be dependable.

Tact—"Yuk! You have bad breath!" How would you feel if the person sitting beside you made this announcement in the presence of the entire class? It would probably embarrass and infuriate you. Even if you did have bad breath, it would not be very kind for someone to embarrass you like that. People can be cruel in the things they do and say. Many people cause unintentional hurt because they lack tact.

Tact is kind, compassionate, and considerate behavior. A tactful person is careful not to offend others by what he says or does. Tactfulness denotes acting with discreet diplomacy. A valuable guideline to help avoid cruelty or crudeness is the application of the golden rule. Doing to others as you would have them do to you is a beginning for developing tact. However, in order to respond with tactfulness, it is also necessary to know information concerning the situation and expectations.

When trying to be tactful, be careful not to lie in order to keep from hurting someone. Try focusing on the positive aspects of situations even if you may not like the entire effect. For instance, if a classmate wears a new dress that you do not particularly like, you may mention how you like the color. If a classmate gets a new haircut that does not seem attractive to you, you can comment about the way it accents her eyes or ask her where she got it cut. In some situations it may be best to avoid making any comment at all. The old saying "If you can't say something nice, don't say anything at all" is still appropriate. By being silent or focusing on positive aspects of a situation, you can gracefully meet many problems and manage to be tactful.

A balanced personality—These four personality traits are some of the more important ones you need to develop. As you work to improve these traits as well as others, you must make sure that you remain balanced. For example, do not become so overly concerned with being tactful that you feel you can never express convictions because they may offend someone. Nor should you remain loyal to an organization when it begins to practice evil. This response is taking a personality trait to the extreme. Be careful to avoid extremes and work to shape a personality that is balanced and pleasing to God.

Section Review

1. Define personality.

2. Identify at least one way that you can exhibit each of the following traits in your relationships with family and friends: humor, dependability, loyalty, and tact.

3. Define loyalty, dependability, and tact.

Learn To Listen

Another important social skill to develop is listening. Many people who have excellent hearing are very poor listeners. Hearing is the ability to perceive sound. Listening is the ability to give your attention to and think about the sounds that you are hearing. It is possible to go through a conversation without ever really listening to what the other person is saying. Have you ever introduced yourself to someone new and found that you cannot remember his name, even though he just told you what it is?

Listening is an art to be developed. It begins with putting the other person first.

You may have heard what he said, but you were not listening.

Becoming a good listener is not difficult. All it usually takes is some self-discipline. When someone talks to you, look directly at him. Learn to concentrate on what he is saying. Try to avoid thinking about what you will say or considering unrelated items. In other words, you must give him your undivided attention. Once you become a good listener, you will probably find that many of your friends will enjoy talking to you more. People enjoy talking to those who listen to them.

Cultivate Communication

Communication is the exchange of information between individuals. You communicate primarily by talking or writing. However, you also communicate by your posture, your tone of voice, your facial expression, and the gestures that you use. When you communicate without using words, it is called **nonverbal communication.** Have you ever had someone tell you, "It is not what you are saying, but the *way* you are saying it, that I don't like." He was indicating to you that he did not like your nonverbal communication.

Communication is essential to building strong, healthy relationships with other people. If you do not talk to your parents, you will probably not feel close to them. How can you expect them to understand *you* if they do not know what you think or what you are doing? Do you really know *them?* If you do not talk to your friends, you may find your friendships drifting apart. You may still be friendly to each other, but the deep-rooted camaraderie will wane. If you value close relationships, you should look for opportunities to communicate with the people you love.

Foster Friendliness

If you want to have friends, you must be friendly. Friendly people attract other people. Have you ever looked at people you know and wondered why they are so popular? Maybe they are not particularly attractive, well dressed, or athletic, yet everyone seems to like them. Their popularity may be due to their friendliness.

What makes a person friendly? Wearing a smile, warmly greeting people, and taking an interest in others are some of the things that distinguish a friendly person. Even a quiet person can be friendly. Most of the time, it takes more effort for an introverted person to be friendly. You do not have to be boisterous or extroverted in order to smile. Try to be extra friendly to everyone you meet today and see whether it makes a difference in the way others treat you. It is difficult to dislike a friendly person.

Initiate New Interests

List the things that you like to do. After you finish this list, make another list of your friends and what they like to do. Are the lists alike? You will usually find that you and your friends enjoy doing similar things. These common interests help to bind you together.

A socially healthy person has a wide variety of interests. If your whole life revolves around one or two activities (such as basketball or piano playing), you will have few things in common with most other people. Playing the piano or practicing basketball can be fun, but there are thousands of other things you might enjoy; just give them a try. Even if you do not want to *do* a variety of things, you can learn about different areas in order to have a broad base of interests.

Employ Proper Etiquette

It is difficult to like people who are brutish or who lack manners. You usually avoid rude people who interrupt when you talk, never wait for their turn, cough in your face, use your property without permission, and do many other things that irritate you. Although none of these actions are against the law, they are not commonly accepted behavior in our society.

President Grover Cleveland committed a faux pas (social mistake) when he added sugar and cream to his coffee then poured a small bit of it into his saucer. His guests, feeling obliged to follow his example, did the same. However, while they were pouring their coffee into their saucers, they noticed too late that Mr. Cleveland had placed his saucer on the floor for his dog.

The rules of common courtesy and proper conduct are called **etiquette.** These rules of conduct or manners may vary among countries or areas. However, the main goal of etiquette is to make everyone feel comfortable. Your parents and teachers are probably your main sources for etiquette information, and you may grow tired of their constant reminders. However, having proper manners may keep you from losing friends or getting into embarrassing situations.

You may think that good intentions excuse poor manners. This is a false assumption. Correct conduct is vital to your reputation as a person, your testimony as as Christian, and your confidence as an individual. Etiquette takes on more value to people when they begin to care about what others think of them (especially when starting to date or to seek employment). It is a boon to your testimony as

Courtly Conduct

Etiquette comes from the French word *estiquet,* meaning "label." This is derived from the Old French verb *estiquer,* "to attach." The word describes the list of rules and regulations that

were posted in the courtyards of feudal castles and palaces. These lists could be torn away and changed as often as desired, sometimes daily. Rules of etiquette can be altered today too, although not so easily.

Two thousand years before the writing of the Bible, an Egyptian named Ptahhotep wrote the first known book on etiquette, *The Instructions of Ptahhotep.* Included in the book were common sense rules for good conduct.

"Let thy mind be deep and thy speech scanty . . . for speech is more difficult than any craft." The ancient manuscript continues with, "If thou hast become great after thou wert little, and hast gained possessions after thou wert in want . . . be not unmindful of how it was with thee before." When it comes to being in the presence of a superior, "laugh when he laughs so shalt thou be very agreeable to his heart and what thou doest will be very pleasant to his heart." Even in 2500 B.C. kindness and consideration were the bases of good manners. Ptahhotep admonished, "Do not talk down to those who know less than you" (Aresty, E. B. *The Best Behavior.* New York: Simon and Schuster, 1970).

Later in the first century A.D. the Talmud was decoded to reveal proper table manners. "All meals were to begin with a prayer that invoked God's blessing and thanked him for his bounty; the proper behavior that was to follow the blessing was then described down to the smallest detail: 'A man should not hold in his hand a piece of bread as big as an egg, but only a piece as big as an olive; otherwise he is a glutton' " (Aresty, p. 22).

In 1290, an Italian monk, Bonvicino da Riva, wrote a book

which extensively discussed proper table manners. He instructed that one should turn the head when sneezing or coughing, not gulp food or liquid in one mouthful, not cross legs on the laid-out table, not lick one's fingers, not pick one's teeth, not stare in others' plates, and (yes, even as far back as 1290) not talk with a mouthful of food.

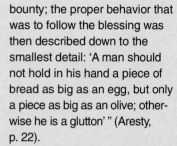

Even George Washington composed his own set of rules in 1747 when he wrote "Reprehend not the imperfections of others for that belongs to Parents, Masters and Superiours"; "Contradict not at every turn what others Say"; "In speaking to men of Quality do not lean or Look them full in the Face." When dining, "Put not another bit into your mouth til the former be

Swallowed"; "Cleanse not your teeth with the Table Cloth, Napkin, Fork or knife." As for other matters of decorum, "Wear not your Cloths [clothes], foul, unript or Dusty"; "Spit not in the Fire"; "Kill no vermin as Fleas, lice, ticks &c [etc.] in the Sight of Others" (Schlesinger, Arthur M. *Learning How to Behave.* New York: Cooper Square Publishers, Inc., p. 5).

Most rules of etiquette that have changed have to do with fad and fashion rather than with respect. For instance, men no longer raise their visor in respect to a lady since they no longer wear armor. However, if a man is wearing a hat, he does tip his hat in respect or greeting to a stranger and removes it altogether when speaking to or in the presence of a lady.

All of these rules of etiquette have changed little during the course of time. They all hold the sensitivities of company and others in esteem. They are manners appropriate for knights and ladies at court as well as for ladies and gentlemen today.

a Christian and to your confidence to know the correct way to behave.

The foundation for good manners lies in three attitudes: a concern for other people, the desire to have other people feel comfortable, and confidence to be at ease in even awkward situations. It has been said that manners are the art of kindness acting in style. Courtesy is bred from an inner spirit of thoughtfulness.

Many people treat etiquette as if having good manners should be avoided. On the contrary, etiquette that is practiced daily becomes a natural habit. In the past, it took some getting used to to learn how to eat with silverware. However, few people today would relish the thought of scooping their food into their mouths with their fingers (or watching other people do so). It takes practice to make good manners flow smoothly into your behavior. The only way to avoid the embarrassment of accidentally using improper conduct is to know and to practice good manners all the time.

Many people question whether to use the continental or the American style of eating. The continental or European method of eating (with fork tines held down in the left hand and knife in the right) began in the 1840s when the English upper class proclaimed it fashionable to quit shifting the fork from right to left. The idea quickly spread to Europe. Being democratic in nature, the Americans refused to follow their contemporaries' uppity customs and chose to retain the common method of fork usage (with fork tines held up in the right hand to eat, and transferred to the left when using the knife for cutting). It is proper to use either method.

The Importance of Love

While social skills such as loyalty, dependability, and friendliness are important, they cannot make up for a lack of love. Love is the most essential ingredient in your life. It is an unselfish desire for another's highest good, an earnest commitment to what is best for others. The evidence of love is giving. If you really love someone, you will give yourself and your things to help him achieve what is best for him.

For Christians, love should be the constant motivation for service, sacrifice, prophecy, and faith (I Cor. 13:2-3). Love also serves as a symbol of Christianity. Love for other Christians is the one characteristic that most effectively shows the world that you are Christ's disciple (John 13:35).

The love that Christ commands His followers to have is not always easy or even natural. You should love your neighbor and your enemy (Matt. 5:44). There should also be a special love for all those who know Christ as Savior (I John 4). Christ is the supreme example of love; it was love that caused Him to die for all mankind. Without love, you cannot be socially healthy or effectively used by God.

Love is more than a feeling. It is action based on an unselfish desire for another's good.

Section Review

1. List the social skills given in this chapter. Beside each, identify at least one way you exhibit that social skill in your relationships with family and friends.

2. How does listening differ from hearing? What are some ways that you can become a better listener?

3. What is communication? What is nonverbal communication? Give one example of nonverbal communication.

4. What is etiquette? What are three foundational attitudes for good manners?

5. What is the most essential ingredient for good social health?

YOU AND YOUR FAMILY

One of the greatest blessings that God has given to you is your family. It is unfortunate that some of the greatest blessings are often the ones least appreciated. Are you thankful for your family? If you are, how do you show your gratitude?

Living with Parents

Your parents are responsible for rearing you and providing for your needs. That is a big responsibility. Without children, your parents would have much more money to spend on the things they want.

A sense of humor strengthens the bonds of family unity.

They would also have more freedom and face less pressure. Yet your parents are usually happy to do without many of the things they want simply because they love you.

Your parents love you, protect you, and provide for you. They have an obligation to God to bring you up in "the way you should go." But the relationship between you and your parents does not depend just on them; it also depends on you. By obeying, honoring, and loving your parents, you can maintain a proper relationship with them.

Obey—Your first obligation to your parents is to obey them. Ephesians 6:1 says, "Children, obey your parents in the Lord: for this is right." When you disobey your parents, you grieve God as well as your parents.

Sometimes you will find it difficult to obey your parents. As you get older, you will begin to feel more independent. This feeling of independence is preparing you to be the man or woman you will soon become. Until God establishes you in a home of your own, however, you must submit to your parents' authority. As an adult you will probably look back and thank God for many of the restrictions that you dislike now. However, it may help at the present to remember that the rules your parents

set are placed by loving concern for your welfare. "Obey them that have the rule over you, and submit yourselves: for they watch for your souls, as they that must give account, that they may do it with joy, and not with grief: for that is unprofitable for you" (Heb. 13:17).

Honor—Another responsibility you have to your parents is to honor them. One of the Ten Commandments that God gave to Moses says, "Honour thy father and thy mother: that thy days may be long upon the land which the Lord thy God giveth thee" (Exod. 20:12). You honor your parents by treating them with respect and esteem. God has promised special blessing to those who honor their parents.

It is out of respect that you should hold the door open for your mother, help with the chores, let your parents have the most comfortable place in the den, and speak with respect. It is a poor testimony to see sons or daughters order their parents around, grunt answers, ignore questions or comments, or yell at them. First Corinthians 13:5 says that love "doth not behave itself unseemly." When you honor your parents, you have the opportunity to show your love and care for them.

Shared experiences, memories, communication, and respect are a few benefits of spending time with parents.

Love—Finally, you should love your parents. Your parents are not perfect. Because they are human, they will make mistakes, sin, lose their tempers, come to poor conclusions, and make inadequate decisions. However, they are God's chosen instruments for training you. Your parents love you and are trying to do what is best for you. God is still in control; He can work all things for good.

Consider your love for your parents. Is your love enduring, forgiving, considerate, and selfless? Review the qualities of love in I Corinthians 13, and see how you rate in regard to your attitude toward your parents. How often do you tell your parents that you love them? Parents enjoy getting a hug or hearing you tell them that you love them. They do not mean to seem snoopy; they want to know you and your interests. They enjoy it when you notice the little things they do for you. Do you love your parents? Do you appreciate them? If you do, be sure to take time today to tell your parents just how much they mean to you.

Living with Siblings

Does the following conversation seem familiar?

"Danny, may I borrow a pair of blue socks?"

"Are you kidding? The last time you wore a pair of my socks, I didn't see them again for six months."

"That was your fault. I put them in your drawer, but your clothes are such a mess that you couldn't find them."

"You put them in my drawer all right—my sweater drawer! You're one to talk about dirty drawers; your whole room looks like a pigpen!"

Any time two people spend much time together, there will usually be some disagreements. However, many siblings (brothers and sisters) have turned their homes into battlefields. Competition

During childhood, sibling rivalries tend to arise quickly and end just as fast.

Oh, Brother!

If you seem to have a problem in the realm of getting along with your brothers and sisters, consider the following tips.

Edify rather than tease. Do not look for ways to aggravate your siblings; instead, seek ways to build up your brothers and sisters in the Lord. Hebrews 10:24 says, "And let us consider one another to provoke unto love and to good works."

Be considerate. Show respect to your brothers or sisters. Be respectful of their privacy and of their property. Share the work that needs to be done. Romans 12:10 clearly states, "Be kindly affectioned one to another with brotherly love; in honour preferring one another."

Communicate by word and deed. Talk with them; take time to get to *know* them. Do you know about the burdens they are bearing? Do you know of their trials or

problems? Let them know that you will be praying for them; let them know that you are there to help. Take time to listen. By the same token, let them know you. Talk to them; let them know of your needs too. "Finally, be ye all of one mind, having compassion one of another, love as brethren, be pitiful, be courteous" (I Pet. 3:8).

Exhibit thoughtfulness. Look for ways to show your siblings that you care. Go out of your way to make special occasions memorable. Any day can be a holiday. Do special things for them. If you have extra time, help them with their chores. Let them know that you are grateful to have them as your brothers or sisters. "With good will doing service, as to the Lord, and not to men" (Eph. 6:7).

Be worthy of respect. First Timothy 4:12 says, "Be thou an example of the believers." Be a model believer in word and deed. Make sure that Christ is evident in your talk and walk, not only outside the home but also within it.

You may say, "But my brother is so mean!" Your siblings may be unkind or inconsiderate. You cannot beat them into having a loving spirit; you cannot force them to obey God's Word. However, you are responsible for your actions. You can do what is right. Let God deal with your siblings; you do what you know to be honoring to the Lord.

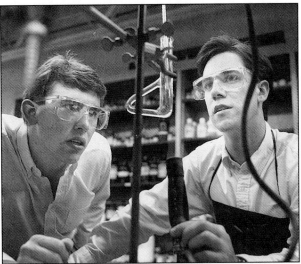

Common interests and respect can result in being friends as well as being siblings.

and fighting between brothers and sisters is called **sibling rivalry.** There are many reasons that some siblings are at odds with each other. Sibling rivalry can be caused by jealousy, vying for affection, pride, lack of respect, refusal to forgive, insecurity, and selfishness. Notice that not one of these reasons is godly.

There is only one solution to the problem of sibling rivalry: love. Love looks at a person's good points instead of focusing on his faults. Love also helps combat wrong attitudes like jealousy, pride, and selfishness. Take a close look at I Corinthians 13:4-7 to see how you rate in being a loving brother or sister. With love and a little effort, you should be able to get along with anyone. According to I Peter 4:8, love covers a multitude of sins.

Section Review

1. What are three obligations that you have in your relationship with your parents?

2. How can you honor your parents?

3. What is sibling rivalry? List some of the causes of sibling rivalry? What is the best solution? Identify ways that this major solution can be shown.

YOU AND YOUR FRIENDS

If your father came in this evening and announced that you were moving to another state, leaving your friends would probably be one of the most difficult things about going. Friends are often so near to the heart that they almost seem to be a part of your family. Because friends are so important, you must be very careful about the type of friends you choose.

Choosing Good Friends

Your closest friend should be Christ Himself. In John 15:13-15 Christ says, "Greater love hath no man than this, that a man lay down his life for his friends. Ye are my friends, if ye do whatsoever I command you. Henceforth I call you not servants;

Being a Friend

"The secret of friendship is just the secret of all spiritual blessing. The way to get is to give" (Black, Hugh. *Friendship.* New York: Fleming H. Revell Co., 1903, p. 46).

The Bible makes it very clear that in order to have friends, you must be one. The responsibility to be a friend rests on both parties. Friendship must be mutually given and equally worked on. Mutual selflessness would be a descriptive term. Friendship often means sacrifice, inconvenience, and abandonment of self-centered goals or activities not by one, but by both.

Because friendship extends well past the head and into the heart, it is vital to be careful whom you befriend. It is well known that "a man is moulded into likeness of the lives that come nearest him" (Black, p. 93). As one preacher aptly described it, "If you want to be an eagle, don't hang around with the buzzards." Be kind and loving to all people, but be selective of those you choose for friends. Most people confuse acquaintance (familiarity) with friendship.

Friends not only like each other because they have common interests or bonds, but friends also love each other. Loving friendship encompasses forgiveness, patience, admonition (giving warning and instruction), and acceptance. Because friends truly care about each other, they present a united effort in growing in the Lord. It is unity in God that binds minds and hearts together. However, friendship is not limited to a unity with those outside the family; friendship should be cultivated between parents and their children, brothers and sisters, and, of course, between husbands and wives.

Kindness and thoughtfulness in the little things are important. Neglect is a sure way to kill a friendship. There is an old Scandinavian saying: "Go often to the house of thy friend; for weeds soon choke up the unused path." (It is important to remember, however, that friendship does not mean being a nuisance. Proverbs 25:17 says, "Withdraw thy foot from thy neighbour's house; lest he be weary of thee, and so hate thee.") In order for any relationship to grow, there must be not only giving of self but also communication and love in action. "Little faults of manner, little occasions of thoughtlessness, or lack of the little courtesies, do more to separate people than glaring mistakes" (Black, p. 149). Be sure to note birthdays, special events, holidays, "unbirthdays," times of trial, and moments of joy. It takes time and effort to be a good friend, but it is well worth both.

for the servant knoweth not what his lord doeth: but I have called you friends; for all things that I have heard of my Father I have made known unto you." What a privilege it is to be the friend of Jesus Christ!

Most of your other friends probably consist of people you have met in your neighborhood, your school, or your church. Young people about the same age who share similar interests usually tend to gather together and eventually become friends. But common interests are not the most important factor to consider when you choose your friends.

If you are a Christian, your closest friends should also be Christians. Other Christians will understand the spiritual battles you face in your life because they are facing similar battles. They can also help you overcome temptation, encourage you during times of trial, and help you live closer to Christ. You have a common bond—Christ.

However, all people who call themselves Christians do not make good friends. Many young people who claim to be Christians use foul language, take drugs, smoke cigarettes, look at lewd pictures, or rebel against authority. These "Christians" can be a terrible influence in your life. They can pull you away from doing those things that you know to be good and right. You should avoid developing close ties with people who would bring you down rather than build you up in the Lord.

Although it may not be good to have unsaved people as your closest friends, you should be friendly to the unsaved people you know. In fact, some unsaved teen-agers act better than many "saved" teen-agers. In the New Testament, Christ is a good example of how to be a friend to the unsaved. He did not allow sinners to influence Him for wrong, but He did treat them with kindness and compassion and shared with them the plan of salvation. You too have the same opportunity and responsibility to reach the unsaved people you know.

Peer Pressure

Peer pressure is the compulsion your friends exert on your life. During your teen-age years, peer pressure is unusually strong and has an effect on most areas of your life (such as your dress, speech, and attitudes). At times peer pressure can be so great that you will be tempted to do things that you really do not want to do just to "go along with the crowd."

The effects of peers on your life often begin very subtly. The progression they follow is clearly shown in Psalm 1. You start by listening to the foolish advice of simple-minded friends (walking "in the counsel of the ungodly"). Soon you begin to think like they think and begin to "hang around" with a crowd that seldom thinks of God and that disobeys His commands (standing "in the way of sinners"). Eventually you become one of the crowd that openly opposes all that God stands for (sitting "in the seat of the scornful").

Although everyone faces peer pressure, it is not always bad. If you are around the right friends, they

Lot's Loss

One of the most vivid illustrations of the potential harm of evil peer pressure is the life of Abraham's nephew, Lot. Apparently Lot knew and loved God when he lived with Abraham. However, the time came when they had to separate, and Lot chose to pitch his tent toward Sodom. He must have known how wicked the Sodomites were, but he liked the comfort of the well-watered plain so much that he was willing to allow this evil influence to enter his life. The next chapter reveals that soon Lot was dwelling in Sodom and fellowshiping with the Sodomites. Lot became so much like the Sodomites that in Genesis 19:1 he is found sitting in the gate of Sodom. Apparently Lot had become a leader in this ungodly city. When God judged Sodom, Lot lost all the possessions that he had accumulated and destroyed himself and his family. Lot allowed peer pressure to rob him of all the blessings that God had given him. Peer pressure can do the same to you.

Fun Today, Funny Tomorrow

Teen-agers are always full of inventive ideas. What is a fun or unusual fad today may seem funny or even odd years later. Shown are some fads from the past.

Imagine walking by a trash can that suddenly wishes you a good day! It was a "barrel" of laughs for these guys.

Most people dunk their doughnuts in milk or coffee. These teens seem to prefer soda with theirs.

may help you to resist doing things you should not do. Teen-agers who sit in church with their parents and friends, take notes, pay attention, and participate in the service are unlikely to slump back, doodle, or be inattentive. Peer pressure can also influence you to do right. If your friends decide to go witnessing with the youth group, they may get you to do what you should do (but may not do on your own).

Sometimes peers encourage friends to do things that are unusual but not really wrong. For example, if everyone you know decides to wear orange and purple socks, you might decide to wear a pair even though you hate the way they look. Peer pressure often influences young people in what they wear as well as in the things they do. Temporary trends of dress and action are called **fads.** Some fads may be morally wrong (for example, if they are immodest). Other fads are not wrong in themselves but may be wrong if they indicate rebellion or snobbishness. Faddish clothes are usually not a good investment because they are often overpriced and go out of

style quickly. You should not expect your parents to keep your wardrobe filled with fad fashion. One measure of maturity is the ability to make wise choices even under peer pressure.

There will be times when you will face immense peer pressure to do wrong. Although choosing the right friends and avoiding certain situations can save you from this pressure some of the time, you *will* face situations when your friends will do their best to get you to do wrong. Christ has promised to give you the strength you need to withstand temptation. You must have the courage to do it!

Cliques

One thing to avoid as you choose friends is the formation of cliques. A **clique** (klik) is a closed or exclusive group of friends who tend to ignore others and share a private interest. Although you will have special friends, you should not exclude others or make other people feel like outsiders. A clique provides a mutual admiration society that is mainly bonded by pride.

A clique tends to focus its attention on a shared interest and on itself. If a group emphasizes itself, there is no room for promoting Christ. Although Christ had a group of close friends (His disciples), His mission was to point men to God and not to applaud only His disciples. "And Jesus went about all the cities and villages, teaching in their synagogues, and preaching the gospel of the kingdom, and healing every sickness and every disease among the people. But when he saw the multitudes, he was moved with compassion on them, because they fainted, and were scattered abroad, as sheep having no shepherd" (Matt. 9:35-36). If you truly love others as Christ commanded, you will avoid forming cliques. But do you desire to serve Christ or do you want to serve your own interests? II Timothy 2:24-25 exhorts, "And the servant of the Lord must not strive; but be gentle unto all men, apt to teach, patient, in meekness instructing those that oppose themselves; if God peradventure will give them repentance to the acknowledging of the truth."

Prejudice

Another problem that young people may face is prejudice. **Prejudice** is the act of forming an opinion of someone or something before knowing the person or all the facts. It is making a judgment in advance. Prejudice is also hostility or suspicion toward other individuals because of their race, religion, or background. African-Americans, Jews, and fundamentalist Christians are a few groups that have been victims of prejudice in recent history. As a Christian, you must love the things that God loves and hate the things that God hates. God hates sin. You must also hate sin and stand against it. But you must also remember that God loved the world and gave His Son to die for the sins of the world. You cannot successfully fulfill God's great commission to evangelize the world if you despise another person simply because he is of a different color or nationality or because he has different customs or beliefs. There should be no room in a Christian's heart for prejudice.

Prejudice: Blind Hatred

The Ku Klux Klan (KKK) is a secret society organized after the United States Civil War. The society uses intimidating tactics to promote the fallacy of white supremacy. The KKK dogma is marked by hostility toward blacks, Jews, Roman Catholics, and foreigners.

Prejudice is one of the strongest evidences of fallen human nature. However, it may not be as blatantly obvious as in this KKK rally. More often, prejudice is evidenced by negative reactions to a person's appearance, culture, economic status, or personal habits.

1. List qualities that you should look for in a friend. Do your current friends meet these standards?

2. Is there a need for unsaved acquaintances? Why or why not?

3. What is peer pressure? What is the danger of peer pressure as revealed in Psalm 1?

4. Is peer pressure good or bad? Why?

5. What is a clique?

6. What is prejudice?

7. Are cliques healthy for a Christian? Is prejudice healthy for a Christian? Why or why not?

YOU AND THE OPPOSITE SEX

It is hard to believe that just a few years ago you hated boys (or girls, as the case may be). Through the years, however, your opinion has changed. Most young people your age are beginning to become very interested in the opposite sex. God gave you this desire; it is perfectly normal. The socially healthy young person should be able to communicate with friends of either sex comfortably. At this stage in your life you should concentrate on getting to know many different people.

Unfortunately, society today tends to push friendships between young men and young ladies toward dating and intimacy before the young people really get to know themselves, let alone each other. This rush for relationships is not only promoted by television and the world but also by many unthinking Christians. It is important to establish friendship between the sexes before dating is even considered. Being able to communicate and to be at ease with the opposite sex without emotional entanglements is important. How can a young person expect to enjoy a date if he cannot even manage to carry on a conversation?

Many young people participate in their church youth groups, Christian school organizations, and other group activities. By getting involved in serving the Lord, young people also avail themselves of the opportunity to build friendships with others, male and female. Social interaction should not be the main reason to join the Bible quiz team, debate society, or visitation program. However, it is a benefit of being involved in various activities.

Dating

When a new father looked into the sweet face of his infant daughter, he proclaimed, "You can start dating when you get to be thirty-five, and not a moment before!" Of course, when that sweet baby grew up, she had an earlier time in mind as to when to begin dating. When you begin dating depends on several things.

First to be considered are your parents' rules. Some parents specify a certain age for their teenagers to begin dating. Many will allow their teens to go only on double dates or group dates. Other parents determine the age to begin dating by the maturity exhibited in the life of the teen-ager. You need to discuss this with your parents. Leave your friends' opinions and their parents' rules out of the discussion. "So-and-so's parents let him date" or "Buddy-buddy thinks I'm old enough to date" has

Fellowshiping and developing communication skills with those of the opposite gender should be the main focuses of dating during teen years.

nothing to do with the principles that your parents hold. You must meet the expectations and obtain the respect of *your* parents. If they have not addressed the subject of dating with you, you can initiate the discussion. It helps to have all the ground rules established before you are asked on a date or ask someone for a date.

When you begin dating, your parents will probably set some guidelines for your dates. However, it is your responsibility to develop, within the rules established by the authorities over you, your own personal standards for your dating behavior. It is important to begin studying and praying about the standards you will have when dating. Specific dating standards should be well established *before* you begin to date. If you cannot decide whether you should or should not act in a certain manner, make your choice on the side of what you think will please Christ the most. What your date thinks of you, what your peers think of you, and what you want to do should all be secondary to pleasing God.

Satan will try to deceive you with thoughts of, "Your reputation will be ruined, and no one will

want to date you if you don't loosen your standards a little." However, the devil is the father of lies. In reality a reputation for low standards will be more costly and will result in future prospects of sleazy dates. A reputation for high standards will bring respect. Who wants to date or eventually marry a person who chooses not to obey God? God's way is always best.

Dating Steadily

Why is it that when two third graders decide to "go steady" the seventh graders laugh? And when the seventh graders start "going together," the high schoolers laugh. When high schoolers start dating steadily, the collegians and adults smirk. However, when students in college steadily date, nobody thinks it is funny. The answer is found in the word *readiness.*

A teen should not decide to date steadily for prestige ("*I* have somebody"), for security ("*I* have a date"), or to hold on to a relationship ("He's *mine,* and he can't date anyone else"). Dating steadily is actually a step in the relationship just prior to marriage. It is a natural stage in the courtship process before engagement that states that both individuals are committed to each other ("*We* are in the process of getting engaged"). It is important to notice that

Dating standards must be based on godly principles, approved by parental authority, and upheld by mature self-discipline.

dating steadily is mutual, a "we" relationship, and is not done for individual purposes or from a "me" motivation.

The reason people tend to deride youngsters who steadily date each other is that the idea that they are ready for marriage or even a step toward marriage is incongruous and inappropriate. They simply are not mature enough or ready to consider marriage in the near future. Dating steadily during the teen-age years is not wise. Relationships need to grow and move forward. Regularly dating the same person during adolescence may lead to a stagnant relationship or one that is too familiar for godly conduct.

There may come a time during your teen years when you experience a great amount of pressure to pair up with one special person. You may even have friends who already have a special girlfriend or boyfriend. Right now, however, it is best to keep your relationships casual and to avoid becoming too familiar with the opposite sex. This will help you resist temptation, protect your sexual purity, and enable you to meet and to date a variety of individuals.

In the past, people often finished school after sixth or seventh grade, married, and faced the responsibilities of rearing a family at a younger age than they do today.

Section Review

1. Explain at least three benefits of getting involved with youth group activities or participating in Christian school extracurricular activities.

2. Diagram the steps of courtship.

3. Explain at least two major considerations that should be clear and established *before* you begin to date.

4. What does it mean to date steadily? What are some of the invalid reasons couples "go together"?

YOU AND ADULTS

Some young people tend to avoid anyone who is over twenty years of age. Christian young people should not have this attitude. Adults can be a great source of wisdom and inspiration to any teen-ager. You should seek opportunities to communicate with older Christians.

It is important as you communicate with adults that you are careful to treat them with respect. Do not interrupt them while they are speaking. (If there is an emergency, say, "Please forgive me for interrupting, but. . . .") You should not call adults by their first name. In many areas it is considered respectful to address adults as "Sir" and "Ma'am." If you are polite and respectful, you will find adults more apt to listen. Concerning listening, be sure to listen to what adults say. Much of what is said is important and will give you an insight into their thoughts, memories, and wisdom. Some people tend to ramble when talking, but be patient, knowing that God can use you to be a blessing to them as much as He can use them to be a blessing to you.

While it is important to treat your elders with respect, you should never allow an adult to convince you to do wrong. There are some adults who **abuse** children and young people. Abuse is treating someone in an improper manner. If an adult begins to use vulgar language around you, makes suggestions about improper behavior, or attempts to touch private parts of your body, you should inform your parents or another adult immediately. Righteous indignation rather than fear or shame is an appropriate reaction if one is ever abused. Abuse does not stop with children; teen-agers, men, and women often face abusive behavior in the world today. Be wary of situations that would place you in danger. Do not be afraid to stand up for what is right, to refuse to go to a dangerous or isolated location, or to get help if you need it.

SUPERIOR SOCIAL HEALTH

Changing social habits is not easy. It takes time, work, and prayer to change attitudes and habits that you have developed for years. But it can be done. If you feel shy and lonely, you can learn to enjoy the company of others. If you do not have many friends, you can learn to make more friends. If you have bad manners, you can learn proper manners. If you have never considered dating standards, seek God's leading and determine them. Set a goal today that aims at superior social health.

Section Review

1. Why should teen-agers take time and effort to talk to adults and elderly people?

2. What are at least three rules of etiquette a teen-ager should keep in mind when dealing with adults?

CHAPTER REVIEW

Terms

extrovert	tact	peer pressure
introvert	communication	fad
social skills	nonverbal communication	clique
personality	etiquette	prejudice
loyalty	sibling rivalry	abuse
dependability		

Content Questions

1. List at least three characteristics that you would expect to find in an extroverted person. Select and list three characteristics that describe an introverted person.

2. Outline the social skills discussed in the text.

3. What is tact? Why should one be sure to exercise tact along with a sense of humor?

4. What are some indicators during and after class that show whether a student was listening to or only hearing the teacher?

5. Why should one practice good etiquette daily?

6. Why should you obey and honor your parents?

7. List three actions that would encourage good sibling relationships.

8. Why should Christian young people seek to have godly friends? How can carnal Christians often be more dangerous than the unsaved?

9. What is the difference between peer pressure, cliques, and prejudice? In which cases could these terms be related?

10. What are some benefits of participating in group fellowships before starting to date?

11. Why should young people discuss dating rules with their parents before they start to date?

Application Questions

1. Why should a person consider improving his social skills?

2. Since it is possible to improve your personality, how could a person who has a tendency to be serious increase his sense of humor?

3. In what ways are verbal communications more harmful than nonverbal communications?

4. You are with your friends and someone begins to tell a dirty joke. Explain what you would say and do in order to deal with this situation.

5. Your best friend has started to drift toward worldly actions and desires. You feel that it is time to break off your friendship. What do you say? What do you do? What are some biblical principles that will help you through this difficult decision?

6. Why must you be armed with more than good intentions when you go out on a date? Before you date, what should you have already established?

Speech-Language Pathologists and Audiologists

Job Description: Speech-language pathologists identify, evaluate, and help people who have speech or language disorders. They work with people who have difficulty communicating due to hearing loss, brain injury, mental retardation, learning problems, cleft palate, or vocal misuse. Audiologists work mainly with the hearing impaired. They test, evaluate, and treat people for hearing problems.

Job Location: Although many speech pathologists

and audiologists enjoy the comfort of an office or clinic setting, many travel to schools, nursing homes, or agencies to deliver services to their clients. Concentration, patience, and attention to detail are essential for the speech-language pathologist and audiologist.

Training Required: A master's degree is necessary in order to obtain a license to practice in either field. Most insurance programs (Medicare, Medicaid) also require at least 300 hours of clinical experience before reimbursement will be given. People who are working on their degrees or accumulating clinical experience are often classified as special education teachers and must receive a practice certificate.

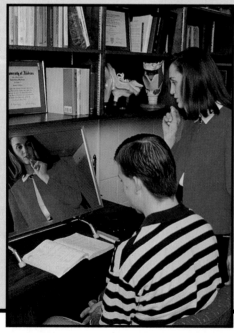

NUTRITION

What was the last thing you stuck in your mouth (other than your pen or your toothbrush)? Was it a handful of potato chips? The final slurps of a strawberry milkshake? Perhaps it was a slice of pepperoni pizza. Now, think back; did you eat or drink to the glory of God? Few people who quote I Corinthians 10:31 have actually considered how a Christian can eat and drink to God's glory.

CHAPTER 5

"Whether therefore ye eat, or drink, or whatsoever ye do, do all to the glory of God."

I Corinthians 10:31

EATING TO THE GLORY OF GOD

A Christian should eat his food with a thankful heart. A thankful heart recognizes that it is God who provides the food. Of course, your dad may have labored to earn money to buy the food, and your mother may have worked hard to prepare it, but it is God who made all these things possible.

Have you ever had to go through a day without any food, or have you always had plenty to eat? Unfortunately, those who have the most are often the ones who complain the loudest. Do you grumble about the food you have, or are you truly thankful for the food God provides for you? Sure, you said grace before you ate, but did you really have a thankful heart?

A Christian should also be careful to maintain a proper attitude about the food he eats. Food should never become the primary focus of a Christian's life. In John 6:27 Christ teaches believers to "labour not for the meat which perisheth, but for that meat which endureth unto everlasting life." There is a difference between appetite and hunger.

Undernutrition *is the lack of essential nutrients due to insufficient food intake.* Malnutrition *is poor nutrition which may or may not be caused by inadequate food intake. Unlike these Kurdish refugees of northern Iraq getting MREs (Meals Ready to Eat) to fight malnutrition, many American teen-agers suffer malnutrition due to poor food choices and terrible eating habits.*

Appetite is a desire for food; **hunger** is the body's response alerting of a need for food. It is important to be able to distinguish between the desire to eat and the need to eat. Some people who have the wrong attitude toward food eat too much. The practice of overconsumption is called **gluttony.** Gluttony is condemned in the Scriptures as a sin.

Due to lack of exercise and overindulgence in food, forty percent of Americans are obese.

Finally, a Christian should be careful to choose foods that do not harm his body. The food you eat influences your health. Be careful to select foods that will help you maintain your temple in optimum condition. Although a Christian should avoid placing too much importance on the food he eats, he can usually work more effectively for God if he observes the rules for good nutrition.

WHAT IS NUTRITION?

What is your idea of a "perfect" meal? Maybe a grilled hamburger, crisp French fries, and a large soft drink would suit your fancy. You could add a huge hot fudge sundae topped with a mountain of whipped cream and nuts for dessert. Or maybe you would prefer a juicy steak, baked potato with all the trimmings, salad, and a thick chocolate shake, with hot apple pie and ice cream for dessert. What is in the foods you like? Are they good for you? These questions and many more are dealt with in the study of nutrition.

Nutrition is the study of food and how it affects health. In underdeveloped countries people are more concerned with getting enough food for survival than with thinking about how food affects their health. Today, however, most people in the United States have more food than they need; yet many suffer from illnesses caused by improper diets. This is mainly due to poor food choices and poor eating habits rather than a lack of food availability. It is important to know how to use the abundant resources that God has given.

Nutritionists, people who devote themselves to the study of nutrition, have become a vital link in solving many dietary problems. Although there has been great progress, research is still incomplete. New information is being discovered; the field of nutrition is constantly changing. Keeping up with the new information will allow you to practice good nutrition in the future, but you must first become aware of the basic terms and facts now available. This chapter will acquaint you with some basic nutritional information.

FOODS CONTAIN NUTRIENTS

There are more than forty substances your body must get from the foods you eat. We call these substances **nutrients.** Essential nutrients include water, vitamins, minerals, amino acids from protein, fatty acids from fat, and sources of calories (proteins, carbohydrates, and fats [lipids]). Without the proper nutrients, your body cannot remain healthy. Nutrients are necessary for almost every body function. If you deprived your body of all nutrients, you would die; but, because God has made your body with the remarkable ability to store and conserve nutrients, you would not die immediately.

Nutrients Supply Energy

One of the most important benefits of nutrients is energy. It takes energy to do everything: to move, to think, to talk, to read. It even takes energy to do "nothing." Your heart must beat, your lungs must function, and your brain must keep them working when you are asleep or at rest.

The amount of energy that you get from any food can be measured. The unit used to indicate the amount of energy provided by a food is called a **calorie**. A calorie (abbreviated as *cal*) is the amount of heat required to raise one *gram* of water one degree centigrade. A kilocalorie (abbreviated as *kcalorie, Cal,* or *kcal*) is one thousand calories. Because calories are small units, most nutritional information is given in kilocalories. However, popular usage usually substitutes the word calorie for kilocalorie. The caloric information on food labels and in cookbooks is given in kilocalories although they are simply called calories. A kilocalorie is occasionally distinguished from a calorie by capitalizing the word *Calorie*. Whenever the word *calorie* is used in this text, it refers to a kilocalorie.

Calorie Expenditure per Hour for Various Activities				
Activity	**Cal./lb./hr.**	**100 lb.**	**120 lb.**	**140 lb.**
Archery	1.80	180	216	252
Baseball	1.86	186	223	260
Basketball	3.78	378	454	529
Bicycling				
slow	1.74	174	209	244
moderate	2.70	270	324	378
fast	4.74	474	569	664
Hiking	2.52	252	302	378
Jogging	4.14	414	497	580
Running	6.00	600	720	840
Soccer	3.54	354	425	496
Swimming				
crawl	4.20	420	504	588
backstroke	4.62	462	554	647
side stroke	3.30	330	396	462
Walking	2.16	216	259	302

The actual calories used will vary according to one's gender and body composition. To determine how many calories you would use during an hour of the above activities, multiply your weight by the calories/pound/hour figure or find your approximate weight column on the chart.

Energy for Metabolism

Your body is like a complex piece of machinery carrying on thousands of reactions. The sum of all the chemical reactions occurring throughout the body is called **metabolism** (muh TAB uh LIZ um). Everything you do (breathe, move, grow) is a part of your metabolism. To carry on these reactions, your body must have a constant supply of energy; it receives this energy through the food that you eat. The amount needed is determined by your **metabolic** (MET uh BAHL ik) **rate.** Metabolic rate is the speed at which your body uses energy for metabolism. Since everyone's metabolism is different, everyone's need for energy (and food) is also different. That is one reason why some people are able to eat more food than other people and not gain weight.

Your metabolic rate changes daily throughout life. There are many factors that affect your metabolic rate. Age is one factor. As you get older, your metabolic rate will begin to slow down. A two-year-old child, for example, has a higher metabolic rate than a sixty-year-old adult. The things you do also affect your metabolic rate. When you exercise, your metabolic rate is higher than when you watch television.

Metabolism *(meta=among;* bole=*change) includes the processes of* catabolism *(kata=down), which is the breaking down of large molecules to simple molecules and energy, and the processes of* anabolism *(ana=up), which is the building of needed body compounds.*

Factors That May Affect Metabolic Rate

Factor	Increased Metabolic Rate	Decreased Metabolic Rate
Activity amount	Active	Inactive
Activity type (considering intensity and duration)	Aerobic (jogging, bicycling, swimming, etc.)	Anerobic (weight lifting, quarter mile sprint, etc.)
Age	Young	Aging
Body composition	Lean	Fat
Body temperature	Fever	——
Emotional reactions	Stress	Calm
Environmental temperatures	Hot or cold temperatures	——
Gender	Men	Women
Growth	Childhood and pregnancy	——
Height	Tall	Short
Nutritional intake	——	Fasting, malnutrition, starvation
Thyroid hormone (thyroxin)	High production in thyroid	Low production in thyroid

SOURCE: *Eleanor N. Whitney, Eva May N. Hamilton, Sharon R. Rolfes,* Understanding Nutrition *(New York: West Publishing Co., 1990), table 12-4.*

Generally, the less active you are the lower your metabolic rate becomes. Your metabolic rate is usually lowest when you are resting. Your lowest metabolic rate is called your **basal** (BAY sul) **metabolic rate.** This is the rate at which your body uses just enough energy to keep your vital functions, such as heart rate and respiration, going.

Metabolism may be easier to understand if you think of your body as a car. Just as a car must have gasoline, your body must have a constant supply of energy (food). When you are resting (car idling), you are still using energy, but your energy needs are decreased. That is your basal metabolic rate. As you

become more active, your body burns more calories, just as driving faster burns more gas. As you continue to burn calories, you will need to replace them by eating (refueling). Neither your body nor your car can run properly without a suitable supply of fuel.

IN SEARCH OF A BALANCED DIET

Balance is important in every area of life, and your diet is no exception. A balanced diet provides the proper combination of nutrients necessary for you to stay healthy. How can you know the proper combination of nutrients for your body? The most widely accepted information comes from the National Academy of Science's Committee on Dietary Allowances. This committee established a **Recommended Dietary Allowance** or **RDA** for most nutrients.

The Recommended Dietary Allowance (RDA) provides a guide for people to determine the amount of nutrients they need each day. The RDA for each nutrient includes a margin of safety to insure that the nutrient intake is sufficient for most people. It is usually useless to take more than the recommended amounts since the excess will be stored or excreted. In fact, taking too many vitamins and minerals in supplemental forms can be dangerous and toxic. Nutrients obtained in quantities that far exceed the RDA are often referred to as **megadoses.** It is best to obtain necessary nutrients by eating a balanced diet rather than depending on nutrient supplements. You can find out how close you are to getting the recommended dietary allowances of many nutrients by reading the labels on the foods you eat.

EXTRA! EXTRA! READ ALL ABOUT IT!

In order for people to easily consider the nutritive value of foods they purchase, the Food and Drug Administration established the U.S. RDA (United States Recommended Daily Allowance) in 1972. Notice that the U.S. RDA and the RDA are two different things. The U.S. RDA used the 1968 RDA from the National Academy of Science to determine the highest recommended daily allowance of each nutrient for an adult. So that consumers

Nutrients	Male 11 - 14 yrs.	Male 15 - 18 yrs.	Female 11 - 14 yrs.	Female 15 - 18 yrs.
Protein (g)	45	59	46	44
Vitamin A (RE)	1,000	1,000	800	800
Vitamin D (mg)	10	10	10	10
Vitamin E (mg)	10	10	8	8
Vitamin K (mg)	45	65	45	55
Vitamin C (mg)	50	60	50	60
Thiamin (mg)	1.3	1.5	1.1	1.1
Riboflavin (mg)	1.5	1.8	1.3	1.3
Niacin (mg equiv.)	17	20	15	15
Vitamin B6 (mg)	1.7	2.0	1.4	1.5
Folate (mg)	150	200	150	180
Vitamin B12 (mg)	2.0	2.0	2.0	2.0
Calcium (mg)	1,200	1,200	1,200	1,200
Phosphorus (mg)	1,200	1,200	1,200	1,200
Magnesium (mg)	270	400	280	300
Iron (mg)	12	12	15	15
Zinc (mg)	15	15	12	12
Iodine (mg)	150	150	150	150
Selenium (mg)	40	50	45	50

Recommended Daily Allowances

RE = retinol equivalent   Figures based on 1989 information.

based on the 1989 RDA. Remember that a diet with less than one hundred percent of the U.S. RDA or Daily Values does not necessarily mean that the diet is deficient, since nutrient recommendations are overestimated. You should daily strive to obtain the highest percentage of RDAs that you can. It is important to read food labels in order to choose foods with the highest nutrient levels. To be a good steward of your temple and of the resources God has given to get food, take time to analyze food labels and "read all about it."

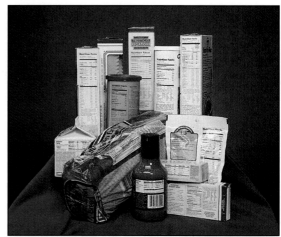

New food labels have replaced the U.S. RDA labels. The main goal of the new labels is to make nutritional information available and understandable to the consumer.

could tell at a glance what the nutrient levels were per serving of a food, the U.S. RDAs were expressed in a percentage on food labels. The U.S. RDA was the standard used in nutrition labeling for years in spite of changes made by the National Academy of Science in the RDA due to medical and nutritional research findings.

News Flash–In the early 1990s, the U.S. RDA was replaced with Daily Values. **Daily Values** represent recommended protein, vitamin, and mineral intakes for an average person in the population

Section Review

1. List three ways a Christian can eat and drink to the glory of God.

2. Explain why many Americans with abundant food availability suffer from malnutrition.

3. List six major nutrients that people must consume in order to maintain good health.

4. What is the difference between metabolism and basal metabolism?

5. What is the difference between the RDA and the U.S. RDA? What happened to the U.S. RDAs in the 1990s?

6. In order to obtain a balanced diet, does a person have to consume 100% of the RDA daily? Explain your answer.

Analysis of a Food Label

Serving Size

Is your serving the same size as the one on the label? If you eat double the serving size listed, you need to double the nutrient and calorie values. If you eat one-half the serving size shown here, cut the nutrient and calorie values in half.

Calories

Are you overweight? Cut back a little on calories! Look here to see how a serving of the food adds to your daily total. A 5'4", 138-lb. active woman needs about 2,200 calories each day. A 5'10", 174-lb. active man needs about 2,900. How about you?

Total Carbohydrate

When you cut down on fat, you can eat more carbohydrates. Carbohydrates are in foods like bread, potatoes, fruits, and vegetables. Choose these often! They give you more nutrients than sugars like soda pop and candy.

Dietary Fiber

Grandmother called it "roughage," but her advice to eat more is still up-to-date. That goes for both soluble and insoluble kinds of dietary fiber. Fruits, vegetables, whole-grain foods, beans, and peas are all good sources and can help reduce the risk of heart disease and cancer.

Protein

Most Americans get more protein than they need. Where there is animal protein, there is also fat and cholesterol. Eat small servings of lean meat, fish, and poultry. Use skim or low-fat milk, yogurt, and cheese. Try vegetable protein like beans, grains, and cereals.

Vitamins & Minerals

Your goal here is 100% of each for the day. Don't count on one food to do it all. Let a combination of foods add up to a winning score.

Nutrition Facts

Serving Size ½ cup (114 g)

Servings Per Container 4

Amount Per Serving

Calories 90   Calories from Fat 30

	% Daily Value*
Total Fat 3 g	**5%**
Saturated Fat 0 g	**0%**
Cholesterol 0 mg	**0%**
Sodium 300 mg	**13%**
Total Carbohydrate 13 g	**4%**
Dietary Fiber 3 g	**12%**
Sugars 3 g	
Protein 3 g	

Vitamin A	80%	•	Vitamin C	60%
Calcium	4%	•	Iron	4%

* Percent Daily Values are based on a 2,000 calorie diet. Your daily values may be higher or lower depending on your calorie needs:

	Calories	2,000	2,500
Total Fat	Less than	65 g	80 g
Sat. Fat	Less than	20 g	25 g
Cholesterol	Less than	300 mg	300 mg
Sodium	Less than	2400 mg	2400 mg
Total Carbohydrate		300 g	375 g
Fiber		25 g	30 g

Calories per gram:

Fat 9   •   Carbohydrate 4   •   Protein 4

Total Fat

Aim low: most people need to cut back on fat! Too much fat may contribute to heart disease and cancer. Try to limit your calories from fat. For a healthy heart, choose foods with a big difference between the total number of calories and the number of calories from fat.

Saturated Fat

A new kind of fat? No—saturated fat is part of the total fat in food. It is listed separately because it's the key player in raising blood cholesterol and your risk of heart disease. Eat less!

Cholesterol

Too much cholesterol—a second cousin to fat—can lead to heart disease. Challenge yourself to eat less than 300 mg each day.

Sodium

You call it "salt"; the label calls it "sodium." Either way, it may add up to high blood pressure in some people. So, keep your sodium intake low—2,400 mg or less each day.

Daily Value

Feel like you're drowning in numbers? Let Daily Value be your guide. Daily Values are listed for people who eat 2,000 or 2,500 calories each day. If you eat more, your personal daily value may be higher than what's listed on the label. If you eat less, your personal daily value may be lower.

For fat, saturated fat, cholesterol, and sodium, choose foods with a low % **Daily Value.** For total carbohydrate, dietary fiber, vitamins, and minerals, your daily value goal is to reach 100% of each.

g=grams (about 28 g=1 ounce)

mg=milligrams (1,000 mg=1 g)

Reprinted with some changes from *How to Read the New Food Label*, American Heart Association and Food and Drug Administration.

ESSENTIAL NUTRIENTS PRESENT IN A BALANCED DIET

You read earlier in this chapter that there are over forty nutrients essential for good health. It would be difficult and time-consuming to study each nutrient separately, but fortunately all of these nutrients can be divided into six different categories. The six types of nutrients discussed in this chapter are water, proteins, carbohydrates, fats, vitamins, and minerals.

Water

Because the cells of your body require an almost constant supply of water, it is one of the most important nutrients. Water is the most common substance in your body. In fact, on the average sixty percent of your body weight is water. In Chapter 2 you learned that water is a major part of your blood, but did you know that there are other parts of your body that are mostly water? Your muscles and your brain are about seventy-five percent water, and even your bones are more than ten percent water.

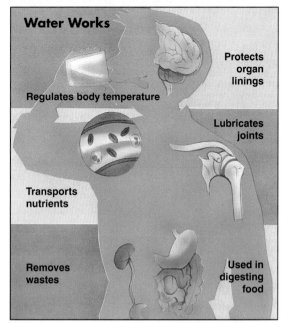

Water Works

Protects organ linings

Regulates body temperature

Lubricates joints

Transports nutrients

Removes wastes

Used in digesting food

It is suggested that a person drink at least one liter (almost 1 quart) of fluid for every 1,000 cal used. Transporting nutrients, removing wastes, regulating body temperature, lubricating joints, protecting organ linings, and digesting food are a few examples of ways the body uses water.

Caffeine Content of Popular Beverages

Item	Caffeine content (mg)	Item	Caffeine content (mg)
Coffee (5 oz.)		**Soft drinks (12 oz.)**	
Drip Method	60 - 80	Jolt	72.0
Instant	30 - 120	Sugar-free Mr. PIBB	58.8
Decaffeinated	2 - 5	Mountain Dew	54.0
		Mello Yello	52.8
Tea, loose or bags (5 oz.)		TAB	46.8
1-minute brew	9 - 33	Coca-Cola	45.6
3-minute brew	20 - 46	Diet Coke	45.6
5-minute brew	20 - 50	Mr. PIBB	40.8
		Dr. Pepper	39.6
Tea products		Pepsi-Cola	38.4
Instant (5 oz.)	25 - 50	Diet Pepsi	36.0
Iced tea (12 oz.)	67 - 76	RC Cola	36.0
		Diet Rite	36.0
Chocolate products		Root Beer	0
Hot cocoa (5 oz.)	2 - 20		
Chocolate milk (8 oz.)	2 - 7		

SOURCE: Kathleen P. Mullen, Robert S. Gold, Philip A. Belcastro, Robert J. McDermott, Connections for Health (Madison, Wis.: WCB Brown and Benchmark Publishers, 1993), Table 14.4.

Choice Beverages

It may seem that drinking six to ten cups of water each day is a tall order to follow. However, the question most people usually ask concerns not how much to drink but what to drink. Americans suffer from a seemingly endless parade of choices. Coffee? Tea? Milk? Soda? Water? What are you thirsting for? Which should you drink? In most cases, the choice is determined by thirst and preference. Take a moment to analyze what is available.

Would you like water or water? What? Water from the tap or bottled water—which should you drink? Bottled water offers purity and taste not available from many water systems. Distilled and de-ionized water is not 100% pure but does come close to it. Many people desire bottled water because of the taste. However, many people drink bottled water out of necessity.

Some water systems have been contaminated with bacteria, toxins (insecticides, herbicides, hydrocarbons such as gasoline or oil), or disease-carrying organisms (pathogens). Other people drink bottled water due to the presence of excessive lead in the water (from lead in the water pipes, water mains, or solder

connecting them). If you are not sure about the quality of your tap water, you can have your water tested. Public water systems check the water regularly; however, it is the responsibility of people with a private well to have their well tested occasionally.

Just because water is bottled does not guarantee that it is pure. As long as the water is bottled in sanitary conditions, water from ordinary water supplies can be bottled and sold. Some companies filter, flavor, deionize, or carbonate water from public water systems in order to enhance the taste.

Sodium (salt) content should also be considered. It is best to drink fluids that are low in salt so that the fluids will not upset the normal potassium and sodium balance in the body. This is especially important to consider when consuming fluids in hot, humid conditions or when engaging in strenuous work or play. In situations where dehydration could occur, the sodium content of the beverage could increase the chances of problems.

What about caffeine? Caffeine is a substance that occurs naturally in over sixty different plants. Caffeine can

be found not only in coffee and tea but also in soft drinks and chocolate products. Because it is a stimulant drug, low doses of it enhance alertness, increase metabolic rate, and keep the consumer awake. Because a tolerance to caffeine can be created over a period of time, increased usage or dependence on it can create problems (nervousness, insomnia, headaches, anxiety, paranoia, depression, and stomach upset). Caffeine is also a **diuretic** (DIE uh RET ik). A diuretic increases the excretion of urine. This can increase possibilities of dehydration in some situations.

In the final analysis, drink nutritiously and wisely. Use a variety of beverages daily to obtain your daily quota of not only water but also other nutrients. A glass of milk enhances your calcium, phosphorus, vitamin A, and vitamin D requirements. Juices contribute to quenching thirst as well as helping to increase vitamin intake. Certainly, it is nice to have some tea, coffee, and soft drinks. However, do not let these beverages be the main sources of your fluid intake. Water is still one of the best answers. Develop a taste for it. Develop a thirst for it.

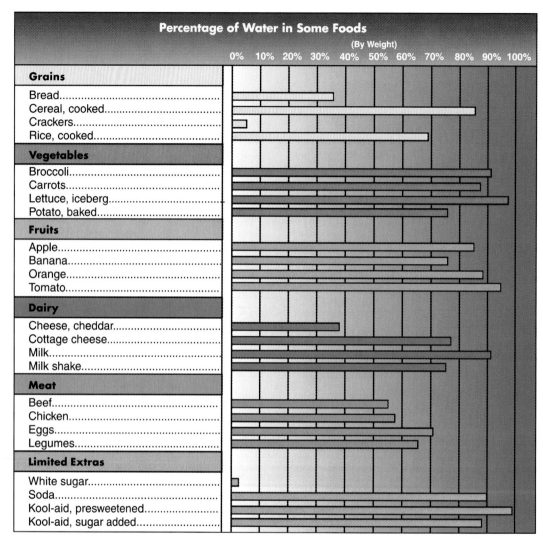

Percentage of Water in Some Foods
(By Weight)

	0%	10%	20%	30%	40%	50%	60%	70%	80%	90%	100%

Grains
- Bread
- Cereal, cooked
- Crackers
- Rice, cooked

Vegetables
- Broccoli
- Carrots
- Lettuce, iceberg
- Potato, baked

Fruits
- Apple
- Banana
- Orange
- Tomato

Dairy
- Cheese, cheddar
- Cottage cheese
- Milk
- Milk shake

Meat
- Beef
- Chicken
- Eggs
- Legumes

Limited Extras
- White sugar
- Soda
- Kool-aid, presweetened
- Kool-aid, sugar added

SOURCE: David C. Nieman, Diane E. Butterworth, Catherine N. Nieman, Nutrition (Dubuque, Iowa: Wm. C. Brown Publishers, 1990), table 12.1.

Your body was wonderfully designed by God to conserve water. Without this ability it would take about 2,500 gallons (9500 L) of water each day to keep all your body systems working properly. To supply your body with this much water, you would have to drink over two glasses of water each second. Although the body conserves most of the water it uses, some water is lost each day primarily through perspiration, vapor exhaled from the lungs, and urine. It is important to replace this water daily. Your body may be able to exist for weeks without food, but you will die in a few days without water. If a person loses six percent of his body water per day, death can result in three or four days. **Dehydration** is the excessive loss of water from the body.

In spite of the fact that water is in all the liquids you drink and most of the foods you eat, most nutritionists recommend that you drink six to ten cups of water a day. This helps replace the water you lose each day and keeps your body working properly. It is especially important to drink extra water when you exercise or work in a hot, humid environment. This aids in replacing the extra water that is lost in perspiration.

If you know ahead of time that conditions for dehydration will be great, you should *prehydrate* (increase body water beforehand). This can be done by drinking two or three cups of water two hours before and two cups of COLD water ten minutes before extended or intensive physical activity. Cold water moves through the stomach faster, allowing absorption to be increased. *Rehydrate* (replace body fluids) by drinking during and after strenuous activity, in the heat, and in humid conditions. You should weigh in before and after vigorous work or workouts. It is suggested that two cups of fluid be taken for each pound lost as sweat. Thirst is not always an adequate guide of the amount of water you need to consume. Drink what you *know* to be good for you, not what you *feel* like drinking.

Section Review

1. Why is water important to the body?

2. Identify three ways that water is lost from the body.

3. How much water intake is recommended in normal conditions?

4. What are three special recommendations that athletes should remember about fluid intake?

Carbohydrates

Carbohydrates supply energy for the body. Each gram of carbohydrate supplies the body with four calories of energy. Starches and sugars are types of carbohydrates. Since calories are needed by the body to supply its daily energy needs, you should strive to get most of your calories from carbohydrates.

Certain "fad" diets require a drastic reduction in the amount of carbohydrates eaten. Because of the popularity of these diets, many people think that they should avoid carbohydrates. The opposite is really true. The type of diet that eliminates carbohydrates is not a healthy diet. In fact, a diet that is high in certain types of carbohydrates (such as starches) may actually be helpful in losing weight.

Vegetables, fruits, cereals, and breads are some of the foods that are good sources of carbohydrates. These foods supply many vitamins and minerals and are important sources of **fiber** in your diet. Fiber is a part of the cell wall (the rigid structure

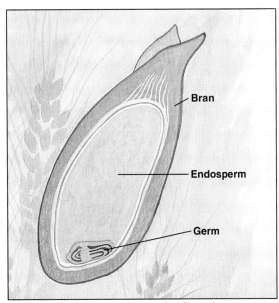

In grains, the bran provides needed fiber; the endosperm provides starch and protein; and the germ provides fat and vitamins. In fruits and vegetables, the skins and cell walls provide cellulose (insoluble fiber).

The Amount of Dietary Fibers Foods Contain

Food	Cal.	Grams of Dietary Fiber
Fruit		0 1 2 3 4 5 6 7 8 9 10
apple (w/skin)	81	
banana	105	
peach (w/skin)	37	
raisins	434	12.6
strawberries	45	
orange	62	
Vegetables, cooked		0 1 2 3 4 5 6 7 8 9 10
beans, string, green	36	
broccoli	20	
potato (w/skin)	115	
Vegetables, raw		0 1 2 3 4 5 6 7 8 9 10
celery, diced	18	
lettuce, shredded	7	
Legumes		0 1 2 3 4 5 6 7 8 9 10
baked beans	235	
garbanzo beans	28	
kidney beans, cooked	230	12.5

*Amounts are either 1 cup, 1 serving, or 1 slice.

Food	Cal.	Grams of Dietary Fiber
Nuts and seeds		0 1 2 3 4 5 6 7 8 9 10
almonds	677	10.7
peanuts	840	11.1
popcorn, popped	25	14
Breads, pastas, and grains		0 1 2 3 4 5 6 7 8 9 10
bagels	163	
bran muffins	112	
bread, French	98	
bread, white	61	
bread, whole-wheat	61	
rice, brown, cooked	232	
rice, white, cooked	225	
spaghetti, cooked	155	
Breakfast cereals		0 1 2 3 4 5 6 7 8 9 10
All-Bran®	212	25.5
granola	503	
oatmeal	311	
corn flakes	883	

* Please note that not all fibers have similar effects; oat bran and wheat bran do not react the same in the body. Therefore, it is important to eat a variety of high-fiber foods.

SOURCE: *Gordon M. Wardlow, Paul M. Insel, Marcia F. Seyler,* Contemporary Nutrition: Issues and Insights *(St. Louis: Mosby Year Book, 1992), Appendix A.*

that surrounds plant cells) in many of the plants that you eat. Your small intestine cannot digest fiber, yet it is an important part of your diet. Fiber adds bulk to your diet and may help you feel fuller when you eat. It also aids the digestive system in the elimination of waste.

You have probably noticed the increased promotion of dietary fiber in advertisements and in lists of dietary requirements. This promotion results from the fact that fiber, normally thought of as only

a help in the elimination of waste products from the body, has also been linked with the prevention of appendicitis, diverticular disease, colon cancer, and the control of diabetes, obesity, and cardiovascular disease.

Dietary fiber is sometimes divided into two different categories: soluble and insoluble. Insoluble fibers such as cellulose, hemicellulose, and lignin pass through the body undigested and thus increase fecal bulk and promote regularity. Soluble fibers such as gums, pectins, and mucilages help to promote the growth of bacteria to attack toxins and bind acids, salts, and toxins. They also aid in the gradual absorption of carbohydrates and thus help stabilize blood sugar levels. Some water-soluble fibers seem to decrease blood cholesterol levels, and therefore reduce the risk of cardiovascular disease.

Although carbohydrates are an important part of a balanced diet, some carbohydrates such as sugars should be reduced. Table sugar or sucrose is just one of the many types of sugar that Americans eat. The average American eats well over 100 pounds of sugar each year. This equals about one-fourth of the total calories that many Americans consume. That is a lot of sugar.

Refined sugar contains no vitamins or minerals; it supplies only calories. Since many Americans get too many calories and not enough nutrients, sugar is not usually a wise choice of food. Although you might be healthier if you never eat sugar again, it is probably not a realistic goal. A more realistic goal may be simply to reduce the amount of sugar that you consume.

In 1977 the Senate Select Committee on Nutrition and Human Needs recommended that Americans reduce their sugar intake by one-half. Obesity, diabetes, heart disease, and behavioral problems are a few of the diseases that have been blamed on excess sugar intake. In spite of an abundance of criticism, the only documented link between sugar and disease is its link with dental caries (tooth decay). However, even if sugar may not cause debilitating disease, it still does not contribute to health.

Millions of Americans have switched to artificial sweeteners to avoid some of the negative effects of sugar. The two artificial sweeteners that are most popular today are saccharin and aspartame (AS pur TAME; Nutrasweet), and both are surrounded by controversy. Saccharin leaves a bitter aftertaste with some users and has been associated with an increased cancer risk. Because of the possible can-

cer risk, the FDA sought to ban saccharin in 1977 but was blocked by Congress from doing so.

Aspartame is 200 times sweeter than sugar and leaves no aftertaste. It is a combination of two natural amino acids and has been found safe by the FDA. However, this finding has been disputed by some scientists who contend that aspartame momentarily breaks down into methanol (a toxic compound) and is then converted into formaldehyde (another toxic compound) before it is changed into carbon dioxide. Clinical studies have failed to demonstrate any health risk, but some scientists believe that the tests have not been adequate to assure safety. However, due to its chemical composition, aspartame is dangerous for people who have the genetic disease of phenylketonuria (FEN ul KEET n UR ee uh; PKU). Warnings are usually placed on

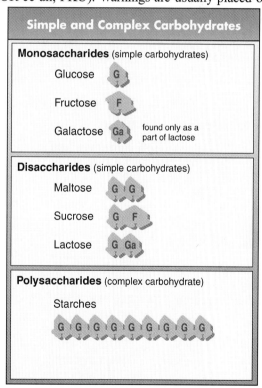

There is more to sugar than granulated table sugar, powdered sugar, and brown sugar. Sugars (saccharides) are often grouped according to their molecular structure (as shown in the box above).

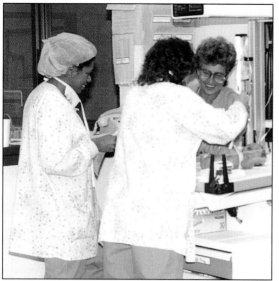

Infants are usually given a test for PKU shortly after birth.

the labels of products containing aspartame. One other drawback of aspartame is that it breaks down when heated.

The FDA has approved aspartame with the assumption that no one will consume more than 50 milligrams per kilogram of body weight a day. This maximum can be reached if a small person drinks a quart of drink sweetened with aspartame and also consumes gum, pudding, cereal, or other aspartame sweetened products on the same day. Limiting aspartame intake to three or four packets of Equal per day has been suggested. Aspartame should not be given to children under the age of two. The best way to avoid problems is to treat aspartame like sugar; limit its consumption and monitor what you eat and drink.

Section Review

1. What is the primary purpose of carbohydrates in the body?

2. List six types of sugars and three examples of starches which supply carbohydrates.

3. Explain why fiber is so important in the diet.

4. Identify four different sources of fiber.

5. What is the major danger proved to be associated with sugar intake? With aspartame intake?

Protein

Another nutrient that supplies energy for the body is **protein.** Like carbohydrates, each gram of protein can supply the body with four calories of energy. Protein is necessary for growth and the repair of body tissue. In fact, tissue building is the main function of proteins in the body, and the production of energy is secondary. Protein is also used by the body to regulate body processes (enzymes, hormones, and antibodies are all proteins).

Protein Quality: Essential Amino Acids—A protein is a substance made of long chains of amino

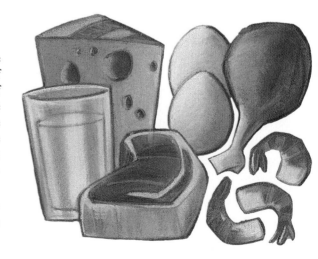

n cells are removed with every bath, so protein and nitrogen lost. Through proper protein intake, proteins are restored cells and tissue are replaced. The skin is totally replaced ry seven years.

production. Body protein (and therefore, nitrogen) is constantly being removed from the body in the form of sloughed off skin, hair, nails, perspiration, urine, and feces (inner linings of organs also lose worn-out cells, which are replaced with new cells).

Because protein is essential for proper growth and development, many people think that by eating extra protein they can develop larger and stronger muscles and improve their health. Unfortunately, extra protein does not result in extra muscle. Exercise, not increased protein, builds muscle. This emphasis on extra protein has been proved to be unnecessary and even harmful for most Americans. The average American gets far more protein than can be used for growth and development. Extra protein does not add muscle but is stored by the body as fat.

Although meat is the most abundant source of protein in our diets, certain plants also contain protein. In general, dairy products, meat, fish, and legumes supply greater amounts of protein than

(uh MEE noh) acids. Called the building blocks of proteins, amino acids are molecular chains necessary for your body to function properly. Although God has created your body with the ability to produce many of the amino acids you need, there are a few that your body cannot produce. These essential amino acids must be provided by the food you eat.

There are twenty amino acids that are important to human nutrition; nine of them are essential. Some proteins contain all nine; such a protein is called a **complete protein**. Most animal proteins are complete. A protein that does not contain all nine essential amino acids is called an **incomplete protein**. Most plant proteins are incomplete. Since a person who eats only vegetables may not receive all the essential amino acids from any one food, he must carefully choose the vegetables he eats. By properly combining a variety of vegetables and grains, he can receive all the essential amino acids.

Protein Quantity: Restoring Nitrogen Needs—
Eating protein is the only way the body obtains nitrogen. Proteins must be taken in enough quantity to provide the necessary nitrogen for amino acid

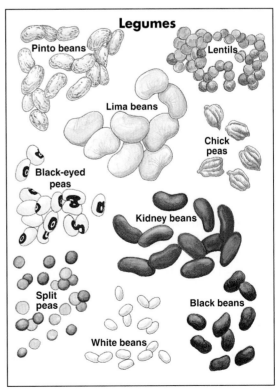

Legumes

Pinto beans · Lentils · Lima beans · Chick peas · Black-eyed peas · Kidney beans · Split peas · Black beans · White beans

grains, fruits, and vegetables. Legumes are beans, peas, and lentils from pods containing one row of seeds. At one time legumes were mainly grouped with meats because of their protein content. However, because of the high level of fiber offered, legumes are now grouped with both vegetables and meats.

Two Little and Too Much—Protein deficiency in the diet is not usually a problem in the United States. However, people in other countries suffer from deprivation and malnutrition. In areas where food is available but there is a deficiency of protein quality or quantity, people may suffer from a condition called kwashiorkor (KWA shee OR KOR). Kwashiorkor symptoms include swelling (of the face, feet, and belly); thinning hair that may become pigmented with streaks or patches of gray, blonde, or red; and discolored, flaking, and cracked skin.

The lack of calories or food for energy in addition to the lack of protein in a diet can result in a condition called marasmus (muh RAZ mus). The main symptom of marasmus is extreme emaciation. The wasting away of body protein tissue makes the sufferer weak, listless, and an easy target for infection and disease.

On the other hand, an excess of protein also produces problems. Too much protein can contribute to obesity since excess protein is stored as fat and many proteins are accompanied by fat. Protein excess can also contribute to dehydration since breaking down proteins requires large amounts of water. The intake of an abundance of protein has also been linked to calcium loss. This especially seems to be a problem if a person eats a lot of meat and avoids dairy products.

Although the amount of protein needed by the body will vary according to a person's age, size,

Kwashiorkor vs. Marasmus

Kwashiorkor comes from a word used in Ghana that means "sickness the older child gets when the next baby is born." This sickness results when nursing mothers wean an infant and place him on a diet of watered down cereal when a new baby arrives. The new baby gets the high-quality protein of milk from the mother, while the older child gets only low-quality protein from the cereal. Kwashiorkor is often equated to the term *red boy* due to the red patches of pigment that appear on the skin. The difference between kwashiorkor and marasmus is that kwashiorkor results from a protein deficiency (quality and quantity) and marasmus (derived from a Greek word that means "to waste") is starvation from the lack of food.

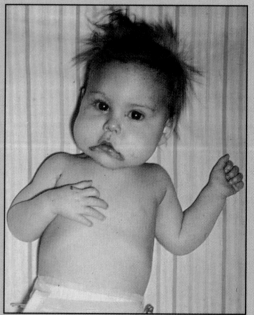

Fluid accumulation in this baby with kwashiorkor can be misleading. Fullness in the face and stomach areas does not result from fat, but from a deficiency of quality protein.

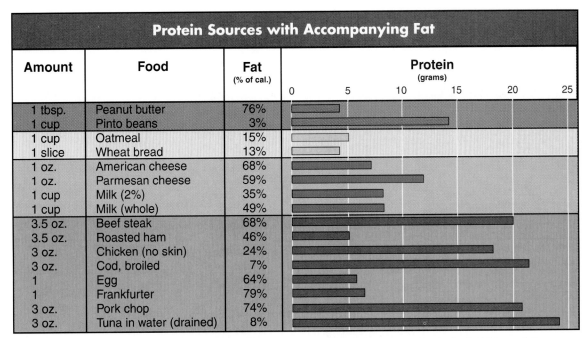

Amount	Food	Fat (% of cal.)	Protein (grams)					
			0	5	10	15	20	25
1 tbsp.	Peanut butter	76%						
1 cup	Pinto beans	3%						
1 cup	Oatmeal	15%						
1 slice	Wheat bread	13%						
1 oz.	American cheese	68%						
1 oz.	Parmesan cheese	59%						
1 cup	Milk (2%)	35%						
1 cup	Milk (whole)	49%						
3.5 oz.	Beef steak	68%						
3.5 oz.	Roasted ham	46%						
3 oz.	Chicken (no skin)	24%						
3 oz.	Cod, broiled	7%						
1	Egg	64%						
1	Frankfurter	79%						
3 oz.	Pork chop	74%						
3 oz.	Tuna in water (drained)	8%						

Protein Sources with Accompanying Fat

SOURCE: Eating to Lower Your High Blood Cholesterol, *NIH Publication Number 92-2920, April 1992, pp. 6-7. Washington, D.C.: U.S. Department of Health and Human Services, National Institute of Health.*

activity level, growth rate, and absence or presence of illness, two or three servings a day of protein food are normally adequate. It is also important to obtain quality protein. Selection of lean protein foods that supply the essential amino acids in themselves (lean meat, fish, poultry, milk, and eggs) or in a combination (fruits or vegetables with grains) is wise.

Section Review

1. What are the functions of protein in the body? What is the primary use of protein in the body?

2. What is the difference between complete and incomplete protein?

3. List at least three good sources of high-quality proteins.

4. Is there a problem with protein deficiency or excess?

Fats

The final nutrient that supplies energy for the body is **fat**. Fats are a concentrated source of energy. Each gram of fat provides nine calories (9 kcal) of energy. This is more than twice as much energy as an equal amount of either carbohydrates (4 kcal) or protein (4 kcal).

Fat also provides other valuable functions in the body. Under the skin, fat acts as an insulator and

The word satiety (suh TEYE i tee) is often used to describe one of the functions of fat in food. Satiety is the feeling of being full or gratified; hunger has been satiated.

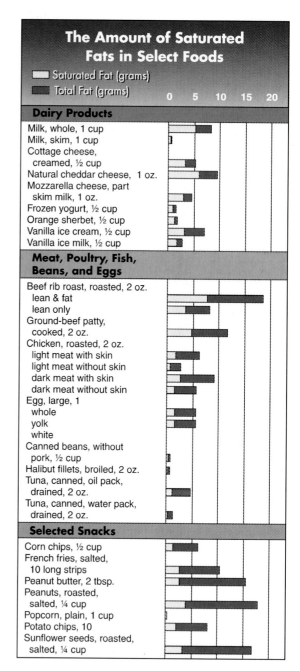

The Amount of Saturated Fats in Select Foods

- ☐ Saturated Fat (grams)
- ■ Total Fat (grams)

Dairy Products
- Milk, whole, 1 cup
- Milk, skim, 1 cup
- Cottage cheese, creamed, ½ cup
- Natural cheddar cheese, 1 oz.
- Mozzarella cheese, part skim milk, 1 oz.
- Frozen yogurt, ½ cup
- Orange sherbet, ½ cup
- Vanilla ice cream, ½ cup
- Vanilla ice milk, ½ cup

Meat, Poultry, Fish, Beans, and Eggs
- Beef rib roast, roasted, 2 oz.
  - lean & fat
  - lean only
- Ground-beef patty, cooked, 2 oz.
- Chicken, roasted, 2 oz.
  - light meat with skin
  - light meat without skin
  - dark meat with skin
  - dark meat without skin
- Egg, large, 1
  - whole
  - yolk
  - white
- Canned beans, without pork, ½ cup
- Halibut fillets, broiled, 2 oz.
- Tuna, canned, oil pack, drained, 2 oz.
- Tuna, canned, water pack, drained, 2 oz.

Selected Snacks
- Corn chips, ½ cup
- French fries, salted, 10 long strips
- Peanut butter, 2 tbsp.
- Peanuts, roasted, salted, ¼ cup
- Popcorn, plain, 1 cup
- Potato chips, 10
- Sunflower seeds, roasted, salted, ¼ cup

SOURCE: Nutrition and Your Health: Dietary Guidelines for Americans, Home and Garden Bulletin Number 232-3, April 1986, pp. 6-7. Washington, D.C.: U.S. Department of Agriculture, Human Nutrition Information Service.

protects the body from extreme temperature changes. It surrounds certain internal organs (such as the kidneys and liver) to protect and to cushion them from physical injury. Fat is also necessary to transport certain vitamins.

Why then do so many people think fat is bad? It is that the typical American eats far too much fat; forty percent of his caloric intake comes from it. Although the right amount of fat in the diet is necessary and useful (it helps to decrease hunger pangs), too much fat can be deadly. Again, balance is essential.

There are two major problems associated with excess fat in the diet. The first problem is that fat in the diet contributes to the weight problem that many Americans experience. As noted earlier, fats are packed with calories. When you eat fat, it is easy to accumulate too many calories. This excess energy is then stored in the body as fat tissue. One pound of body fat provides 3,500 calories. Accumulating too much fat tissue in the body has been associated with diabetes, arthritis, and heart disease.

Second, a diet that is high in fats often results in an abundance of fatty substances in the blood. Among the most dangerous of these substances is **cholesterol**. Cholesterol is a fat-related substance that is produced

Cholesterol Wars: HDL vs. LDL

Recent studies have shown that a high level of cholesterol in the blood is an important contributor to heart disease. Doctors and patients are becoming much more aware of the importance of controlling cholesterol levels. There is evidence, however, that not all cholesterol is the same. Cholesterol links with protein for transportation in the blood stream, and there are several different ways they combine. Some combine to form relatively dense fatty substances (called HDL), and others combine to form fatty substances that are less dense (called LDL). Interestingly, one seems to protect the heart while the other appears to harm it.

The "bad guy" seems to be LDL. LDL appears to contribute to a type of blood vessel disease in which fat deposits build up on the blood vessel walls. This disease is called **atherosclerosis** (ATH uh roh skluh ROH sis). Atherosclerosis can cause interference of blood circulation. If the blood is interrupted from flowing to the brain, a stroke can occur. If the blood is kept from flowing to the heart, a heart attack can result.

HDL appears to be a "good guy." HDL may actually be beneficial in preventing and reducing atherosclerosis. Currently most medical efforts are directed at reducing the total cholesterol level. Some physicians believe that raising the amount of HDL in comparison with total cholesterol is more important than reducing the total cholesterol level.

What determines the amount of HDL that you have? Scientists are not certain of all the things that influence the amount of HDL in the body, but they have observed that certain families seem to have higher levels of HDL. This is one reason many scientists believe that heredity plays an important role in cholesterol level and the level of HDL. Scientists have also observed that HDL levels are usually higher in women than in men.

There is nothing you can do to change your heredity or your gender, but exercise does appear to help raise HDL levels. Running in particular seems to raise the level of HDL in the blood. Whatever your heritage or gender, screening your diet in order to lower total fat intake and engaging in moderate exercise may help you to avoid or delay the onset of heart disease.

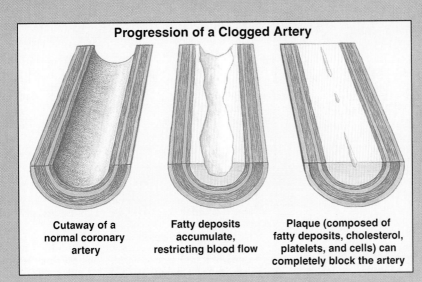

Progression of a Clogged Artery

Cutaway of a normal coronary artery

Fatty deposits accumulate, restricting blood flow

Plaque (composed of fatty deposits, cholesterol, platelets, and cells) can completely block the artery

by the liver and is needed for good health. As much as 80 percent of the cholesterol found in the body is produced by the liver. It is also present in many of the fatty foods that Americans eat.

There is evidence that a diet rich in cholesterol can increase the amount of cholesterol in the blood stream, and this increase can result in a greatly increased chance of heart disease. If the cholesterol level in the blood becomes too high, it can often be reduced by changing the diet. Cholesterol is found only in products from animal sources and not in products from plant sources. Certain foods such as egg yolks, liver, and shellfish contain high levels of cholesterol and may need to be eliminated. However, increased consumption of poultry, fish, legumes, and lean meat combined with more fruits, vegetables, and grains will also promote lower cholesterol levels.

Another way you can help reduce the amount of cholesterol in your diet is to choose the right kind of fats. There are two types of fats: saturated and unsaturated. **Saturated fats** are fats that generally come from animals and are solid at room tempera-

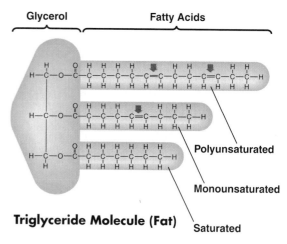

Triglyceride Molecule (Fat)

The distinction between saturated and unsaturated fats pertains to the hydrogen atoms they contain. Saturated fats are filled with hydrogen atoms and cannot accept any more hydrogen atoms. Unsaturated fats can accept more hydrogen atoms.

ture. Have you ever watched your mother fry bacon? What happens when the bacon grease cools?

Cholesterol Content Of Common Foods

Grains	Cholesterol (mg)	Meats	Cholesterol (mg)
Grains	0	Meats	
Fruits	0	pork chop (3 oz.)	83
Vegetables	0	chicken, drumstick	41
Dairy		chicken, breast (½ cup)	73
		beef, steak (3 oz.)	67
whole milk (1 cup)	33	hotdog, beef & pork	23
low-fat milk (1 cup)	22	hotdog, chicken	45
skim milk (1 cup)	4	brains (3 oz.)	1,696
yogurt (whole milk, 1 cup)	30	liver (3 oz.)	410
nonfat yogurt (1 cup)	4	egg, yolk (1 large)	213
cheddar cheese (1 oz.)	30	egg, white (1 large)	0
American processed cheese (1 oz.)	27	shrimp (3 ½ oz.)	195
mozzarella (part skim milk, 1 oz.)	15	lobster (1 cup)	104
ice cream, rich (16% fat)	88	flounder (3 oz.)	58
ice cream, regular (11% fat)	59	tuna, canned water pack (3 oz.)	28
ice milk (4% fat)	18	Limited Extras	
soft serve ice cream (3% fat)	13	butter (1 tsp.)	11
sherbet (2%)	14	margarine, all vegetable (1 tsp.)	0
		bacon fat (1 tsp.)	26

SOURCE: Eating to Lower Your High Blood Cholesterol, NIH Publication Number 92-2920, April 1992, p. 44. Washington D.C.: U.S. Department of Health and Human Services, National Institute of Health.

Dietary Fats

Food Item	Cholesterol (mg/tbs.)	Fat (grams)	Saturated fat	Polyunsaturated fat	Monounsaturated fat (Fatty acid content normalized to 100%)
Canola oil	0	14	6%	31%	63%
Safflower oil	0	13.6	10%	77%	13%
Sunflower oil	0	13.6	11%	69%	20%
Corn oil	0	13.6	13%	62%	25%
Olive oil	0	13.5	14%	9%	77%
Soybean oil	0	13.6	15%	61%	24%
Mayonnaise	8	10.9	16%	54%	30%
Salad dressing	4	4.9	16%	56%	28%
French dressing	0	8.81	16%	39%	45%
Margarine	0	11.4	17%	34%	49%
Peanut oil	0	13.5	18%	33%	49%
Chicken fat	11	12.8	31%	22%	47%
Bacon fat	84	14	37%	12%	51%
Lard	12	12.8	41%	12%	47%
Beef fat	14	12.8	52%	4%	44%
Butterfat	31	11.5	66%	4%	30%
Coconut Oil	0	13.6	92%	2%	6%

SOURCE: Nutrition and Your Health: Dietary Guidelines for Americans, *Home and Garden Bulletin Number 232-3, April 1986, pp. 6-7. Washington, D.C.: U.S. Department of Agriculture, Human Nutrition Information Service.*

Bacon grease is a saturated fat. Saturated fats are primarily found in animal products (meat and dairy products) and in tropical oils from the coconut and palm plants.

Unsaturated fats come primarily from plants and are liquid at room temperature. Cooking oil is an example of an unsaturated fat. Unsaturated fats may be saturated by a chemical process and sold in cans as shortening. Even though these fats come from plants, they have been changed into saturated fats.

Nutritionists have found that saturated fats appear to be much more dangerous than unsaturated fats. Saturated fats raise the cholesterol level in the blood while unsaturated fats may reduce it. Nutritionists recommend that Americans reduce the amount of fat they eat from about forty percent of their total calories to below thirty percent and that most of it be unsaturated.

Although fat is necessary in the diet, it is important to notice the *amount* of fat in your food choices. The *types* of fat that you eat should also be monitored. Choose foods that are low in fat content, low in cholesterol, and low in saturation. It is your choice; make it wisely.

Section Review

1. Are fats useful to the body? How?

2. In what ways can fats be harmful to the body? Be specific.

3. Which food groups do not have cholesterol?

4. How are saturated fats dangerous to health?

Vitamins

Do you ever take vitamin pills? Does your mother ever make you finish the food on your plate so that you will "get all your vitamins"? What are vitamins anyway, and why are they so important?

Vitamins are chemicals derived from living things which are essential for life. These nutrients are needed by the body in small amounts to help regulate metabolism. Because your body cannot make most vitamins, you must get them from the foods you eat. A shortage of certain vitamins can result in serious disease.

There are two types of vitamins needed by the body: water-soluble vitamins and fat-soluble vitamins. **Water-soluble vitamins,** such as the B vitamins and vitamin C, dissolve in water. Because they dissolve in water, any excess taken is excreted by the kidneys. Since water-soluble vitamins are not stored in the body, it is vital to get the proper amount of these vitamins daily.

Many Americans die each year from vitamin poisoning. Vitamin supplements with more than 100% of the RDAs increase the risk of vitamin toxicity.

Remember that bigger does not mean better, and more is not always good.

Fat-soluble vitamins do not dissolve in water and are transported and absorbed by the body in fats. There are four fat-soluble vitamins: A, D, E, and K. Because these vitamins can be stored in the body, special care must be taken to avoid the harmful effects that can come from getting too much. High intake of vitamins A or D can be very dangerous.

Since vitamins occur naturally in food, most nutritionists agree that the best way to get your vitamins is through a balanced diet. Studies show, however, that the diets of many Americans are not providing the necessary vitamins. Because it is often difficult to change eating habits, many people attempt to achieve a healthy diet by taking extra vitamins. These vitamins are often sold in pills and are called **vitamin supplements.**

Should you take vitamin pills? This is a controversial topic in nutrition with no right answer that will apply to everyone. A Christian realizes that God designed the body to get necessary substances from food. However, the diet that is actually being used may differ greatly from the type of diet that God designed for best health. Age, size, activity, sickness, and food intake all influence dietary needs and choices. A daily multivitamin supplement may be helpful in supplying the vitamins not obtained from your diet. However, no nutritionist knows all the substances a body needs and the correct amount for each nutrient. This is part of the reason that it is best to get vitamins through a balanced diet.

Overview of Vitamin Needs and Functions

Vitamin	Amount	Major Sources	Major Functions	Signs of Deficiency
B_1 (thiamine)	Male: 1.5 mg Female: 1.1 mg	Pork, peas, sunflower seeds, wheat germ, pasta, legumes	Used in energy metabolism	*Beriberi:* damages nerves, cardiovascular systems, and muscles; inability to walk
B_2 (riboflavin)	Male: 1.8 mg Female: 1.3 mg	Milk, meat, yogurt, mushrooms, dark green vegetables, beans	Used in energy metabolism; supports vision and skin health	*Ariboflavinosis:* cracks at mouth corners, skin rash, hypersensitivity to light
Niacin (vit. B_3, nicotinic acid, nicotinamide, niacinamide)	Male: 20 mg Female: 15 mg	Meat, tuna, poultry, fish, peanuts, mushrooms, potatoes, dried peaches	Used in energy metabolism; supports healthy skin, nervous, and digestive systems	*Pellagra:* weak muscles, no appetite, diarrhea, skin blotches
B_6 (pyridoxine, pyridoxal, or pyridoxamine)	Male: 2.0 mg Female: 1.5 mg	Potatoes, watermelon, bananas, poultry, fish, meats, whole grains	Amino acid metabolism, fatty-acid use	Depression, anemia, smooth tongue, cracked mouth corners, dermatitis
B_{12} (cobalamin)	Male: 2.0 µg Female: 2.0 µg	Meat, fish, eggs, milk, cheese, kidneys, liver	Formation of red blood cells, functioning of nervous system	Rare except in vegetarians; *anemia:* exhaustion
Folic acid (folate, folacin, pteroylglutamic acid)	Male: 200 µg Female: 180 µg	Leafy green vegetables, liver, wheat germ, peas, beans	Formation of red and white blood cells, aids in cell division	Anemia, fainting, fatigue, depression
Pantothenic acid	Male: 4-7 mg Female: 4-7 mg	Meat, fish, poultry, nuts, whole-grain cereals and bread	Metabolism of fats, carbohydrates, proteins	Vomiting and fatigue
Biotin	Male: 30-100 µg Female: 30-100 µg	Found widely; egg yolk, kidneys, liver, yeast, nuts	Formation of fatty acids, energy release from carbohydrates	Scaly dermatitis, fatigue, muscle pain, abnormal heart action
C (ascorbic acid)	Male: 60 mg Female: 60 mg	Citrus fruits, melons, tomatoes, green pepper, strawberries, leafy green vegetables	Formation of connective tissues, red blood cells; helps absorb iron	*Scurvy:* tender skin; weak, bleeding gums; swollen joints
A (retinol, retinal, or retinoic acid)	Male: 1,000 RE Female: 800 RE	Fortified milk, yogurt, cheese, liver, dark green and orange vegetables	Vision, maintenance of membranes, tooth and bone growth	Scaliness of skin, faulty teeth and bones, *nyctalopia* (night blindness)
D (calciferol or cholecalciferol)	Male: 10 µg Female: 10 µg	Fortified milk, eggs, exposure to sunlight (sunshine vitamin)	Regulation of calcium and phosphorus for strong teeth and bones	*Rickets:* soft bones; *osteomalacia:* bone softening
E (alpha-tocopherol, tocopherol, or tocotrienol)	Male: 10 mg Female: 8 mg	Vegetable and seed oils, leafy green vegetables, whole-grain cereals	Prevention of oxidation of vitamin A and fatty acids	*Anemia,* degeneration and pain in calf muscles
K (phylloquinone or naphthoquinone)	Male: 65 mg Female: 55 mg	Liver, cabbage, potatoes, peas, leafy green vegetables	Synthesis of blood-clotting substances and protein	*Anemia,* defective blood coagulation

mg = milligram   µg = microgram   RE = retinol equivalent

As you learned earlier, you should avoid taking large amounts of certain vitamins. Some people think that because a small amount of a certain vitamin helps them feel better, more will make them feel great. This is not true. Balance is the important principle to remember. Large doses of certain vitamins can be fatal. You should not take megadoses of any vitamin without first consulting your doctor.

Section Review

1. Do vitamins supply energy in metabolism?

2. What are the two major groups of vitamins, and which vitamins are included in each group?

3. Which group of vitamins can be toxic if taken in excess? What causes this group more likely to be toxic than the other group?

4. What is the best way to obtain vitamins?

5. Which vitamin is called the "sunshine vitamin"? Why?

Minerals

In addition to vitamins, there are other substances that the body must have in small amounts. These substances are called **minerals.** Minerals are different from vitamins in that vitamins come from organic (carbon-containing) substances, and minerals come from inorganic sources. Minerals are smaller than vitamins and therefore more stable in the body. Minerals help to regulate important body processes, and some serve to form parts of the body. For instance, some minerals help in normal muscle and nerve activity, others help control body water levels, and still others help form bones and teeth.

There are two major groups of minerals, **macrominerals,** also called the major minerals, and **trace minerals,** called minor minerals. As suggested by the name, macrominerals are present in the body in large quantities (about five grams of each in the body of an average adult). For instance, the largest amounts of minerals in the body are calcium (about two pounds) and phosphorus (about one and a half pounds). Calcium, phosphorus, magnesium, sulfur, potassium, sodium, and chloride are the seven macrominerals.

Although the trace minerals are less abundant in the body, they are not less important. Four of the trace minerals—iron, iodine, zinc, and selenium—

The behavior called pica is illustrated by children and pregnant women who eat nonfood substances. Children are noted for eating dirt and sand; pregnant women (especially those in poverty) are known to eat clay and laundry starch. Pica can cause an iron deficiency.

Overview of Mineral Needs and Functions

Mineral	Amount (ages)	Major Sources	Major Functions	Signs of Deficiency
Macrominerals				
Calcium	1200 mg (11-18)	Milk, cheese, dark green vegetables, sardines, enriched grains and cereals	Bone and tooth formation, blood clotting, nerve and muscle functions	Stunted growth, less bone mass
Phosphorus	1200 mg (11-18)	Milk, cheese, meat, poultry	Form bones and teeth; acid-base balance; genetic code, energy, and cell functions	Not known
Magnesium	Male: 270 mg (11-14); 400 mg (15-18) Female: 280 mg (11-14); 300 mg (15-18)	Dark green leafy vegetables, legumes, nuts, whole-grain products	Bone formation, teeth maintenance, building protein, nerve and muscle functions	Weakness, muscle spasms
Sulfur	None given	In all proteins	Component of proteins	Not known
Potassium	Minimum of 2000 mg	Fruits and vegetables, whole grains, meat, milk	Fluid balance, nerve and muscle functions	Muscular weakness, irregular heartbeat
Sodium	Minimum of 500 mg	Salt, soy sauce, most processed foods	Fluid balance; nerve function	Muscle cramps, reduced appetite
Chloride	Minimum of 750 mg	Same as for sodium	Acid-base balance; part of stomach acid	Muscle cramps; less appetite and growth
Trace Minerals				
Iron	Male: 12 mg (11-18) Female: 15 mg (11-18)	Meats, eggs, legumes, whole grains, green leafy vegetables, dried fruits, oysters	Needed to carry oxygen in blood and body cells	Iron deficiency anemia, weakness, lowered immunity, *pica*
Iodine (iodide)	0.15 mg	Iodized salt, fish, shellfish	Component of thyroid hormones	*Goiter* (enlarged thyroid), *cretinism* (retardation)
Zinc	Male: 15 mg Female: 12 mg	Meats, seafood, poultry, whole grains	Part of enzyme; helps form proteins	Growth failure, impaired immunity
Selenium	Male: 40 µg (11-14); 50 µg (15-18) Female: 45 µg (11-14); 50 µg (15-18)	Seafood, meats, whole grains	Part of enzyme, functions in close association with vitamin E	Muscle pain, heart disease
Copper	1.5-3.0 mg	Seafood, nuts, whole grains, organ meats	Part of enzymes, needed to utilize iron	Anemia
Fluoride	1.5-4.0 mg	Drinking water and tea, seafood	Maintenance of tooth and maybe bone structure	Higher frequency of tooth decay
Cobalt	Same as vitamin B_{12}	Animal products	Part of vitamin B_{12}	Same as vitamin B_{12} deficiency
Chromium	0.05-0.2 mg	Meats, fats, vegetable oils	Release energy from glucose	Loss of insulin efficiency
Manganese	2.5-5.0 mg	Nuts, whole grains, legumes	Part of enzymes	Poor growth
Molybdenum	0.075-0.25 mg	Legumes, tomatoes, milk, whole grains, cereals, carrots, strawberries	Works with enzymes	Not known

SOURCE: Wayne A. Payne and Dale B. Hahn, Understanding Your Health *(Muncie, Ind.: Times Mirror Mosby, 1989), table 5-2.*

have been researched enough to establish set recommended daily allowances. Copper, manganese, fluoride, chromium, and molybdenum are also needed by the human body. Although specific amounts have not been established for these minerals, tentative ranges for safe and adequate daily intakes have been set.

One of the trace minerals iron is highly deficient in many diets. Iron enables blood to carry oxygen and carbon dioxide to and from body cells. It is also a component of several enzymes and proteins. Although it is needed only in small amounts (12 mg for males 11-18 and 15 mg for females 11-18), iron deficiency is a problem. Iron deficiency can be caused by inadequate intake, loss of blood, poor absorption in the small intestine, frequent donations of blood, pica, and drugs (antibiotics, laxatives, and aspirin). Because of increased body growth and development, teen-agers need higher amounts of iron than children or many adults.

Iron deficiency and **anemia** (uh NEE mee uh; pallor, fatigue, and weakness caused by severe deficiency) can usually be avoided through good nutrition. Oysters, spinach, lima beans, beef liver, and legumes tend to top the list of good iron sources. Red meats, legumes, molasses, dried fruits, and enriched cereals and grain products are also good sources of iron.

As stated earlier, calcium and phosphorus are the most abundant minerals in the body. (Ninety-nine percent of the body's calcium and eighty-five percent of the body's phosphorus are found in the bones.) Adequate calcium intake usually insures adequate phosphorous intake. Most Americans do not get enough calcium and need to increase their calcium consumption. Milk and milk products are good sources of calcium. However, tofu, dark green leafy vegetables, sardines, and enriched grains and cereals also provide calcium.

Many older Americans, especially women, suffer from a bone disease called **osteoporosis** (AHS tee oh por OH sis). Many experts encourage teen-agers and young adults to build maximum bone

mass in their younger years so that losses of bone in later years will be minimized. Consumption of calcium, phosphorous, magnesium, vitamin D, and weight-bearing exercise (such as walking or aerobics) have been recommended for increasing bone mass.

The minerals potassium, sodium, and chloride are usually grouped together because they are **electrolytes** (carry an electrical charge when dissolved in water). These aid in balancing the water in and around body cells. Although exact RDA has not been set for the electrolytes, a minimum amount of 2,000 mg of potassium, 500 mg of sodium, and 750 mg of chloride has been given.

While sodium is a necessary part of a healthful diet, the average American gets many times more sodium than he needs. It has been recommended that salt (sodium chloride) intake should be limited to less than 6 grams (2,400 mg of sodium) per day. Most Americans consume about 8,000 mg of sodium daily. This is in great excess of what is good for the body. It is believed that an abundance of sodium in the diet leads to high blood pressure. However, the

Sodium advertisements must meet specified standards.
  Unsalted—no salt added during processing
  Sodium free—less than 5 mg
  Very low sodium—less than 35 mg
  Low sodium—less than 140 mg
  Reduced sodium—25% less sodium

link between a diet high in sodium and high blood pressure has not been conclusively established. Evidence is strong enough, though, for most medical and scientific communities to recommend a reduction in dietary sodium intake.

One of the biggest contributors to sodium excess in the diet is ordinary table salt (sodium chloride). How many times have you seen people sit down to eat and sprinkle salt over their food before tasting a bite of it? The wise consumer should avoid salting food before tasting it. Do not develop a taste for salt, and omit salt whenever possible. For instance, use spices, herbs, or fruit juices rather than salt to season food.

Sodium is added for seasoning not only at the dinner table and in the kitchen but also at the factory when many foods are made and processed. For instance, dry and canned soups made at the factory usually have much more sodium in them than homemade soups. Frozen TV dinners and entrees usually have higher sodium levels than the same foods made at home.

Read the labels to see what is in processed foods. Remember that salt is not the only key word in reading labels (salt, garlic salt, celery salt, etc.). Watch for other sodium names in food products (MSG is mono*sodium* glutamate; baking powder and baking soda are *sodium* bicarbonates; *sodium* caseinate is a thickener; *sodium* benzoate is a preservative; *sodium* citrate is a buffer in soft drinks and fruit drinks; *sodium* nitrite is a curing agent in meat; *sodium* phosphate is a buffer; and *sodium* saccharin is a sweetener).

Popcorn! Potato chips! Tortilla chips! Peanuts! Pretzels! Come get your sodium snacks! Americans are avid munchers and many do not realize the amounts of sodium they ingest. Pizza, burritos, spaghetti, pickles, sardines, olives, hot dogs, sausage, ketchup, soy sauce, and barbecue sauce are a few food favorites that have high sodium levels. Even some cereals and cheeses contain high amounts of sodium. Watch out and be aware of what you eat. Do not get in the habit of developing a taste for salty foods. Remember to control your eating habits; do not let food control you.

Ways to Reduce Sodium Intake

1. Taste food *before* salting.
2. Omit salt if possible.
3. Use spices, herbs, and fruit juices for flavoring.
4. Cut down on using convenience foods.
5. Read food labels; use products with the least sodium content.
6. Avoid salty snacks.

Section Review

1. Make a list of the seven macrominerals and five trace nutrients. Beside each, write one good reason that you should be sure to get sufficient amounts of it.

2. Why is calcium and phosphorous intake so important for teen-agers?

3. Which mineral should be decreased in consumption? Give suggestions as to how this can be done.

THE BASIC FOOD GROUPS

You may be wondering how all this information on vitamins, minerals, proteins, fats, and carbohydrates can help you. After all, how often do you go to the store and ask for a half pound of carbohydrates? It would be pretty unusual to go to a restaurant and order a vitamin or mineral sandwich. Instead, you eat things like hamburgers, potatoes, oranges, bread, and cereal. Although you are not

Recommended Daily Servings from Each Food Group

Study Hint
The following jingle may help you remember the food pyramid information:

Two, three
Two to four,
Three to five,
Six or more

Two servings

Three servings

Two to four servings

Three to five servings

Six or more servings

The food pyramid published by the U.S. Department of Agriculture is now the accepted format for the food groups and servings per day.

expected to compute RDA intakes daily, a knowledge of nutrients and RDA needs is important. Understanding nutrient needs and reading labels enable you to know which nutrients should be increased or decreased in your diet. Nutrient information also provides you with the ability to choose the best food for your money.

Most people do not have time to consistently or daily figure out their RDA for the nutrients of the foods they eat. Fortunately, nutritionists have devised a simple way to keep track of basic nutrient intake by dividing most of the foods eaten into basic food groups. These food groups are designed to help you get an adequate supply of needed nutrients. The basic food groups provide an excellent guide for good eating habits.

The Meat Group and Meat Alternatives

The meat and meat alternatives group supplies proteins, vitamins, and minerals (such as iron and phosphorus). This group is valued as a source of protein and iron, but it can also be a dangerous source of fat. You can reduce the amount of fat from this group by selecting lean cuts of meat, trimming excess fat, reducing the amount of beef and pork eaten, and increasing the use of legumes.

A serving consists of two to three ounces of lean, cooked meat, poultry, or fish without bone. One egg; $\frac{1}{2}$ cup cooked dried beans, peas, soybeans, or lentils; two tablespoons of peanut butter; or $\frac{1}{4}$ to $\frac{1}{2}$ cup nuts, sesame seeds, or sunflower seeds count as one ounce of meat, poultry, or fish. You should get two servings from this group each day. However, most Americans eat much more than two servings each day.

The Milk Group and Milk Products

Milk and milk products provide certain vitamins (riboflavin, and vitamin D and vitamin A when fortified), minerals (especially calcium and phosphorous), fats, and protein. Milk products are the primary source of calcium in the American diet. The milk and cheese group includes milk, cheese, and milk products such as ice milk, ice cream, cottage cheese, and yogurt. An eight-ounce cup of milk is one serving. Servings from this food group are usually based on the amount of calcium they contain. For example, one cup of plain yogurt is equivalent to one cup of milk, one ounce of cheddar or Swiss cheese equals about $\frac{3}{4}$ cup of milk, and $\frac{1}{2}$ cup of ice cream or ice milk equals about $\frac{1}{3}$ cup of milk.

Because you are entering a period of rapid growth and development, this food group is especially important. While adults may need only two servings from this food group, teen-agers need three servings each day. Selecting products from this group that have reduced fat content (such as skim milk instead of whole milk) will give you the needed vitamins and minerals while decreasing your fat intake.

The Fruit Group

This group used to be included with the vegetable group, but the necessity of obtaining more varied sources of vitamins, minerals, and carbohydrates caused the formation of this separate group. Fruits are major contributors of vitamins A and C. Dried fruits are good sources of iron and potassium. Besides being high in vitamins and minerals, fruits are good because they are low in fat and contain no cholesterol. Fruits are also excellent providers of fiber. This is especially so if the peel is eaten whenever possible.

It is necessary to obtain a good source of vitamin C every day and vitamin A every other day. Fruits make this goal easily attainable. Vitamin C is readily available in citrus fruits (oranges, tangerines, grapefruits, etc.). Strawberries, papayas, cantaloupes, mangoes, and watermelon are also good sources. Cantaloupe, mangoes, papayas, apricots, and watermelon are also good sources of vitamin A. It is easy to remember the necessary serving amounts. One medium piece of fruit, $\frac{1}{2}$ cup of juice, $\frac{1}{2}$ cup of cooked, canned, or frozen fruit, or $\frac{1}{4}$ cup dried fruit provides one serving of this group. It is suggested that you eat a variety of fruits and obtain two to four servings daily.

The Vegetable Group

Vegetables are also valuable sources of carbohydrates, vitamins, minerals, and fiber. You need three to five servings from this group each day. Vegetables also provide vitamin C (broccoli, brussels sprouts, green peppers, cauliflower, spinach, or tomatoes). Deep yellow or dark green vegetables (squash, sweet potatoes, carrots, tomatoes, broccoli, spinach, mustard greens, turnip greens, parsley, asparagus, and romaine lettuce) are also good sources of vitamin A. Some typical servings in this food group are $\frac{3}{4}$ cup of vegetable juice, a wedge of lettuce, a bowl of salad, or one medium potato.

Because of a lack of high-quality vegetable sources in fast-food restaurants, a lack of time to eat wholesome meals, or a dislike of vegetables, many teen-agers do not get enough vegetables in their daily diet. Although you may not like all vegetables, the variety of foods that are available in this group should allow you to find many that you enjoy. If you are willing to try new foods with an open mind and work to cultivate a taste for foods that are good for you, you will find it easy to obtain the three to five servings each day.

The Bread Group and Grain Products

Breads and cereals provide carbohydrates, vitamins (especially the B vitamins), minerals (such as iron and magnesium), protein, and fiber. The bread and grain group includes all foods made with whole grains or enriched flour or meal. Some examples are bread, pancakes, cooked or ready-to-eat cereals, flour, noodles, and rice. A typical serving of this group would be one piece of bread; one biscuit; $\frac{1}{2}$ to $\frac{3}{4}$ cup of cooked cereal, cornmeal, grits, macaroni, noodles, rice, or spaghetti; or one ounce of ready-to-eat cereal. You need six or more servings daily.

Although you may be eating enough foods from this group, you may be making some poor nutritional choices. For example, you may be choosing foods from this group that are not as nutritious as others. Whole-grain products, such as whole-wheat bread, are often more nutritious than refined products such as white bread. While white bread may be enriched to include some vitamins and minerals, there is a greater variety of nutrients in whole-wheat bread. Another example of a poor nutritional choice from this food group involves breakfast cereals. Many cereals are filled with sugar. For a healthy diet you should choose cereals that do not have sugar added or that include only a small amount of sugar. The benefits of making this good nutritional choice will decrease, however, if you add sugar to the cereal. Adding ingredients such as sugar, syrup, or butter increases the caloric value of breads and cereals with little or no increase in their nutritional value.

Limited Extras

This food group contains a category of foods common in the American diet. These are the fats and sweets. Foods such as mayonnaise, butter, margarine, candy, sugar, syrups, and soft drinks are included in this category. Also included are refined but unenriched breads, pastries, and flour products.

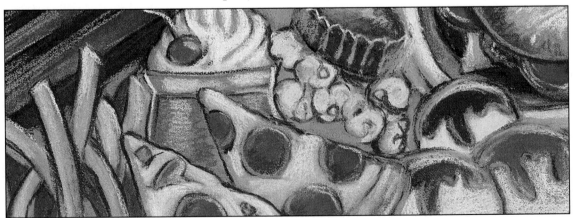

Right Choices for Healthy Nutrition

Great Choice!
These are low-caloric foods.

Careful!
These are mid-caloric foods.

Think Twice!
These are high-caloric foods.

Meat and Meat Alternatives
2 servings per day

2 - 3 oz. poultry
2 - 3 oz. fish
2 eggs
1 - 1½ cups cooked legumes

2 - 3 oz. beef
2 - 3 oz. pork
1 - 1½ cups refried beans

2 - 3 oz. hot dogs
2 - 3 oz. sausage
4 tbsp. peanut butter
½ - 1 cup nuts or seeds

Milk and Milk Products
2 - 3 servings per day

1 cup non-fat milk
1 cup buttermilk
1 cup skim milk
1 cup low-fat milk
1 cup low-fat yogurt
2 cups low-fat cottage cheese

1 cup whole milk
1½ oz. cheddar cheese
2 slices packaged cheese
1 cup fruit-flavored yogurt
2 cups cottage cheese

1 cup custard
1 cup pudding
1 cup milkshake
1 cup ice cream

Fruit
2 - 4 servings per day

1 med. apricot
1 med. orange
1 med. peach
½ grapefruit
1 melon wedge
½ cup berries

1 med. apple
1 med. banana
1 med. pear
½ cup canned fruit

¼ cup dried fruit

Bread and Grain Products
6 or more servings per day

1 slice bread
1 small roll
1 pancake
1 tortilla
½ cup whole grains

½ - ¾ cup rice
½ - ¾ cup cereals
½ - ¾ cup pastas
  (macaroni, spaghetti, etc.)
1 muffin
1 biscuit
½ hamburger bun

1 waffle
1 bagel
1 piece cornbread
½ cup presweetened cereal

Vegetables
3 - 5 servings per day

½ cup broccoli
½ cup Brussel sprouts
½ cup cucumbers
½ cup green beans
½ cup green peas
½ cup mushrooms
½ cup tomatoes
½ cup squash
1 cup spinach
1 cup mustard greens
1 cup collard greens
1 cup cabbage
1 cup lettuce

1 potato
½ cup corn

1 sweet potato
½ cup avocado

Limited Extras
Limited or no servings per day

spices   coffee   diet soft drinks
herbs   tea

High in fat
margarine   salad dressing   cream
butter   cream cheese   gravy
oils   mayonnaise   sauces

High in salt
pretzels   potato chips   olives
pickles   corn chips

High in sugar
cake   sweet rolls   syrup
pie   doughnuts   gelatin
candy   soft drinks   sugar
jelly   cookies   honey

These foods have little to offer you except many "empty calories."

Many of the foods in this group are often referred to as **junk foods**. Junk foods have little or no nutritional value. While you could eliminate these foods and probably be healthier, a more balanced approach may be to reduce the amount of these foods that you eat. Try drinking water instead of a soft drink when you are thirsty. Although you may not think you could ever give up candy bars, you could probably eat a favorite fruit as an occasional substitute. A little junk food eaten in addition to a balanced diet probably will not hurt you, but be careful to remember God's command for moderation that is given in I Corinthians 6:12: "All things are lawful unto me, but all things are not expedient: all things are lawful for me, but I will not be brought under the power of any."

Section Review

1. For your room, develop a reminder chart of the basic food group requirements.

2. What special vitamin requirements should you remember when consuming foods from the fruit group and vegetable group?

3. Write down all the things that you have eaten in the last two days. After dividing everything into the basic food groups, determine which groups you tend to be deficient in or excel in. How many servings of water did you obtain each day? Did you meet the vitamin requirements referred to in question 2?

CURRENT CONCERNS ABOUT FOOD

The last fifty years have brought many changes in the way Americans live. Among the things that have changed are the foods that Americans eat. While many of these changes have improved the health of most Americans, there are some changes that remain controversial. The following topics will address some of the current concerns about food.

Food Additives

Any substance that is added to food is called a **food additive.** There are thousands of substances that are now being added to our food. There are about 2,800 substances that are intentionally added to food. Well-known substances such as sugar, salt, and corn syrup are the most commonly used additives. Together with citric acid, baking soda, vegetable colors, mustard, and pepper, they account for ninety-eight percent, by weight, of all food additives used in this country.

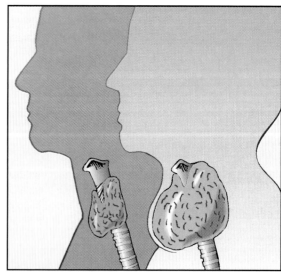

Too little or too much iodine can cause the formation of a simple goiter, a large projection from the throat that may have to be surgically removed. The incidence of goiter in the United States was lowered in the 1930s by adding iodine to salt. In some underdeveloped countries, iodine deficiency and goiter are still common today.

Many additives, such as those in hot dogs, are intentionally added to preserve the quality and safety of the product. Intentional additives are added to increase nutrition or color. Incidental additives get into foods through growing, storing, packaging, or processing stages.

Additives can be used to keep food from spoiling, to give more pleasant coloring, to increase certain vitamins and minerals, to improve the taste or texture, or to improve quality in many other ways. These uses can be organized into four primary purposes of additives:

- To maintain or improve nutritional value (fortifying with vitamins and minerals)
- To make food more appealing (coloring agents, sweeteners, natural and synthetic flavors)
- To maintain freshness and retard spoilage
- To aid in processing or preparation (emulsifiers and stabilizers)

Because many of these substances do not occur naturally in our food supply, some people question whether they are safe to eat. Some additives have been linked with cancer. Others cause severe allergic reactions. Since it is difficult to know whether an additive is safe and because there are so many additives in the food eaten today, many people would like for the use of additives to be drastically reduced.

Other health experts believe that most additives are harmless and that many actually improve health. For example, the iodine that is added to salt in iodized salt and the vitamin D that is added to milk in fortified milk have been helpful in improving health. Additives that prevent spoilage have

saved many people from severe illness or even death. These experts believe that most of the fear people have of additives is unnecessary.

A good approach to food additives is to recognize that many are not harmful and that some actually improve health. Those additives that are potentially harmful should be eliminated or used with caution.

Processed Foods

Think of all the foods you see in your local grocery store. How many of them have you seen growing in a garden? For instance, have you ever seen a jelly tree or a pudding plant? Obviously, many of the foods now available are not grown but are made in a factory. These manufactured foods are called **processed foods**. They are often high in sugar, salt, and other food additives; many have little nutritional value. Unfortunately, processed foods have replaced more natural foods in the diets of many Americans. Most people would benefit by reducing the amount of processed foods they eat.

Natural Foods

In reaction to the abundance of processed food in the American diet, many health conscious Americans have turned to **natural foods**. Natural foods

Make it a practice to use the more natural forms of food rather than processed ones.

Vegetarian Dietary Habits								
	Fruits	Nuts	Grain	Vegetables	Legumes	Dairy	Eggs	Meat, Fish, & Poultry
Fruitarian—eats only fruits, nuts, honey, and/or olive oil.	limited	limited						
Vegan—avoids all foods of animal origin, even dairy products and eggs.			Flour					
Lacto-vegetarian—avoids eating animal flesh and eggs but uses dairy products.			Flour					
Lacto-ovovegetarian—avoids eating any animal flesh but uses dairy products and eggs.			Flour					
Semi-vegetarian—avoids only certain kinds of fish, meat, or poultry.			Flour					selected
Nonvegetarian—eats all types of foods.			Flour					

SOURCE: Janet L. Christian and Janet L. Greger, *Nutrition for Living* (New York: The Benjamin/Cummings Publishing Co., Inc., 1991), Figure 8.4.

are supposed to be foods that are not processed and do not contain artificial ingredients. Natural foods are often organically grown (without the use of chemical sprays or fertilizers).

While consuming more natural foods can contribute to a more healthful diet, many foods that are labeled "natural" actually differ little from other unprocessed foods. However, many people prefer or, because of allergies, need foods that have no preservatives in or chemical contaminants on them. These products are available in health food stores and special food sections in many grocery stores. Since there is no official standard for classifying a food as a "natural food," the most consistent distinction is the cost. "Natural foods" are often much more expensive than unprocessed foods.

Vegetarian Diets

Another thing some Americans are doing to improve their health is to stop eating meat. A person who does not eat meat is called a vegetarian. A vegetarian diet can be a healthful diet; however, vegetarians must take extra care to make sure their diet contains all the nutrients needed by the body (such as complete proteins).

Today there are many false religions that preach the virtues of a vegetarian diet. While eating less meat may be a healthful goal, you should guard against any religious influence that attempts to restrict your liberty to eat meat. In I Timothy 4:3, the Scripture clearly teaches that "commanding to abstain from meats" is a mark of the devilish doctrine that will be prevalent in the last days.

Section Review

1. True or False—Food additives are bad. Defend your answer.

2. Write a convincing explanation of why it is best to eat natural rather than processed foods.

3. What are two things to be aware of when considering a vegetarian diet?

DIETING AND WEIGHT CONTROL

Dieting is the practice of changing the amount or the type of food you eat. Some diets are designed for weight gain, to reduce some specific substance like cholesterol or sodium, or to increase athletic performance (such as carbohydrate loading). However, the desire for weight loss is the main reason for dieting. Some studies show that over half of the adults in America are overweight and millions are on diets to try to lose weight. Dieting is a popular American habit.

Crash Diets

Many diets are designed so that the dieter can lose five, ten, even twenty pounds in a single week. Diets that call for a drastic change in the way you eat and are supposed to result in rapid weight loss are called **crash diets**. Any diet that varies greatly from a balanced diet or that aims at reducing weight more than one to two pounds per week is probably not a healthful diet.

Hundreds of diet books have been written by self proclaimed "experts" that market a variety of approaches to dieting. Some of these diets are consistent with acceptable nutritional guidelines and simply market a different approach to accepted standards. However, many exotic and nutritionally deficient diets are also being marketed. Some are even marketed by medical doctors. Credentials, such as a medical degree, do not necessarily imply

a sound approach. Any diet plan that varies greatly from the balanced diet described in this chapter should be viewed with great skepticism.

The Rebound Effect

Almost any diet can result in some weight loss. Few diets, however, are successful in keeping weight off after it has been lost. This explains why most dieters do not get increasingly thinner. Many dieters gain back the weight they lose. This pattern of weight loss-weight gain-weight loss-weight gain is sometimes called the rebound or yo-yo effect.

Many times those who experience the yo-yo effect become heavier than when they began dieting. Even those who do not gain more weight are often less healthy than they were before they began. Most people who lose weight by dieting lose both muscle and fat tissue. When this weight is gained back without an exercise program, the weight that is regained is almost entirely fat. The result is a person who may weigh the same but who has more fat tissue. Studies also show that the yo-yo effect often raises blood pressure in some individuals.

Effective Dieting

Everyone knows that people gain weight because they eat too much. Right? Not necessarily! Recent studies suggest that if you are overweight, it is probably due more to a lack of exercise than to excess food. Therefore the best way to deal with a weight problem is usually to exercise more and to

eat a balanced diet. In fact, dieting may cause your body to lower its metabolic rate. A lowered metabolic rate will make losing those extra pounds even harder.

Successful dieting requires determination and patience. Determination is important because eating habits are not easy to change. Patience is important because a healthful diet is one that results in a gradual weight loss (one to two pounds per week). Many people are not satisfied with a gradual weight loss. They want an instant diet that produces instant results. That is why crash diets are so popular. The problem is that instant success is usually followed by instant failure. A successful diet is a diet that results in a lifelong change in the way you eat.

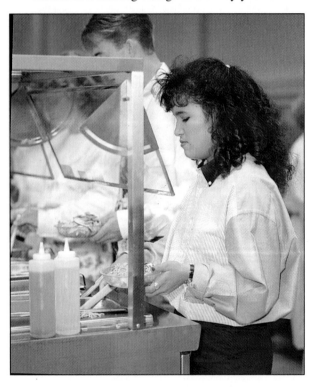

At this stage of life it is usually not advisable to diet because a teen-ager's growing body needs the variety of nutrients received in a regular balanced diet. Weight loss of more than ten pounds should be attempted only under the supervision of a physician.

The importance of maintaining a nutritious diet with gradual and lifetime changes rather than crash dieting or rebound dieting cannot be overemphasized. Consistent exercise (not just vigorous exercise once in a while which causes stress on the body and heart) is also important in weight control. Walking, swimming, aerobics, and floor exercise all aid in muscle tone and cardiovascular conditioning (improvements in heart, arteries, and lungs). A good diet program should also include psychological support. Many dieters give up because of the difficulty of "going it alone." Even though you may not be dieting, perhaps you can be an encouragement to someone who is.

Eating Disorders

There are times when the current emphasis on slimness contributes to certain types of eating disorders. **Anorexia nervosa** (AN uh REK see uh nur VO suh) is a disorder in which a person eats almost nothing. Anorectics may eventually starve themselves to death or cause irreparable damage to their hearts and bodies. Although the anorectic may be a mere walking skeleton, he sees himself as fat and needing to lose weight. A related eating disorder is **bulimia** (byoo LEEM ee uh). A person suffering from bulimia will often eat large portions of food and then, in an attempt to keep from gaining weight, immediately cause himself to expel the food consumed.

Both of these eating disorders can impair health. The heart may pump inefficiently, blood pressure can fall, the lining of the digestive tract can be damaged, the lungs can become infected, teeth may become eroded, and the kidneys and bladder can become infected. Because of the lack of necessary nutrients, brain activity can become abnormal, causing disturbed sleep and unrest. Continual practice of anorexia nervosa or bulimia can result in heart failure, kidney failure, and death.

Although anorexia nervosa and bulimia seem to be nutritional problems, they actually stem from emotional and spiritual problems. Young women who suffer from a poor self-concept (focusing on

ost anorexics have a distorted body image in that they see
emselves as fat, no matter how much weight they lose.

themselves rather than on Christ) seem to be especially susceptible to anorexia or bulimia. Self-centeredness or rebellion seem to be the core causes. Anger, resentment, bitterness, and pride may also be involved. These problems lead to other dilemmas such as becoming overdemanding of self, expecting total self-control, and emphasizing self-perfection. The anorectic must determine to accept God's will, to live for God's glory, and to submit to God's control rather than to focus on self and to give in to Satan by heading for self-destruction.

SUMMING IT UP: SIX GUIDELINES TO GOOD EATING HABITS

As you can see by now, nutrition is a fascinating yet complex area of study. Can you learn to eat a more healthful diet without remembering all the details about nutrition? Fortunately the answer is yes. The U. S. Department of Agriculture and the U. S. Department of Health and Human Services have analyzed current information about nutrition and reduced all this information to seven dietary guidelines. Six of these apply directly to you and your diet.

Dietary Guidelines

1. **Eat a Variety of Foods**
2. **Maintain Ideal Weight**
3. **Avoid Too Much Fat, Saturated Fat, and Cholesterol**
4. **Eat Foods with Adequate Starch and Fiber**
5. **Avoid Too Much Sugar**
6. **Avoid Too Much Sodium**

Eat a Variety of Foods

You learned earlier that your body needs about fifty different substances to stay healthy. Since no single food contains all of them, the best way to insure you get all the substances you need is to eat a variety of nutritious foods. Get the many nutrients needed by the body by choosing foods you like from the basic food groups.

Maintain Ideal Weight

How much do you weigh? Are you overweight or underweight? Do you know what your weight should be? Probably the best person to help you with this question is your doctor. He knows your state of development and the type of body that you have; he can help you determine whether you have a weight problem. When comparing body weight to weight and height tables, he will take your body composition into consideration. A body builder may weigh the same as an obese person but have increased weight due to muscle mass rather than fat. Some people have heavier bone mass than others, and weigh more because of their larger frames.

The best time to solve any weight problem is when it is a small problem. Good eating habits such as eating slowly (it takes about twenty minutes before your body feels full), eating smaller portions, and avoiding seconds may help you control a small weight problem before it becomes a big problem. When controlling weight, nutritious eating and a consistent exercise program go hand in hand.

Avoid Too Much Fat, Saturated Fat, and Cholesterol

As you have read earlier, these substances have been associated with heart and blood vessel diseases. Recent research shows that teen-agers who maintain diets high in saturated fats and cholesterol or who smoke are as susceptible to developing atherosclerosis as adults with the same habits.

Be selective in your food choices. Opt for baked or broiled meat rather than fried. Choose poultry or fish rather than red meats. Choose lean rather than fat portions of meat. Eat more from the fruit, vegetable, and bread and grain food groups. Drink skim or low fat milk rather than whole milk. Cut down on the use of butter, fats, and oils.

Eat Foods with Adequate Starch and Fiber

Starches (complex carbohydrates) supply the body with energy, and fiber aids digestion and

These foods are high in starch and fiber, two things most Americans do not get enough of.

Snacking on fruit can be a delightful way of obtaining fiber and natural sugar.

elimination. Most Americans should eat more starch and fiber than they currently are eating.

Eat more vegetables, dried beans and peas, fruits, breads, cereals, pasta, and rice. Eat fruit and vegetable skins when possible (cleaned but not pared apples, peaches, potatoes, carrots, etc.).

Avoid Too Much Sugar

The average American gets one-fourth of his calories from sugar. Sugar provides only calories. Since many Americans get too many calories and not enough nutrients, the amount of sugar they eat should be reduced. Avoid excessive snacking on candy bars, candy, soda, cake, cookies, and other sweets. In order to avoid dental caries, be sure to brush and floss your teeth regularly.

Avoid Too Much Sodium

The average American eats far more salt than he actually needs, and salt is a major source of sodium in the American diet. Many scientists believe that too much sodium can result in high blood pressure. High blood pressure is a dangerous but common disease in the United States today. Use salt sparingly at the table and in cooking. Eat salted snacks such as chips, crackers, pickles, pretzels, and nuts in moderation. Remember, many seemingly "non-salty" foods are actually high in sodium; so read the label.

These basic nutritional guidelines summarize many of the vital facts given in this chapter. As you have heard before, the key to nutrition, as in many other areas in your life, is balance. By avoiding the extremes, you can enjoy the healthful benefits of a balanced diet. It is not easy to change your eating habits, but the advantages of a healthful diet are certainly worth the effort. After all, as the maintainer of the temple of God, you are responsible to make wise choices in nutrition. As this chapter's verse states, "Whether therefore ye eat, or drink, or whatsoever ye do, do all to the glory of God" (I Cor. 10:31).

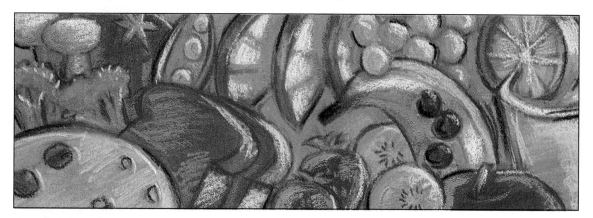

Section Review

1. Why is it unwise to indulge in crash diets or rebound diets?

2. What are three important parts of an effective weight-control diet?

3. What is the difference between anorexia nervosa and bulimia?

4. Without looking in your text, list the six dietary guidelines.

CHAPTER REVIEW

Terms

appetite

hunger

gluttony

nutrition

nutrients

calorie

metabolism

metabolic rate

basal metabolic rate

Recommended Dietary Allowance (RDA)

megadoses

Daily Values

dehydration

diuretic

carbohydrates

fiber

protein

complete protein

incomplete protein

fat

cholesterol

atherosclerosis

saturated fats

unsaturated fats

vitamins

water-soluble vitamins

fat-soluble vitamins

vitamin supplements

minerals

macrominerals

trace minerals

anemia

osteoporosis

electrolytes

junk foods

food additive

processed foods

natural foods

vegetarian

dieting

crash diet

anorexia nervosa

bulimia

Content Questions

1. Why should a Christian be concerned about his nutrition?

2. What is the difference between appetite and hunger?

3. True or False—Calories are bad. Justify your answer.

4. When is your metabolic rate usually at its lowest?

5. How can the RDAs affect you?

6. Which nutrient groups primarily provide energy?

7. Which nutrient group is mainly used to build body tissues and regulate body processes?

8. Why should a vegetarian be aware of complete and incomplete proteins?

9. Which nutrient groups are needed in small amounts to sustain health?

10. In addition to consuming food from the basic food groups, you should be sure to consume _____ glasses of water daily, a source of _____ every day, and a source of _____ every other day.

11. Why should weight loss diets be planned to be long-term rather than short-term?

Application Questions

1. What is the difference between malnutrition and undernutrition? What are some ways to alleviate these problems?

2. How has the breakdown of traditional family life added to the increase of poor nutritional habits? Be specific.

3. Formulate a vitamin supplement standard. Should you take vitamin supplements? Why or why not?

4. Imagine that your parents are going on an emergency trip for five days. They have asked your elderly great-aunt (Aunt Gladys) to stay with you and your siblings. You have assured them that they need not worry; you will plan the meals, go shopping, and help Aunt Gladys with the cooking. Write your meal plans (breakfast, lunch, snack, and dinner) for five days. Be sure to follow the basic food groups and the dietary guidelines. For extra credit, make a grocery list of items needed for the week.

5. Suppose you need to gain weight. Determine a five-day eating and exercise regimen that should increase your weight nutritiously.

6. Imagine that you and your best friend decide to lose five pounds and get into shape. Plan a week's eating and exercise regimen that will fit into your normal school routine. Set goals, standards, and rewards.

Dietitians

Job Description: Dietitians are professionals trained in the science of nutrition. Clinical dietitians work with doctors to coordinate the nutritional intake of patients. Because these dietitians work mainly with the sick, they are often called therapeutic dietitians. Community dietitians work with human services agencies and health maintenance organizations to counsel, evaluate, and teach individuals or groups about proper nutrition. Many work with nursing homes, schools, institutions, and home-delivered meal services to insure nutritional meal planning. Others provide nutritional counseling for diabetics, the elderly, and those with special nutritional problems (obesity, allergies, high blood pressure, high cholesterol).

Job Location: Most dietitians work forty hours a week; however, some are required to work weekends if they are employed by hospitals, nursing homes, or institutions. The environment where dietitians work varies. Those who mainly counsel, instruct, or do research usually have their own offices, classrooms, or laboratories. Dietitians who manage the kitchen and food preparation must work in hot, steamy kitchens and serving areas.

Training Required: A bachelor's degree in nutrition, home economics, foods, or institutional management is basic. Registered dietitians must complete additional classroom and clinical education before taking the registration exam. Graduate degrees are usually required of dietitians who are teachers, researchers, or administrators.

EXERCISE

In I Timothy 4:8, Paul instructs Timothy about the value of bodily exercise. There are two important ideas in this verse. The most important idea is that exercise is not nearly as profitable as godliness. Godliness has eternal value while exercise has only temporal value. Second, this verse points out that there is some value in bodily exercise. It will never prepare you for heaven, but it is valuable for increasing efficiency in this life.

CHAPTER 6

"For bodily exercise profiteth little: but godliness is profitable unto all things."
I Timothy 4:8

Although there are Christians who place too much emphasis on exercise, those Christians who abuse their bodies by not getting enough exercise are usually in the majority. A Christian should never seek to glorify his own body but should seek to glorify God through his body. That is what God commanded in I Corinthians 6:20. Since your body is the temple of the Holy Ghost, you should take proper care of it; exercise is an important part of caring for your body.

Exercise is an important influence on your health. It can be an exciting way for you to become more effective in almost everything you do. The following pages will help you learn how to make exercise and physical fitness work for you.

WHAT IS PHYSICAL FITNESS?

Huge muscles. Tremendous strength. Terrific speed. Amazing power. The ability to leap tall buildings in a single bound. That is fitness! Right? Wrong! This "superman" idea of fitness is not only wrong but also harmful. It is harmful because it overemphasizes some aspects of fitness and ignores others. The most damaging result of the "superman" idea is that it causes many people to mistakenly believe that they can never be fit. You can be physically fit. It will take time and work, but you can do it.

There are two basic reasons most people are not physically fit. The first reason is laziness. There is no pill that will make you fit; there is no magic machine that will whip you into shape while you relax. Even reading about fitness will not do it; fitness takes work.

The second reason many people are not fit is that they do not know enough about fitness. Some people think fitness is something that only athletes can achieve, or they may not know how to train properly. Many people do not even understand why physical fitness is important.

What does physical fitness mean? **Physical fitness** is the ability to complete each day's activity with energy and alertness, to participate in the things you enjoy with vigor, and to respond to

strenuous activities or emergencies without undue stress. As you can see from this definition, fitness is practical. It is not concerned with spectacular feats, but with daily needs. After all, how important is being able to lift more weight than anyone in your class if you cannot stay awake during school or if you lack the energy to enjoy special activities with your friends?

Most students can increase their fitness level by simply going outside and *moving*. Just about anything that gets you moving and keeps you moving (walking, running, jumping, biking, skipping, swimming) will help develop fitness. If you really want to be physically fit, you should first learn some basic training principles. These principles are important because they can help you choose good activities, avoid bad ones, and use your time wisely.

Principles of Training

Physical fitness is not attained by accident; you must choose to work at it. The work you do to become fit is called your *training program*. There are four factors that determine how effective your training program will be.

These same principles can be applied to many other types of work. For instance, if you are given the job of weeding the garden, your success will be determined by what you do, how hard you work at it, how long you work at it, and how often you do it. As you study the different factors that affect training for physical fitness, a comparison to keeping weeds out of a garden may be helpful.

Factors Affecting Physical Fitness

1. *The type* of exercises you do
2. *How hard* you exercise
3. *How long* you exercise
4. *How often* you exercise

Type of Exercise

The first thing that influences the effectiveness of your fitness program is the type of exercise you choose to do. You should choose exercises that closely resemble the result that you want to achieve. If you want to improve your time in the 100-yard dash, you should run short sprints rather than long distances. If you want to be able to do more sit-ups, you should do sit-ups regularly. Pushups, hang gliding, or running short sprints will do little to increase the number of sit-ups you can do. Fitness experts call this principle **specificity** (SPES uh FIS i tee). Specificity refers to the exercises that best improve specific muscle groups. Choose exercises that closely relate to the desired result.

Think of how this would apply to keeping weeds out of the garden. There are all kinds of useful things to be done in a garden, but few will get rid of weeds. For instance, your garden may need to be fertilized, pruned, or watered, but none of these actions kill weeds; some of them may even help the weeds to grow better. It takes specific action to kill weeds. Likewise it also takes specific exercises to promote certain types of fitness.

There are many areas of physical fitness that can be improved. Cardiorespiratory endurance, muscular strength, muscular endurance, flexibility, and body composition are components of physical fitness. When working on a specific area, it is important not to neglect other areas of fitness. In many cases, however, exercises work together to help improve overall fitness.

Intensity of Exercise

Intensity is how hard you work. For exercise to be effective, you must work harder than usual; this is called the **overload principle.** As your body adapts to new and more difficult demands placed upon it, your physical fitness begins to improve.

Caution must be used when increasing intensity. As exercise becomes more intense, the chance of injury becomes greater. An injury can often cause the loss of much of the progress previously achieved. The goal of your exercise program should be to *train and not strain* your muscles. This is especially important to remember when you are beginning an exercise program. If you try to do too much too soon, you will probably hurt yourself and become discouraged. A proper progression rate is

Although soccer requires extensive leg and foot work (specificity), endurance, strength, and flexibility must also be developed.

important. When you begin an exercise program, start slowly and increase gradually. As long as you reach your goal, it matters little if it takes you a little longer than someone else. Fitness is not a race; it is a habit.

Consider your garden again. If you go out to your garden and pull only one weed every ten minutes, you will not accomplish much. The intensity is just too low to be effective. Generally, the harder you work, the more weeds you will pull (the overload principle). However, if you work so hard that you strain your back or get blisters all over your hands, you may not be able to garden again for weeks. All the time you are out because of your injury, the weeds will be growing again. You would have been better off taking care not to strain or injure yourself and accomplishing the task carefully and gradually.

Finally, if you work so hard that you dread going back into the garden again, you will probably find excuses for not weeding as often as you need to. Working too hard in your garden can make you hate weeding. Likewise, working too hard at your exercise program can make you hate exercise. Exercise is work, but it should not result in misery and severe pain.

Duration of Exercise

Another factor that will affect the success of your exercise program is how long your workout lasts. This is the **duration** of the exercise. You must exercise long enough to make your body work more than usual, or you will not improve. If you lift weights for thirty seconds every day, you probably will not see much improvement in strength. Again, it is like weeding a garden. If you weed for only a minute or two, your efforts will not produce much improvement. Exercise takes time. Exercise slowly and deliberately, and do not quit too soon; keep going.

To maintain a level of fitness, the more intense your exercise, the shorter the duration needs to be. When you begin a training program, exercise for a longer duration and increase the intensity gradually.

One must exercise at least 20-30 minutes in order to metabo... fat. The body uses up other stores of energy before it begins use stored fat energy. Remember that it takes 3,500 calories make one pound of body fat; therefore, the body must use up 3,500 calories to get rid of one pound of fat.

However, if you desire to increase your level of fitness, both intensity and duration should be increased.

Frequency of Exercise

Frequency is the final factor that will affect the success of your exercise program. Frequency is how often you exercise. Obviously, if you have a long, hard workout, but you do it only once every month, improvement will be slow in coming. For most exercise programs to be successful, you must do them at least three times per week.

Even if you get every weed out of your garden, some will probably grow back in just a few days. You cannot weed once and forget about weeding for the rest of your life. You must weed regularly, or there may be little evidence that you ever weeded at all.

One of the greatest hindrances to a training program is the lack of planning. Most people who do not exercise have failed to plan a specific time for exercising. If you do not schedule your swimming, walking, or aerobics, you probably will not remember to do it or will run out of time. Be sure to place your exercise plans on your calendar. Arrange to have a friend or friends exercise with you to make your exercise time more fun and to encourage yourself to follow through with your intentions.

Delight or Drudgery

Exercise can be one of the most enjoyable activities of your day. It can also be a dreaded affliction. Exercise can keep you out of the hospital or put you in the hospital. The difference between an exercise program that harms and an exercise program that helps is directly related to how you structure your workout.

Section Review

1. What is the value of bodily exercise as compared to the value of godliness?

2. What is physical fitness?

3. Why is the proper progression rate important in an exercise program?

4. How often should one exercise?

COMPONENTS OF FITNESS

Who is the fittest person you have ever seen or read about? What measure of fitness did you use to come to your conclusion? Is there any single measure of fitness that will tell who the fittest athlete is? Not really. If endurance is chosen to measure fitness, the fittest person might be a marathon runner. If strength is chosen as the test, the marathon runner might finish far below most football players. If flexibility is the measure for fitness, a gymnast might be classified as more fit than either the marathon runner or the football player.

As you can tell from these examples, there is no single measure of fitness. Instead, fitness is made up of five different components: cardiorespiratory fitness, muscular strength, muscular endurance, flexibility, and body composition. Although you may be very fit in one component, you are not truly physically fit unless you are fit in all five.

The Five Components of Fitness

- Cardiorespiratory fitness
- Muscular strength
- Muscular endurance
- Flexibility
- Body Composition

To be considered aerobic, an exercise must be done continuously so that the heart rate is in the target heart rate zone for at least twelve minutes.

Cardiorespiratory Fitness

Cardiorespiratory fitness refers to the ability of the heart, lungs, and blood vessels to efficiently supply oxygen to the muscle cells when under exertion. Because cardiorespiratory fitness deals with the heart, it is the most important component of fitness. You can live without great strength or flexibility, but you cannot experience longevity with a weak cardiorespiratory system. A person with a weak cardiorespiratory system will not be able to physically meet the demands of an active and vibrant life.

Heart rate—If you are in good cardiorespiratory condition, your heart should efficiently pump blood through the many miles of your blood vessels to each of your body's cells. The more efficiently your heart works, the fewer times it will have to pump.

The number of times your heart beats each minute is your **heart rate.** Your lowest heart rate, the rate your heart beats when you are at rest, is called your **resting heart rate.**

What are the characteristics of a fit cardiorespiratory system? How can you know whether you are fit? Your resting heart rate is an indicator of your cardiorespiratory fitness. As you become more fit, your resting heart rate will slow down. The reason the heart rate slows as a person becomes more fit is that the heart can pump more blood with each contraction. The average resting heart rate for adults is between seventy and eighty beats per minute. Highly trained athletes often have heart rates ranging from forty to fifty beats per minute, and some have rates in the low thirties.

Aerobic exercise—Aerobic (eh ROH bik) means "with air or with oxygen." You are an aerobic organism—you must have oxygen to survive. **Aerobic exercise** refers to any type of exercise that requires large amounts of oxygen for extended periods of time. Cardiorespiratory fitness is improved by regular aerobic exercise. How can you tell if an exercise is aerobic? Do you have to measure the amount of oxygen you breathe? Fortunately not! Aerobic exercises should be continuous and rhythmic in nature such as walking, jogging, biking, rope jumping, or swimming. Remember, aerobic means that there should be a constant increased supply and use of oxygen during the exercise. You should be breathing deeply and rapidly but not gasping for breath.

It is possible to measure the amount of oxygen that a person uses during exercise. This is called oxygen consumption or oxygen uptake. The easiest way to keep track of cardiorespiratory improvement is by checking your heart rate. As you exercise, your heart must beat faster to supply your body with the extra oxygen it needs. Aerobic exercise raises the heart rate high enough and long enough to make the heart work harder than it usually does. As you recall, this is called overloading. The body adapts to the new demands placed on it and thus becomes more fit.

Get the Beat—Heartbeat That Is

Have you ever exercised to the point that you felt like a throbbing artery? Perhaps you exercised so hard or for so long that your heartbeat was ringing in your ears. You may have felt that you could take your pulse simply by listening to it. Actually, taking your pulse is almost as easy.

Determining the rate at which your heart is beating (pulse) is not complicated. The pulse is usually taken at locations where an artery passes near the surface of the skin. The two most accessible pulse points are located near the radial artery and the carotid artery. The pulse at the radial artery can be felt by placing the index and middle fingers of one hand on the wrist of the other hand near the base of the thumb. Try it. Did you feel the beat? The pulse at the carotid artery is felt by gently placing the in-

dex and middle fingers on either side of the Adam's apple on the neck. It is simple to find, right?

Now that you can easily locate the pulse, count the number of beats your heart beats in thirty seconds. Use a watch or clock with a second hand. In order to determine your pulse in beats per minute, simply multiply the number obtained earlier by two. Practice getting your pulse by determining your pulse per minute when sitting, after walking up and down the stairs briskly two times, and after doing thirty jumping jacks. It is important to take your pulse within five seconds after exercising since your pulse rate will slow down rapidly. Did you get the beat? Good! Now, work on improving your heart rate through good nutrition and consistent exercise.

Target Heart Rate Formulas

Below are the two formulas for figuring your lowest target heart rate and highest target heart rate, which together determine your target heart rate zone.

Lowest Target Heart Rate

$$T=0.60(M-R)+R$$

Highest Target Heart Rate

$$T=0.80(M-R)+R$$

Note: For each formula, M=Maximum heart rate (220−age) and R=Resting heart rate (taken just before getting up in the morning).

If Ashley, a twelve-year-old student, has a resting heart rate of 75 beats per minute, her lowest and highest target heart rates would be calculated as follows.

Lowest Target Heart Rate

$$M=220-12=208$$
$$R=75$$

$$T=0.60(208-75)+75$$
$$T=0.60(133)+75$$
$$T=79.8+75$$
$$T=154.8 \text{ or } 155 \text{ beats per minute}$$

Highest Target Heart Rate

$$M=220-12=208$$
$$R=75$$
$$T=0.80(208-75)+75$$
$$T=0.80(133)+75$$
$$T=106.4+75$$
$$T=181.4 \text{ or } 181 \text{ beats per minute}$$

Ashley's target heart rate zone would be between 155 and 181 beats per minute. She should start her exercise program by trying to obtain the lowest target heart rate. As she becomes better conditioned, she should increase her goal within her target heart rate zone.

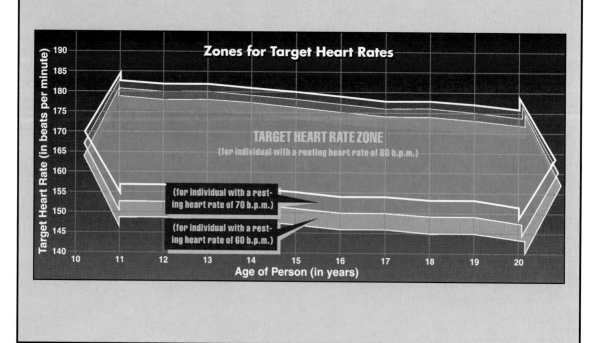

Zones for Target Heart Rates

TARGET HEART RATE ZONE
(for individual with a resting heart rate of 80 b.p.m.)

(for individual with a resting heart rate of 70 b.p.m.)

(for individual with a resting heart rate of 60 b.p.m.)

Target Heart Rate (in beats per minute)

Age of Person (in years)

target heart rate zone, simply figure out the lowest target heart rate (0.60 [sixty percent]) and the highest target heart rate (0.80 [eighty percent]). If your heart rate is not maintained at the target level for most of your exercise time, your cardiorespiratory fitness may not improve greatly.

Using the chart or equations in the box on page 140, can you determine your target heart rate zone? When you exercise, take your pulse and evaluate your cardiorespiratory fitness. Strive for improvement.

Focus on aerobic exercise—Aerobic exercise must be intense enough to raise your heart rate to your target level. If you do not raise your heart rate to the target level, you may not achieve enough overload to give you the improvement desired. Most exercise experts also recommend that you keep your heart

Cardiorespiratory endurance increases through consistent aerobic exercise.

Although you are an aerobic organism, God has designed you with the remarkable capacity to do some work without adequate oxygen. *Anaerobic* means "without air or oxygen." **Anaerobic exercise** is intense exercise that is done without adequate oxygen. Anaerobic exercise cannot be continued for long periods of time. The 100-yard dash, sprinting, and running up stairs are examples of anaerobic exercise.

Target heart rate—In an earlier chapter you learned the importance of goals. Goals give you something to work for. You are more likely to be successful when you set definite goals. Goals should be specific and realistic. A *target heart rate zone* can provide such a goal. Your **target heart rate** is the heart rate you should try to maintain during aerobic exercise. Try to exercise within your target heart rate zone. In order to determine the

rate at the target level for an accumulation of twenty to thirty minutes a day. You should plan to exercise three to six days a week if you want to improve.

Many sports (such as golf or bowling) do not get the heart rate up high enough to be aerobic. The

Because just playing baseball does not maintain their target heart rates, many baseball players do aerobic exercises for cardiorespiratory fitness.

actual playing of other games (such as baseball, football, and even tennis) has frequent stops that allow the heart rate to drop under the target level. Sports can contribute to cardiorespiratory fitness, but sports are usually not an efficient method of developing cardiorespiratory fitness.

The most efficient means of developing cardiorespiratory fitness is through a regular program of certain types of aerobic exercise. How many activities can you name that can get your heart rate up to your target level and keep it up there for at least twenty minutes? Running, cycling, swimming, walking, jumping rope, stair climbing, cross-country skiing, rowing, and aerobic routines are a few of the activities you might name. There is much to think about when determining which exercise to do. Consider the following information concerning some of the most popular aerobic exercises.

Running or jogging is a popular aerobic exercise. Jogging provides a good aerobic workout quicker than many other aerobic activities. Because it can be done almost anywhere and at almost any time, it is a very convenient method of exercise. It is also inexpensive. About the only investment necessary is a good pair of running shoes. Running shoes are an important investment for the jogger. Every runner should wear a quality pair of running shoes. You can avoid many injuries by choosing proper shoes.

Although jogging is an excellent form of aerobic exercise, there are some problems with jogging. First, jogging may be too intense an activity for some people. This is usually not true with junior high school students. However, if you have been inactive for more than four weeks or are overweight, it is best to start with a walking program and build up to a jogging program. Jogging can also

Caution Conscious Concepts

Before you go walking, jogging, running, or engage in outdoor sports, be sure to consider potential dangers. Remember that it does not have to be dark for attackers to act. The following guidelines may help.

- Do not go alone; exercise with a friend or friends.
- Avoid dark or isolated areas.

- Tell someone where you are going and when to expect you back.
- Do not wear headsets. They may tempt someone to rob you, and they hinder you from noticing potential danger.
- Do not wear jewelry or expensive watches or clothes.
- Wear reflective clothing or light-colored clothing in the evening.

be damaging to and a problem for people who have suffered joint disorders or injury to the lower back, knee, calf, shin, ankle, or feet. Finally, jogging only exercises the heart and legs; it does little to condition the upper body. Jogging is not for everyone. Is it for you?

It may surprise you that walking is an aerobic exercise. A vigorous walk can be as effective an exercise as jogging. You get almost the same effect aerobically from walking three miles as you do from running three miles. Of course, walking three miles takes longer than jogging three miles, but both can improve your fitness. However, walking is much safer. Walking provides a safe exercise for many who cannot jog.

When you walk to improve your cardiorespiratory fitness, you should walk briskly. Be sure to walk continuously without stopping. As fitness increases, intensity can be increased by holding weights in your hands (ankle weights are not recommended). Increasing the incline and the distance walked can upgrade your program. Decreasing the time in which you walk a certain distance also increases intensity. Remember that, like jogging, walking gives your legs a good workout but does little to condition the upper body. You should wear similar shoes for walking as used for jogging. A good pair of shoes may help you avoid unnecessary injuries. Walking takes a little longer to do, but the benefits are well worth the time and effort taken.

Riding a bicycle is an enjoyable hobby for many Americans. In many countries, however, the bicycle is more than a hobby; it is a major form of transportation. The fact that many of these people have healthier hearts than many Americans is partly due to the amount of time they spend on their bikes. Cycling is almost as convenient as jogging and walking. Many errands can be accomplished on bicycle rather than by car. Riding a bicycle is also good because the bike supports your weight and may not be as damaging to the joints as jogging can be. In order to reduce injury to the knee joints, be sure that the seat is high enough to let your leg extend fully when the pedal is at the bottom.

There are a few problems with cycling, however. Cycling is more expensive than jogging or walking, and like jogging and walking, riding the bicycle does not develop the upper body. Also, because it is easy to coast on a bike, many people do not keep their heart rates up while cycling. Finally, there is always the danger of having an accident on a bicycle. However, many people enjoy safe and convenient exercise on stationary bicycles in their homes.

The final aerobic exercise focused on at this time is swimming. Swimming is a great aerobic exercise. It conditions the entire body. There are fewer injuries from swimming than from most other aerobic exercises.

Probably the biggest problem with swimming is inconvenience. Few people have a pool readily available all year long. Some people are afraid of water. Swimming also requires more skill than walking or jogging. Although swimmers often avoid disabling injuries, some suffer from irritations and infections of the ears and eyes. Swimming does not help one lose fat and does not build or maintain bone density (since it is not a weight-bearing exercise). Nevertheless, if you can swim and have access to an indoor pool, swimming may be another aerobic exercise that you can do.

No matter which aerobic exercise you choose, remember to be consistent and careful. Work up to your goal gradually. Vary your exercise for diversity. Increase your workout for overload and a challenge. Keep on doing what you know to be good for you. Get up and get going!

Section Review

1. Which is the most important of the five components of physical fitness?
2. Why is cardiorespiratory fitness important to the body's functioning?
3. What are the differences between aerobic and anaerobic exercise?
4. Why is the target heart rate important in the success of an exercise program?
5. What is your target heart rate zone? Show your calculations.

Muscular Strength

The second component of fitness is muscular strength. **Strength** is the ability of your muscles to exert force. This is accomplished by the ability of your muscles to contract. If you are lifting weights, rearranging your furniture, or holding a child, your strength would be measured by the maximum amount of weight you can lift. Any pushing, pulling, or lifting that takes all your effort provides a test of your strength.

Would you like to have strength like Hercules or to have the ability to lift boulders and uproot trees? Although it would certainly be impressive, you seldom need that much strength. The strength that is important for fitness is the type of strength you use every day. Everyone ought to be strong enough to open the door, to carry groceries, or to unscrew a jar of pickles. You should also develop enough strength to pursue recreational and fitness activities (tennis, volleyball, baseball) without causing muscle injury. Additional strength to lift heavy objects or to use massive tools must sometimes be developed by some people as a result of their occupation.

You can increase your strength by doing exercises that require so much effort that you can complete them only a few times. For example, if you were lifting weights to build strength, you would use weights that were so heavy you could lift them only a few times. Remember what this is called? Yes, it is the overload principle. As you exercise the muscle, the muscle fibers increase in size and strength. Girls should not worry about developing

A successful muscle-building program must use the four principles of training: type, intensity, duration, and frequency.

1. The specific muscle to be developed must be exercised.
2. The muscle must be worked harder than normal (overload).
3. The duration of exercise must increase gradually (progression).
4. For greatest results, the muscle must be worked three times a week with a day of rest between workouts.

bulging muscles. God made women with the ability to develop in muscle tone (firmness) more than in muscle bulk. Because there is a lot of stress on your body during these exercises, you must be careful to do each one properly. Strength exercises that are done improperly can cause serious injuries.

Muscular Endurance

Muscular endurance is closely related to muscular strength. **Muscular endurance** is the ability of muscles to exert force many times. This means that muscle contraction is not only exerted but is sustained or repeated. The amount of weight you can lift is a test of your strength. The number of times you can lift a lighter weight is a test of your endurance. Muscular endurance is needed more often for daily activities than muscular strength.

Muscular endurance is built by doing certain exercises many times. If it takes all your effort to do an exercise five times, you are building strength.

If you work at repeating an exercise fifteen, twenty, or fifty times, you are building muscular endurance.

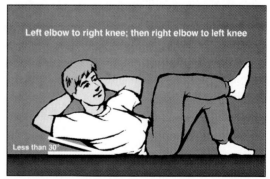

The term sit-ups *has been replaced by* crunches *or* roll-ups. *Traditional sit-ups let the back muscles take over the work of sitting up rather then letting the abdominals and the obliques do the work. Crunches are done with the knees bent and only partially coming to a sitting position. The head and neck are lifted no more than 30° off the floor (the lower back never leaves the floor). Cross-over crunches can be used to work the obliques and to help flatten the stomach.*

Isometric, Isotonic, Isokinetic . . . Isosore

Muscular strength can be built by isometric (EYE suh MET rik) or isotonic (EYE suh TAHN ik) exercises, but muscular endurance can be built only by isotonic exercises. During an **isometric exercise,** your muscles exert force against an object that does not move. Pushing against a wall, pulling up on the chair you are sitting in, and pressing your hands together are examples of isometric exercises. During an **isotonic exercise,** your muscles exert force to move an object. This can be done by lifting barbells (two-handed lifts) or dumbbells (one-handed lifts) repeatedly. If you desire to increase strength, more weight should be lifted with fewer repetitions. If endurance is the goal, then less weight and more repetitions should be done.

In the past, many exercise experts claimed that isometric exercise was the best way to build strength. Today, however, many believe that the more natural, common movements performed during isotonic exercise make it a better method of training. Also, the blood pressure can rise dramatically during an isometric contraction. This can be especially dangerous for those

who already suffer from hypertension or heart problems. Some isometric exercises may be beneficial, but isotonic exercises should be chosen for most muscular strength and endurance training.

Isotonic exercises usually include calisthenics and weight lifting. **Calisthenics** (KAL is THEN iks) are bodybuilding exercises that develop muscular strength and tone. Sit-ups, pushups, pull-ups, chin ups, and knee bends are examples of calisthenics. These are excellent not only for increasing body tone but also for increasing flexibility and balance. Strong abdominal muscles help the lower back and overall posture. Strong muscles, ligaments, and tendons can better absorb shock and stress, reducing the risk of injuries. However, calisthenics do not rate high on the list for aerobic improvement. Calisthenics must be done quickly and continuously for at least twelve minutes before they can be considered an aid in cardiorespiratory fitness. They are best included in the warm-up and cool-down stages of an exercise program, done after aerobic exercise, or done on alternate days of an aerobic program.

Another type of exercise is isokinetic exercise. In **isokinetic exercise** an exercise machine is used to provide consistent resistance through the entire range of motion. In isotonic exercise, the greatest effort is used at the beginning and at the end of the movement. However, in isokinetic exercise, the exercise machine forces the user to exert consistent overload on the muscles from the start of the movement through to the finish. Although isokinetic exercise is usually more effective than isometric or isotonic exercise, not everyone can engage in this type of exercise because of the cost of the equipment.

No matter which type of exercise you use to increase muscular strength and endurance, be sure to strive for balance. Balance is important not only in the components of fitness but also in motives. Fitness should be a tool to make you a better servant for Christ and not a method to increase self-esteem. Pride in looks or ability does nothing to glorify God, your Creator and Master. Say with John the Baptist, "He must increase, but I must decrease" (John 3:30).

Flexibility Workout

Hip Flexor Stretch

Lower Back Stretch

Lower Back Stretch

Saddle Sit Toe Touch

"Pec" (Pectoralis) Stretch

Ankle Rotation and Toe Points

Upper Arm Stretch

THIS   NOT

Arched Back Stretch

Hamstring Stretch

Neck Stretch (ear to shoulder)

Calf Muscle Stretch

Torso Stretch

Many gymnasts begin training at four or five years of age; however, flexibility should be and can be developed throughout one's lifetime.

Flexibility

Flexibility is the ability to bend the joints and stretch the muscles through a full range of motion. It is the degree of movement possible around a joint and its muscles. The ability to touch your toes with your legs straight is a test of flexibility.

Flexibility is beneficial in preventing injury, in improving posture, and in helping performance. As you get older, particularly if you do not exercise regularly, you may find that you are not as flexible as you used to be. However, just like any other component of fitness, flexibility can be improved by training.

Stretching exercises are used to develop flexibility. Some stretching exercises are illustrated above. It is important to do your stretching exercises slowly, without bouncing. Excessive bouncing during stretching can result in injury to the muscles and joints. Stretching should be done just to the point of discomfort (a feeling of tautness in the muscles). Your breathing rate should be normal; do not hold your breath. Hold the stretch for twenty to forty seconds; gradually increase the time. Stretching should be done after other exercises or activities in order to help reduce soreness and to stretch muscles shortened during workouts.

Body Composition

The size and strength of your muscles depend on three factors: heredity, diet, and exercise. These factors coupled with age and gender affect your body composition. Body composition refers to the

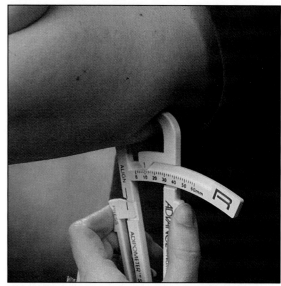

Skin calipers measure body fat. WARNING! Some people may not measure as being overweight but actually are overfat. Many people are thin and look average in weight but have no muscle tone or energy. These individuals may appear to be in peak health, when they are actually in need of physical conditioning.

comparative amounts of body tissue, muscle, bone, and fat. Obese people or extremely emaciated people are not usually seen as being pictures of fitness. Body composition does not refer to how much a person weighs; **body composition** is the proportion of body fat to lean body mass.

The amount of fat on the body can be measured by using a skin caliper. Skin fold measurements are usually taken on the right side of the body. Two or three measurements should be taken at each site and averaged. Girls are usually measured with a vertical skin fold at the triceps (back of the upper arm) and above the hip bone. Boys are usually measured under the shoulder blade and front of the thigh. These measurements then indicate the percentage of fat in body composition. The most accurate method of testing for fat is hydrostatic weighing which is weighing underwater; however, this cannot be done without using expensive facilities. The simplest way to check for body fat is to see if you can pinch an inch. If you can pinch an inch or more beside your navel when standing, you probably have too much body fat.

Mesomorph
broad-shouldered, well-muscled

Endomorph
short, round, obese

Ectomorph
tall, thin

Body composition is greatly affected by heredity. People inherit tendencies for their somatotype (body type) as well as their rate of metabolism. Exercise and nutrition can be used to alter body composition no matter which somatotype or metabolic rate a person possesses.

Strength and Beauty

How important is looking good to you? Do you want to win or be on the team? Certainly! What are you willing to do in order to be a winner? Hopefully, you have your priorities in the right order. However, many teen-agers are tempted to throw all caution away and are blinded by pride and ambition. In order to have the winning edge or have a muscular physique, many people have fallen prey to the power of anabolic steroids.

Anabolic steroids are drugs that are similar to male hormones. Although they do produce accelerated muscle, bone, and red blood cell growth, their effects can be deadly. Many athletes have paid the price with their reputations (Ben Johnson, a Canadian track athlete stripped of his gold medal in the 1988 Olympics) and with their lives (Lyle Alzado, a former NFL football player with the Los Angeles Raiders, who died in 1992 after suffering with inoperable brain cancer. There are also numerous accounts of former steroid users who died of liver cancer, heart attacks, and heart disease).

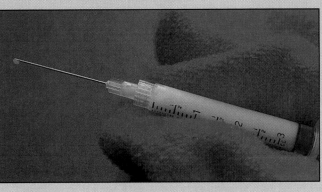

Steroids can produce increased facial hair growth, deepening of the voice, oily skin, acne, sweating, and baldness in women and young people. It can also cause the long bones of the adolescent body to stop growing. Increased fluid retention in the body tissues, hypertension (high blood pressure), high cholesterol levels, liver disorders (cysts, cancer, duct obstructions), and atherosclerosis have been associated with steroid intake. It is believed that anabolic steroids can also harm the body's immune system. Other side effects such as muscle cramps, gastrointestinal distress, puffing of the face, swelling of feet and legs, trembling, jaundice, darkening of the skin, headaches, and dizziness have been reported. Violent tendencies and aggressive behavior also seem to be increased with steroid usage.

There are other problems that can be traced to steroid use; however, the main reason a Christian should not use steroids is that it is wrong. Most steroid use is illegal except when prescribed by doctors for arthritis, tendonitis, or treating other injuries. Steroids are drugs that, whether made synthetically or of human growth hormones, can cause irreparable damage to the body. In a way, steroids are addictive drugs. In order to maintain the muscle mass provided by the drugs, steroid use must continue. The permanent damage that may occur to the body for temporary gain is a foolish waste.

There is no beauty, honor, or sense in obtaining temporary strength and momentary glory at the cost of your reputation, your health, and your life. Remember, you would not be the only one damaged if you used steroids. As a result, the cause of Christ, the temple of the Holy Ghost, and a servant of God suffer the consequences. As Joshua told the children of Israel in Joshua 24:15, "Choose you this day whom ye will serve." Do you desire to be known for godly strength and beauty, or will you seek temporary and selfish, perhaps even deadly, gain?

The distribution of body fat differs between the genders. Women tend to store fat on their legs, hips, and upper arms while men usually store fat in the abdominal region. Body fat distribution is also influenced by heredity. The pattern and predisposition for fat storage is in the genes. Age, gender, heredity, diet, and exercise work together to determine body composition. There is not much you can do to change your age, gender, or heredity, but you can use diet and exercise to improve your body composition. Eat right, do right!

Section Review

1. What is the difference between muscular strength and muscular endurance?

2. Is there a difference between isometric, isotonic, and isokinetic exercise? If so, what?

3. Are there any benefits of flexibility? List some.

4. What are five factors that determine body composition? Which factors can be controlled?

5. Why should a Christian refuse to use anabolic steroids?

THE UPS AND DOWNS OF EXERCISE

Exercise is like getting up in the morning: sometimes it is easy and sometimes it is difficult. Most of the time the hardest part is continuing once you get started. Many people begin an exercise program and fail to keep it up. It does little good to start exercising unless you keep exercising. Here are a few suggestions that may help.

Dress Up

When you go to church, you dress in your church clothes. You may wear a suit and tie or a special dress. You may not feel that a suit and tie are very comfortable, but you tolerate them because you want to look your best. You "dress up" for church by choosing clothes that are appropriate.

When you get ready to exercise, you should "dress up" for exercise, just like you dress up for church. Does that mean you should pick out a coat and tie or your best dress and hose to exercise in? Of course not! Your dress clothes would not be any more appropriate for exercise than your warm-up suit would be for church.

The Lowly Sneaker

The lowly sneaker has been exalted to a status of unbelievable glory. Also known as the tennis shoe, athletic shoe, or by brand name (Adidas, Converse, Nike, Reebok), the sneaker is a commodity that has undergone remarkable changes. Waldo Semon, who invented synthetic rubber during World War II, never dreamed that his discovery would be used for footwear. Since synthetic rubber provides hard-wearing, waterproof soles and comfort, the athletic shoe has been a popular choice in leisure and sports. The uppers, soles, tread, cushioning, and heel design vary to meet the needs of different activities.

For instance, shoes for running are made with features different from a court shoe, which differs from an aerobic shoe. When purchasing running shoes, consider the uppers. Nylon or synthetic uppers are usually chosen for running or walking shoes because they provide support and will not stretch with wear or when battered by puddles, mud, and gravel. Leather uppers are durable and give support, but they will stretch. Canvas does not provide enough support. Running shoes need to be flexible, especially at the ball of the foot. It is also good for the shoe to be light in weight. Cushioning in shoes is important for shock absorption. Air and foam have been used between the sock liner and sole to increase comfort and shock resistance. The soles of the running shoe are usually made of long-wearing materials and have deep or waffled tread for good surface grip. In order to provide a stable and broader base of support, the heel of the running shoe is usually flared.

This differs from the court shoe, which is used for activities such as basketball or tennis. Because the wearer is usually on a surface protected from the elements, leather uppers are used (or a combination of leather and nylon). The sole is firm with a smooth tread, and the heel is not flared, a feature which enables the wearer to shift directions easily and still provides side-to-side support.

The aerobic shoe has leather or nylon uppers and is very flexible at the ball of the foot. This highly cushioned shoe helps to absorb the shock of constant workouts and has no heel flare. Although most aerobic shoes have a smooth tread, some have a "dot" to facilitate pivoting.

Some companies provide a cross-training shoe that is an all-purpose type of shoe. It is designed for flexibility, without a flared heel, and is usually of leather. Some companies provide air insole units at the heel and forefoot for shock absorption. Others design shoes with pumps to provide a personalized fit. No matter which type of shoe you choose, an accurate fit is vital.

When choosing your shoes, consider your foot, not the brand name of the shoe, the price, or the look. Are your feet straight or curved? Do you have high arches or are you flat-footed? Do you need extra ankle support? Does the heel fit snugly and the toe box offer just enough room? Where is the shoe the most flexible? Is it cushioned in the best places for you? When it comes to purchasing athletic shoes, be sure that you make a wise and knowledgeable investment. Find a knowledgeable salesman and discuss your needs with him; good advice is important. Did you choose the right shoe? Then get those shoes on and get going!

Although exercise clothing can be stylish and expensive, expensive clothing is certainly not necessary. Exercising in nice clothes may help you feel better about yourself, but often the people who spend the most money on their exercise clothes are those who exercise the least. All you really need are clothes that are clean, modest, and comfortable. Because exercise involves movement, you should choose clothes that are loose and that do not restrict your movement. You should choose shoes that protect your feet and that are right for the type of exercise you are doing. You should completely avoid any type of clothing (such as vinyl sweat suits) that is designed to make you sweat more by making you hotter. Such clothing can be both uncomfortable and dangerous.

Show Up

Sometimes the most difficult part of exercise is getting started. Once you start, however, you often find it is not as bad as you thought it might be. That

Time for Fitness

Plan for exercise; put it into your schedule. It is recommended that you exercise three or four times each week with a day of rest in between workouts (or at least alternate vigorous and easy days).

is why it is important to do some things to help you to "show up" for exercise each day.

One way to encourage yourself to show up is to schedule your exercise time. Important things must be scheduled. If there were not a scheduled time for you to be at school each day, who knows when or whether you would show up. If you want to keep on an exercise program, you should have a regular time allotted for it each day. There is no one time that is best for everyone. Choose a time that you are most likely to stick with. You may want to avoid vigorous exercise right after a large meal (it slows digestion and makes you feel uncomfortable) or right before you go to bed (it can keep you awake), but about any other time is fine.

You may also exercise more often if you take a friend along. Exercising with a friend is more enjoyable than exercising alone. Your friend may also encourage you to show up when you do not feel like exercising. However, do not feel that you always have to have someone else to exercise with. Friends are not always free at the same time you are, and some friends may be better at talking you out of exercising than they are at talking you into exercising.

Warm Up

Before you start exercising vigorously, you should take time to warm up. Do some type of easy

If you have a friend who will exercise with you, you will be more likely to keep exercising regularly.

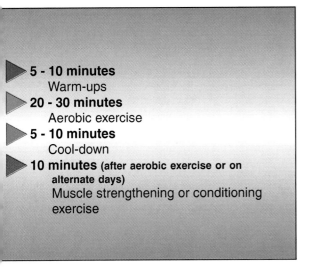

> **5 - 10 minutes**
>   Warm-ups
> **20 - 30 minutes**
>   Aerobic exercise
> **5 - 10 minutes**
>   Cool-down
> **10 minutes** (after aerobic exercise or on
>   alternate days)
>   Muscle strengthening or conditioning
>   exercise

exercise that raises your heart rate slowly. Then take time to stretch out the various muscle groups. Warm-up can make it easier for your body to adjust to the increased demands of heavy exercise and is important in reducing injuries.

Warm-ups should be suited to the individual as well as to the activity that will be done after warm-ups. A good warm-up normally lasts from five to ten minutes. Although the intensity and duration of warm-up may vary, the purpose is to increase the body temperature and get the body ready for exercise. Sweating is usually a good indicator of a sufficient warm-up.

Cool Down

Cooling down is just as important *after* vigorous exercise as warming up is *before* vigorous exercise. When you work out, extra blood is channeled to the muscles. Cooling off gradually helps to channel the blood back to the heart. If you do not take time to cool down, blood may pool in the veins and cause you to feel light-headed. There is also increased danger of heart disorders if you do not keep moving until your breathing and heart rate return close to normal. Cooling down also helps to relax muscle fibers that have been tensed and stressed.

To cool down you should continue to move but at a reduced pace. For instance, if you are jogging,

you might walk to cool down. You may stretch and do some flexibility exercises following an invigorating swim. Take about five minutes to cool down; cooling down should cause the heart rate to come down as gradually as it went up.

Slow Down

Surprisingly, an important thing you must learn about exercise is when to slow down and when to stop. Exercise can cripple and cause problems if it is not done properly. This is not a big danger for most junior high and high-school students, but it is a very big danger for some people.

Exercise is often hard and uncomfortable work, but it should not cause severe pain. Many people have taken to heart the concepts of "no pain, no gain!" and "go for the burn." Yes, exercise may cause some discomfort; however, pain is the body's way of signaling the need to stop. Continuing the exertion or "working through" the pain can cause muscle strain and increase the chances of injury. If it really hurts—*stop!* If your muscles begin to quiver as they burn, it is time to stop. Exercising when in pain may be great for your character, but it could be harmful to your body.

> **Danger signals in exercise include—**
>
> - **Chest pain.**
> - **Breathing problems.**
> - **Dizziness.**
> - **Continued joint or muscle pain.**
> - **Unusual color or volume of urine.**
> - **Recurring headaches, nosebleeds, fainting, or numbness.**

Turn Down

Exercise can be expensive. Pulse meters, stopwatches, exercise bicycles, pacers, club memberships, weight-reducing machines, sauna baths, and vibrators are a few items that are sold to help you get into shape. Some of these can be useful, but many are useless or unnecessary.

The most useful equipment for a successful exercise program is a watch with a second hand. Remember that no matter which machine you purchase, the machine is useless if it is not used. There is no machine that can magically get you into shape while you relax. Turn down any gadget or plan that promises you lost pounds or improvement of fitness without effort. Most likely the only thing you will lose is your money.

Section Review

1. What are a few suggestions you might give to a friend who would like to begin or maintain an exercise program?

2. Why is a time to warm up important in an exercise program?

3. Why is a time to cool down important in an exercise program?

4. When is it necessary to slow down or stop exercise?

THE RISKS AND BENEFITS OF EXERCISE

Work and exercise contribute to making you happy and healthy, but both can be overdone. God created you with a need for rest. Rest allows your body to recover from the stresses and strains of your daily routine. Without proper rest, your body will deteriorate.

Rest does not always mean that you should do nothing. Changing your workouts so that you exercise different muscles on different days can allow the muscles to recover. Alternating hard and easy workouts can be another way of allowing your body to recover. You should never make yourself a slave to a stopwatch. If you do not feel good—*slow down!*

You should also make sure you get enough sleep each night. There is no specific amount of

Planning Your Fitness Program

1. See your doctor.
2. Set your goals.
3. Plan your fitness program.
4. Put variety and enjoyment in exercise.
5. Get a friend to join you for encouragement.
6. Use proper warm-up and cool-down procedures.
7. Keep a written record of goals, progress, and evaluations.

sleep that is right for everyone, but most teen-agers need about eight to nine hours of sleep each night. If you feel like you cannot stay awake during the day, it may be because you are not getting enough sleep at night. If you use your time wisely, you may be surprised at how much you can get done and still get to bed early.

The Perils of Exercise

The Risks of Exercise—Recently, many people have become concerned about the risk of exercise. News accounts telling of people who have died while exercising have caused some people to be afraid of exercising. Is exercise dangerous for you? Although this is a difficult question to answer for everyone, the answer for most is definitely *no!* If you are healthy, exercise is not a hazard; in fact, it can help protect you. However, exercise can be a problem for people with previous health problems (heart problems, high blood pressure, knee injury, shin splints, diabetes).

Exercise puts stress on the heart. For those people with diseased hearts, the extra stress could produce a heart attack. The important thing to remember is that these people do not die because of exercise; they die from heart disease. Even for these people, exercise may be the most effective medication available. However, their exercise program should be carefully guided by a physician.

Anyone who plans to begin an exercise program should have a thorough physical examination first. This becomes increasingly important as you get older. If you go to the doctor periodically, he probably will let you know if there is any reason for you to avoid certain types of exercise.

The Pitfalls of Exercise—Because exercise is so important and because the effects of exercise are often so dramatic, it is necessary again to emphasize the importance of balance. Even good things, like exercise, can become harmful if they are not kept in a proper perspective.

How can exercise become harmful? When any type of care for the body becomes more important than spiritual health, it has become a curse. There

are a few people today who seem to live to exercise. They spend more time exercising than they spend on any spiritual activity. These people often develop a pride in the way their bodies look or in the way they perform. They glorify their bodies. First Timothy 4:8 points out that any type of bodily discipline is profitable only temporarily. Godliness or spiritual discipline is profitable now and for eternity. Obviously, those things that have eternal value are more important than anything that has only temporal value.

Others make sports an idol in their lives. An idol is anything you love more than God. These people think about sports, dream about sports, talk about sports, practice sports, and become upset when anything interferes with the time they spend in sports. They seldom find time for God, yet they say they love God. If God has blessed you with the ability to play a sport, be thankful but do not let it become too important.

The Benefits of Exercise

No one knows all the benefits of exercise. It often seems that new benefits are being found constantly. Exercise can strengthen the heart, reduce the heart rate, lower blood pressure, improve posture, and help reduce extra weight. People claim to work better, sleep better, be friendlier, study better, get sick less, and benefit in hundreds of other ways when they exercise. Exercise has been used to maintain muscle and bone density so that middle-age and elderly days are filled with action rather than sedate onlooking.

Exercise can improve you. If you desire to be all that you can be for the Lord, exercise can help you to run a better race and to finish your course. Instead of letting fat tissue build in and around your muscles, use strength training exercises to build muscle. This should not be done only for an improved appearance, but mainly for improved physical health. For instance, strength training exercises have been shown to improve the quality of life (prolonged mobility, increased stamina), build strong bones, prevent injuries, and reduce back pain.

It is a good testimony for Christ's soldiers to look sharp and lean, but it is more important for them to be able to follow the Lord's commands and do battle for God. Incorporate endurance training

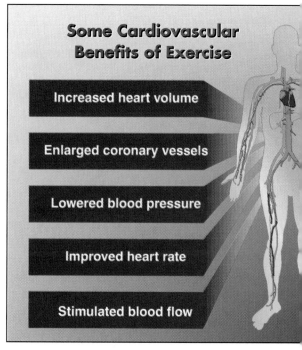

exercises to enable you to keep going and get much accomplished. A fit soldier that can keep on doing his work is a valuable asset. Aerobic training helps the soldier of Christ to keep his physical heart and respiratory systems strong. No matter how you look at it, Christians need to be fit for service. It is your choice—exercise it!

Section Review

1. How does rest contribute to physical fitness?

2. What is a risk of exercise to a teen-ager?

3. Discuss two ways that an overemphasis on exercise can be harmful.

4. What are some of the benefits of exercise?

CHAPTER REVIEW

Terms

physical fitness

specificity

intensity

overload principle

duration

frequency

cardiorespiratory fitness

heart rate

resting heart rate

aerobic exercise

anaerobic exercise

target heart rate

muscular strength

muscular endurance

flexibility

isometric exercise

isotonic exercise

isokinetic exercise

calisthenics

body composition

anabolic steroids

Content Questions

1. Why are most people not physically fit?

2. What are four basic principles that should be considered when developing a training program? Explain why each is important in an exercise plan.

3. What is the overload principle? How does it produce improvement in one's physical fitness?

4. What are the five components of physical fitness?

5. What is *cardiorespiratory fitness?*

6. What is the easiest way to measure one's cardiorespiratory fitness?

7. Why is it important to know your resting heart rate?

8. What are two examples of aerobic activities? What are two examples of anaerobic activities?

9. What are the four stages of an exercise workout? (This should not be confused with the four principles of training.) Write the suggested amounts of time each phase should take.

10. How can the "no pain, no gain" attitude hinder rather than help a fitness program?

11. How often should a person exercise?

12. What is a major reason for Christians to exercise?

Application Questions

1. Which aerobic activity discussed in the text is best suited for you? Considering your needs, schedule, and abilities, which exercise is best for you to do? Explain.

2. What spiritual benefits are possible in improving physical fitness? In what ways can physical fitness be a spiritual hindrance to Christians?

3. Construct an exercise program for your friend who must rest her foot because of a minor sprain (she cannot run or jump).

4. What are your priorities? Make a list of things that must be done in the next two weeks. (Be sure to include church services, youth activities, school obligations, family commitments, personal devotions, and exercise.) Put them in order of importance. Make a schedule of daily plans to include all of your activities. Be sure to plan to exercise at least three times a week for at least thirty minutes. Now follow through on your plans. Did you accomplish more than you thought you could? Did you get everything done? Evaluate your week.

Coaches

Job Description: The field of athletics is filled with a variety of job opportunities. Coaches, umpires, and referees are needed from little league to professional levels in all of the sports. Sports instructors teach the rules and skills of sports to individuals or groups. Athletic trainers are needed in amateur and professional sports to evaluate, guide, and advise athletes. Recreational workers organize athletic activities in camps, senior centers, retirement centers, and youth sports.

Coaching can be entered into as a profession (junior high or high school coach, recreational worker) or as a hobby (community or church team coach, referee, or umpire).

Job Location: Coaching locations vary depending on the sport and the job requirements. Some sports lend themselves to indoor facilities (skating, volleyball, basketball, gymnastics), while others usually take place in outdoor facilities (baseball, football, soccer, track and field, tennis, golf). Of course, travel is a

necessary factor to consider in coaching. If the team or athlete being coached is of amateur, little league, junior high school, or high school nature, travel is usually short distances. However, some coaching opportunities call for cross-country or world travel to national and international competitions.

Training Required: Coaching in schools should require a coaching minor or a major in physical education and a teacher's certificate. However, some jobs in athletics require special licenses or permits. For instance, athletic trainers should earn a certificate from the National Athletic Trainers Association (NATA), which requires the applicant to pass a written examination and to have two years of experience under the supervision of a NATA-certified trainer. Each sport usually has a national organization or association that establishes trainer qualifications and guidelines.

UNIT 2

Defending Your Temple

Unit II Objectives

Chapter 7—Safety
- Discern between depending on God's protection and being presumptuous.
- List points to remember in response to fires, falls, firearms, and fatal substances.
- Discuss how electrical hazards can be avoided and how to respond to electrical accidents.
- Identify precautions to consider in promoting personal, pedestrian, bicycle, car, water, and recreational safety.
- Describe how to react properly to lightning, floods, hurricanes, blizzards, tornadoes, and earthquakes.

Chapter 8—First Aid
- Identify the purpose of first aid and the benefits of knowing first aid.
- Explain why a person should receive first aid training.
- List basic emergency measures to be taken.
- Differentiate various types of injuries, wounds, burns, and emergencies.
- Apply the correct emergency procedures of first aid in proper order.

Chapter 9—Diseases
- Differentiate between infectious diseases and noninfectious diseases.
- State the lines of defense with which God has equipped the human body for battle against pathogens.
- Describe ways to prevent exposure to pathogens and the spread of disease.
- Defend and practice God's plan for STD prevention.
- Identify the major factors that appear to contribute to chronic disease.

Chapter 10—Personal Hygiene
- Identify the basic parts of skin, hair, a nail, a tooth, an eye, and an ear.
- Explain and practice ways to protect skin, hair, nails, teeth, eyes, and ears.
- Discuss problems that can occur in the skin, hair, nails, teeth, eyes, and ears.

Chapter 11—Environment and Health
- Explain why man should be viewed as a consumer and a manager.
- Discuss the impact man can have on the atmosphere, hydrosphere, and lithosphere.
- Explain the basic theory of global warming and point out which factors are true and which parts are speculation.
- Indicate ways to prevent air, water, and land pollution.

Chapter 12—Drugs, Alcohol, and Tobacco
- Classify alcohol and tobacco as drugs.
- Explain the difference between drug misuse and drug abuse.
- List five major groups of drugs and give examples of drugs that are included in each group.
- Identify harmful effects of drugs, alcohol, and tobacco on the body and ways these substances can be a danger to others.

Chapter 13—Growth and Development
- Describe the development of an unborn child.
- Discuss mental, emotional, social, physical, and spiritual changes that occur during adolescence.
- List four guidelines for knowing God's will.
- Identify general rules of conduct when dealing with the elderly.
- Discuss ways of comforting the grief stricken.

Have you ever known an accident-prone person? You know, the type who falls up the stairs, trips over his own feet, or injures himself at every sporting event. Many people have accidents because of a lack of coordination or concentration; some even presume that an accident could never happen to them. Attention to the little things can make a big difference in your safety at home, in school, or during recreation.

CHAPTER 7

"Jesus said unto him, It is written again, Thou shalt not tempt the Lord thy God."
Matthew 4:7

GOD'S PROTECTION AND YOUR RESPONSIBILITY

It is sometimes said that the Christian doing the will of God is immortal until God is through with him. The idea is that God's protection is greater than any threat the Christian might meet. Certainly the Lord can protect the Christian from any peril.

It is also clear from Scripture that the Lord watches over and cares for every Christian. Matthew 6 points out that God provides for your daily needs and even numbers the hairs of your head. The first chapter of Hebrews says that the angels of God minister to the saints (1:14), and Psalm 34:7 points out that the angel of the Lord camps around those who fear Him to deliver them.

Francesco Montemezzano, The Archangel Gabriel, Bob Jones University Collection of Religious Art

Since God's concern and power are so great, why should the Christian even be concerned about safety? Matthew 4:5-7 helps answer this question. God was concerned about Jesus and promised in His Word to take care of Him. When the Devil took Jesus up to the pinnacle of the temple, he quoted Scripture that promised God would protect Christ. Yet Jesus refused to place Himself in danger. He said, "Thou shalt not tempt the Lord thy God" (v. 7).

By refusing to place Himself in unwarranted danger, Christ refused the sin of **presumption**. Presumption is taking undue advantage of a person's kindness. For instance, if your friend offered you some potato chips and you took the whole bag, that would be presumptuous. Although God watches over and protects you, He expects you to act responsibly. Learning and then practicing good safety principles is an excellent way to do this.

The Risks of Life

Almost everything you do in life involves some risk. **Risks** are the dangers you face each day. They can occur at home, at school, at work, and in fact, just about anywhere. When you think of the risks you face each day, what keeps you from living in a constant state of panic? Most people avoid panic by rarely thinking about what could happen. Like the rich fool in Luke 12, they live each day as if they will never die. This attitude is wrong, but what should your attitude be?

First, you should make certain that you are right with God. Someday you will stand before Him and be judged. No risk in this life can compare with the awesome fact that you will face God and give an account of your life.

Second, you should trust God's care. Romans 8:28 promises that everything will work together for your good if you are living for God. God loves you, and He has promised to take care of you.

Third, you should choose your activities carefully. Every time you decide to play a sport, ride in a car, or climb a tree, you are choosing activities that will increase your risks. A mature person evaluates both the risks and benefits of an activity and

...nsider whether it is really worth the risk before you jump.

then chooses those activities in which the benefits are greater than the risks. For example, you may choose to play basketball but decide that mountain climbing is too risky.

Finally, you should develop a safety-conscious attitude. Many of the injuries and deaths that occur today can be prevented if people are just cautious. You do not have to eliminate the things you like to do; just be careful. For example, riding your bicycle involves some risk. If you decide to ride your bicycle without using your hands, you increase the risk. If you decide to ride your bike without using your hands as well as travel on the wrong side of a busy road, you will probably have an accident in only a matter of time. A safety-conscious teen-ager would never try such a stunt.

Accidents

The greatest danger to teen-agers comes from accidents. In fact, more teen-agers are killed in accidents than are killed by cancer, heart disease, or any other cause. You can understand then why the teen-age years are sometimes called the "accident-prone years."

What Is an Accident?—An **accident** is an unexpected event that causes injury or death. Most people think accidents are unavoidable and uncontrollable risks of life. Although many accidents are unexpected, most can be prevented. Usually accidents do not result from failures of equipment or from circumstances that are beyond human control; most accidents are caused by human mistakes. Many accidents can be avoided by changing the way people act.

Preventing Accidents—There are at least three things you can do to prevent accidents. First, you can become more safety conscious. Many accidents are caused by carelessness. Just thinking about safety and becoming more cautious can probably prevent most accidents.

Although safety should be a personal mandate, laws have been enacted to protect the young citizens of America (such as requiring infants to be placed in car seats).

In Acts 27:9-10, Paul demonstrates a safety-conscious attitude. Because Paul had appealed to Caesar, he was being sent to Rome. Sea travel was especially dangerous during that time of the year (late fall or early winter); so Paul and his companions were stuck in an uncomfortable port. Because the port was so uncomfortable, the centurion escorting Paul persuaded the owner of the ship to attempt a dangerous journey to Phenice, a more comfortable port. Paul strongly argued for the postponement of the trip because of the danger involved, but his advice was ignored. The ship was eventually lost, and the occupants narrowly escaped death. A disregard for safety can often be tragic.

Because teen-agers take more risks than older individuals, teens have a higher incidence of accidents. Teens who show off by doing dangerous stunts are mainly demonstrating immaturity. A safety-conscious attitude may sometimes result in some teasing from your friends, but it may also keep you from spending the rest of your life in a wheelchair.

A second way to prevent accidents is to learn about some of the common causes of accidents and how to avoid them. Although it is impossible to learn safety rules for every situation, you can learn safety measures that will protect you from many accidents. Common sense and a cautious attitude will help you make right decisions most of the time.

Finally, learning new skills well can also prevent accidents. When you do not have the skill that is necessary to respond to unusual circumstances, you are more likely to be hurt. For example, an inexperienced driver may not know what to do when beginning to slide on a patch of ice. This lack of skill could cause him to react incorrectly and could even kill him. Poor skill can result in fatal mistakes. Reacting properly when an accident does occur may keep it from becoming serious.

As you read the rest of this chapter, you should begin developing a safety-conscious attitude. You can do this by learning more about the dangers you face every day, what you can do to avoid them, and how to react when an emergency does occur.

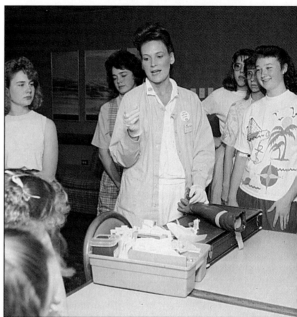

To help you respond correctly in an emergency, you should take a CPR class from a qualified instructor. Classes are also available in first aid and baby-sitting safety.

Section Review

1. Give an example of avoiding personal responsibility while taking undue advantage of another's kindness.

2. List four guidelines that help develop a correct attitude toward the risks of life.

3. Explain how learning a skill well can promote safety. Give an example other than the one written in the text.

HOME SAFETY

There's No Place Like Home! This thought reflects most people's view of home as a happy, secure place. If danger or stress threaten, the usual feeling is that everything will be all right if you can just make it back home. But did you know that your home can also be a place of danger? In a typical home there are hundreds of **hazards**. Hazards are dangerous situations or things.

A big-game hunter faces many hazards in the jungle. He may face hostile natives who might try to boil him in oil if they catch him. He may trip on the uncertain surface of the jungle floor and roll down a steep embankment. He may face the terror of a wildfire. And, of course, he faces the constant danger of attack from wild animals.

The typical home also contains hazards that could make a big-game hunter quiver with fear. There is the occasional threat of boiling oil (like when your mother is frying food). Each day you face the uncertain surface of sliding rugs and slippery tile. Treacherous inclines (like your stairs) are often hidden in darkness. A fire in your home may be just as dangerous as any wildfire, and there is always the danger of attack from hostile natives (like your brother).

While the danger from some of these hazards may be remote, some are very real dangers in your home. Millions of injuries occur in homes each year. Most of these injuries can be prevented. You can make your home a safer place to live in by becoming aware of the hazards that are common in a home and helping to guard against them. Fires, falls, firearms, and fatal substances are common dangers that you can guard against.

Fires

Fire is one of the most serious dangers that could threaten your home. Entire families are sometimes killed in home fires. Even those who survive a fire may be permanently disfigured or disabled. The destruction of property and irreplaceable items (photos, antiques, heirlooms) can also be emotionally devastating.

Preventing fires—The best way to prevent the tragedies that result from fire is to eliminate the conditions that cause fires. The kitchen is a common source of fire hazards. Although a kitchen fire can result in a major house fire, many of the burns and injuries that occur in the kitchen do not result from major fires. Hot pans, hot food, and boiling liquids are often the cause of painful burns.

To prevent fires and burns, take special care when cooking. When food is cooking, it should not be left unattended. Hot pans should be kept away from the edge of stoves and counters, the handles of pans should not stick out over the edge, and appliance cords should not hang from the counter. Make certain that kitchen appliances are turned off when they are not in use. Thick, *dry* potholders or oven mitts (and not the dish towel) should be used

A little break in a wire, a minute away from the grease pan, or a small amount of burning oil or food can lead to major damage and danger.

Be a Smoke Detector Inspector

Before you or your family purchases a smoke detector, be sure to investigate the product thoroughly. Cheap is not always best, and expensive does not insure quality. Consider these purchasing guidelines.

- Look for a seal of a national testing laboratory.
- Are batteries readily available and long lasting?
- Does the alarm have a warning system that signals when batteries need replacing?
- Can the alarm be tested easily?
- Is it loud enough to wake those who are sleeping in the house, even if doors are closed?

More than one or two detectors are usually needed in the average home. A detector should be placed on each level of the home (upstairs, main floor, basement) and outside each sleeping area. Detectors should be placed on the ceiling or four to twelve inches from the ceiling if hung on the wall. However, be careful not to place them too close to a corner (four inches away from the closest wall) or near a window, door, or vent. Drafts from these could cause the smoke initially to by-pass the detector. Also be sure not to place detectors too close to

the kitchen, bathroom, or garage where steam, exhaust, or fumes could initiate false alarms.

Smoke detectors are a worthwhile investment. However, remember that most smoke detectors use batteries for power. These detectors are useless if worn-out batteries are not replaced. Alarms should be checked at least once a month, and the batteries should be replaced once a year. They also need to be kept clean and dust free in order to keep them in prime working condition. Do you have enough detectors? Are they properly placed and maintained? Be a detector inspector and check into it today.

flash point of gasoline is −50° F (−46° C). This is why gasoline should never be stored in the home (not even in the basement). Mowers and other equipment should be fueled outside with the aid of a spout or funnel. Be sure to move away from gasoline fumes before starting the engine. Engines should also be cool when fueling. If you run out of gasoline, let the engine cool down before refilling the tank. Never use gas or combustibles as cleaners because any fumes or residue left can cause a fire. Flammable materials must always be handled, stored, and discarded with care.

Heating systems, such as stoves, heaters, and fireplaces, are also common sources of home fires. Check and clean these systems regularly. Each year have a qualified technician service home furnaces. Chimneys should be cleaned and inspected yearly because a buildup of creosote can cause chimney and house fires. Creosote is a flammable residue that collects in chimneys. Be sure that a metal or glass fire screen is placed in front of each fireplace.

to remove pots, pans, or dishes from the range, oven, or microwave. Steam is hotter than boiling water; so be careful to lift covers away from you to avoid steam burns. Do not cook while wearing loose clothing (floppy sleeves, scarves, and ties) that could catch fire on a burner as you lean over the range. Because grease and old food particles can ignite, be sure to clean appliances, toasters, ranges, and ovens regularly.

Grease fires are a common danger in the kitchen. Never throw water on a grease fire. Throwing water on a grease fire may cause the fire to spread. If the fire is in a cooking utensil, simply cover it to smother the fire. Use a kitchen fire extinguisher or baking soda (*not* baking powder) to put out a grease fire.

Keep **flammable** materials away from any source of heat. A flammable material is any substance that can catch fire easily. Old papers, oily rags, and gasoline are examples of flammable materials. Piles of drapes, papers, and clothing can catch on fire if they get too hot. Be sure not to store gas, kerosene, paint thinner, or lighting fluids where the fumes can ignite. Even pilot lights have been known to inflame fumes.

Flash point is the temperature at which a substance will produce a vapor that can ignite. While the flash point of turpentine is 95° F (35° C), the

When grilling, never use gasoline to light coals that have already been lit. Gasoline fumes are highly combustible and can cause an explosion.

Keep heaters at least three feet from anything that could burn. Turn off portable heaters before leaving the room or going to bed.

Other appliances such as refrigerators, ranges, and televisions should be cleaned regularly behind and underneath in order to prevent fire. Although they will not cause fires, water heaters set at high temperatures can cause burns. The temperature of 120 °F (49 °C) is recommended, since the water will be very hot but will not scald a person quickly.

Matches, lighters, and cigarettes also cause fires. Matches and lighters can be dangerous if handled carelessly. Be sure to place all matches and lighters out of the reach of small children. Do not use them unless you have a specific reason. It is also a good practice to moisten matches before discarding them. Smoking has caused numerous home fires when lighted or smoldering cigarettes have been tossed or have fallen on flammable materials (such as rugs and pillows).

When a fire does occur, it is imperative to become aware of it immediately. If a fire is detected early enough, escape is usually possible. A smoke detector can provide that early warning. Smoke detectors have been installed in many American homes and have saved many lives. In fact, having adequate detectors in the home cuts in half the risk of dying in a home fire!

Responding to Fire

The next thing you should do is to let others know about the fire and to get everyone out of the house. This is called **evacuating** your home. You and your family should plan how to evacuate your home before a fire occurs. Everyone should know at least two ways out of every room. Part of the plan should include a place for everyone to meet once they are out of the house. It is especially important to have a specific meeting place so that everyone can be accounted for in case some family members must use different exits. Many people have been killed because they went back into a burning building to rescue someone who was already out. Never go back into a burning building; stay out!

Careful adherence to fire safety rules may keep you from placing yourself and others in jeopardy.

Be sure to practice your evacuation plan regularly. A drill should not be treated like a race; caution and care should be taken. Practice the drills, blocking off certain exits and pretending that there is smoke and that there are no lights. Because fires are such frightening experiences, it is essential to know what you are going to do in advance.

As you evacuate, there are a couple of important things to remember. First, smoke and toxic gases are just as deadly as flames. Many people who die in fires are not killed by the flames but by inhaling too much smoke and deadly gases. Since smoke and hot gases rise, the best air is usually found several inches off the floor. Get on your hands and knees and then crawl out of the house immediately.

Use the *back* of your hand to feel the door, the doorknob, and the door frame before opening it. If a door feels hot, you should try to find another escape route. If the door is cool, cautiously open it. Be ready to slam it shut if smoke or fire threaten from the other side. Close all doors behind you to help slow down the spread of fire and smoke.

Call the fire department or 911 as soon as possible. If the fire is out of control, do not make this call from your home; go to a neighbor's home. When you contact the fire department, immediately tell them that you are reporting a fire. State your address, the phone number you are calling from, and directions to your home. Stay on the phone until the fire truck arrives or until the dispatcher assures you that he has all the information he needs.

If you are ever trapped in a burning building, close all doors between you and the fire. Stuff cracks and vents with moistened towels, clothing, or cloth to keep smoke out. If there is a phone, call the fire department and tell them exactly where you are. If possible, use a moistened cloth to cover your nose and mouth. Get to a window and signal for help by waving a flashlight or light-colored cloth.

If you or your clothing ever catch fire, remember to STOP, DROP, and ROLL. Use your hands to cover your face.

Fire can be very destructive. It can destroy property and cause the loss of life. It can permanently scar and disable. No one knows when or where the next fire will start; so make sure you are prepared.

Section Review

1. Define the words *hazard, flammable, flash point,* and *evacuation.*
2. Why would an ABC fire extinguisher be best for kitchen use?
3. Why should you never squirt gasoline on a barbecue grill or refuel a gas tank with a hot engine?
4. If you were to catch on fire, what should you do?

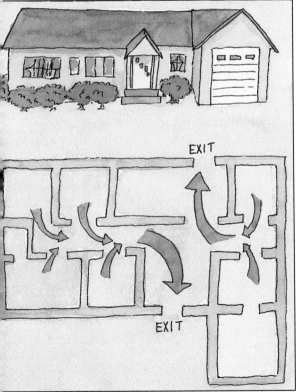

EXIT

EXIT

A basic evacuation plan should be made for each home and practiced periodically.

Falls

Falls are another danger in the home. Although you can fall at any time and in any place, there are a few hazards in the home that increase the likelihood of falls. As a safety-conscious person, be aware of these and eliminate as many as you can.

A common cause of falls is tripping over objects. Look around your home. Are there small rugs placed at the top or the bottom of stairs? Are wires or cords stretched across the room? Are objects such as toys or clothing left on the floor where people walk? Each of these is a potential hazard. It takes only a little extra effort to put things back where they belong. You can make your home a neater and safer place to live if you make this a habit. Remember, safety is everyone's responsibility; move any hazardous obstacle, even if it is not yours.

Stairs and hallways should be well lighted. This is especially important if children or elderly people are in the home. Night-lights placed in strategic spots can help to make your home a safer place.

Slipping on slick surfaces is another cause of falls. Wet tile, waxed floors, and slippery throw rugs are a few of the hazards that cause people to fall. Clean all floor spills immediately. Reroute traffic around wet areas. Using a little extra caution to secure sliding throw rugs to the floor can also prevent falls in your home.

Bathtubs and showers can also be dangerous. Rubber mats are often used in tubs and showers to prevent slips. However, be aware that rubber mats that are worn and have a layer of soap build up on them can be as dangerous as the tub surface. Grab bars in the bathtub and shower can make them safer.

Finally, there is danger in standing or climbing on chairs, counters, tables, or other props. Do not use stools or chairs for climbing; ladders are much safer. Keep in mind, though, that even a ladder can be dangerous. The distance between the base of a ladder and the wall that it is propped against should be one-fourth the height of the ladder. Never place a ladder on a slippery surface. Be sure not to stand on the top rung of a ladder, and never lean away from the ladder that you are standing on.

Many times it is not the fall that causes danger, but the objects that a person can hit in a fall that can be lethal. For instance, a fall in the living room may be harmless unless the person hits his head on the corner of coffee table or on the edge of the fireplace bricks.

Many falls are not caused by problems in the home, but by footwear. Be careful when walking on slick floors in hose or socks. It takes only a moment of careless haste to cause a bad fall. Sometimes broken sandals or thongs can be the culprits. Heels that are too high or that have a loose tap can trip a person. Trips are fun only if they are planned.

Firearms

Many people have guns in their homes. Always use special care around them. Firearms are deadly; they were designed as weapons and can kill. Never use guns as toys or point them at anyone, even if they are not loaded. Thousands of people have been killed with "unloaded" guns. Treat every gun like a loaded gun.

You should never handle a gun without your parents' permission and before you have received proper training. Brothers, sisters, parents, and friends have been killed in accidental shootings. You can protect those you love by using great care around firearms. If anyone who is not qualified to handle guns determines to show you his firearms, get out or get away. Do not stand around to debate the issue with him. Immediately leave and notify an authoritative adult.

Make sure that all weapons are stored out of the reach of children. Firearms should be stored unloaded in a locked gun cabinet. Ammunition should be placed in a separate, locked container. Do not play with ammunition; it can also be dangerous.

Guns must be loaded, unloaded, cleaned, and handled with great care. In fact, cleaning and playing with guns are the major causes of firearm fatalities. Never point a gun at an unintended target. If the gun is loaded, the safety latch or button should be in place. Make it a habit to keep the barrel pointed in a safe direction. Handguns should be carried with the barrel pointed down. Do not place your finger on the trigger until you are ready to shoot. Guns should be unloaded before climbing a tree or a fence, jumping a ditch, or propping them

More than just wild game is killed each year with firearms. Keep in mind that even BB guns or small caliber firearms can maim or kill. Each year more than 1,500 Americans die in gun-related accidents.

against a tree, post, table, or car. Whether the firearm is a BB gun or a .357 magnum, safety glasses should be worn when firing. Target practice should be done only at approved ranges. Using firearms requires an attitude of safety, self-control, and responsibility.

Section Review

1. List five major causes of falls.

2. Complete this important saying, "Treat every gun like _____."

3. Your friend wants to show you his father's gun. He starts to take it out. What should you do?

Fatal Substances

Toxic substances enter the system through more ways than just swallowing them. Most people assume that poisoning refers only to the problems of accidentally drinking furniture polish, eating toxic mushrooms, or consuming spoiled food. Poisons enter the body through four major ways:

1. **Ingestion**—swallowing the poison.
2. **Inhalation**—breathing poisonous fumes.
3. **Absorption**—poisoning through unbroken skin.
4. **Injection**—poisoning through punctured skin.

Ingested Poisons—Teen-agers beware! You probably think that poisoning due to ingestion happens only to small children. Unfortunately, poisoning is the main cause of home accidents during adolescence. This is mainly because of the number of teen-agers taking drugs or medications that are not prescribed for them or taking them in the wrong amounts. Taking drugs or medication that is not prescribed for you is not only wrong but also extremely dangerous. It is important to read the label to make sure that the medicine in hand is the one you need; do not take medicine in the dark. Do not think that if a little medicine is good, taking more medicine than what is prescribed is better. It is very *dangerous!* Read and follow the directions given.

Not all toxic substances seem to be dangerous. For instance, most people would immediately avoid insecticides, kerosene, or cleaning agents. However, lotions, ointments, paint, glue, and many plants are toxic. Children have been known to eat newspaper, hardware (screws, bolts, nails), small toys, and sewing notions (buttons, thimbles, pins). Although these items may or may not be poisonous, they could present the danger of choking, suffocation, or internal injuries. Some old toys, furniture, and walls have coatings of lead-based paint. These could be dangerous if chewed on or consumed.

The intake of lead can cause lead poisoning. Lead can gradually accumulate in body tissues and cause physical damage. It can sometimes be found in old paint, soil (contaminated from flaking lead-based paint and lead from car exhaust or manufacturing), drinking water (from lead pipes), and leaded crystal or dishware. Research shows that lead-crystal decanters and glasses can leak lead into beverages and juice held in them. Ceramics, pottery, and glazed dishware made in foreign countries often have extremely high lead content in the glazing. If you are given such a piece of pottery, use it for decoration but not for serving or storing food and beverages.

Beware of keeping medicine in purses or cars (aspirin, allergy pills, ointments); these could easily be taken by children. Keep in mind that even cosmetics, colognes, and shaving cream can be toxic. Do not refer to medicine as candy. Flushing all old medications down the drain is a good way to discard potential poisons.

Vitamin and mineral supplements, especially those with iron, should be treated like medicine and should be kept locked up. Colorful, fruit-flavored vitamins can be a temptation to children; there are more than 30,000 reports of children swallowing too many vitamins each year. Be sure to place all toxic and dangerous items behind locks or out of the reach of children.

Become familiar with poisonous plants that could be in or around your home. Sometimes only a portion of a plant is toxic. For instance, *solanine* (SOH luh NEEN) is a toxin present in potatoes. This toxin is mainly found in the green portion underneath the potato skin; it increases during sprouting or exposure to light. If the green areas that contain

Toxic Plants

amaryllis bulbs	daffodil bulbs	jasmine	philodendron
angel's trumpet	daphne	Jimson weed (thorn apple)	poinsettia
antheriums	dieffenbachia	larkspur	poison hemlock
azaleas	elephant's ear	lilies	pokeweed stems & roots
bittersweet seeds	English ivy	lily-of-the-valley	rattlebox
buttercups	foxglove	mistletoe berries	rhubarb leaves
caladium	holly berries	mountain laurel	sweet pea seeds
castor beans	jack-in-the-pulpit	mushrooms (some kinds)	tansy leaves & flowers
cherry tree twigs or leaves	hyacinth bulbs	nightshade	wisteria seeds & pods
chrysanthemums	hydrangea bulbs & leaves	oleander	yew

the toxin are removed, the rest of the potato is perfectly safe to eat.

Have the telephone number of your poison-control center posted by each telephone. If you suspect that a poison or accidental overdose has been consumed, call immediately. Not all poisons react immediately; some take hours before serious side effects begin to appear.

It is also important to note that the build-up of bacteria in foods can cause food to spoil or become toxic. For instance, just a small amount (the size of a grain of salt) of the bacterial toxin for **botulism** (BOCH yoo LIZ um) can kill several people within an hour. This toxin develops in an **anaerobic** environment (no oxygen present) and is mainly found in improperly canned low-acid foods. It is best to boil home canned meats and vegetables for at least twenty minutes to destroy any botulinal toxins within; however, not all toxins or bacteria can be destroyed by boiling. Never eat food taken from a can that is not properly sealed or is puffy; these are indicators of contamination.

Many people fall prey to what they think is the flu but, in reality, is food poisoning. **Salmonella** bacterial contamination is a major cause of foodborne illnesses. There are more than 2,000 kinds of

Destroying Angel
Poisonous

Meadow Mushroom
Nonpoisonous

Which is which? Do not take a chance by picking your own mushrooms for eating. Mushrooms can be unpredictable. Some are toxic only at certain stages of maturity or seasons; others are always toxic. Some mushrooms which are normally harmless can have a toxic effect when eaten by a person on certain medications.

salmonella, and each type can cause food contamination. Salmonella is most commonly introduced into the body by consuming contaminated meat, poultry, fish, eggs, or milk products (custard, cheese, ice cream). Salmonella infections have risen greatly since it has invaded the meat and poultry sources. Be sure that poultry is thoroughly cooked before consuming it. Because microwave cooking or grilling on a barbecue does not insure thorough cooking throughout the meat, it is wise to use other methods for primary cooking of pork and poultry (braise or boil the meat first).

Salmonella bacteria are now commonly found in eggs (even though the eggs may not be cracked). It is recommended that raw eggs or foods with eggs not thoroughly cooked in them (such as batter or dough made with eggs) should not be eaten. It is wise to avoid eating eggs cooked with the yolk still runny since it is difficult to determine if lingering bacteria have been destroyed.

Do not eat moldy food. (Moldy, solid cheeses can be trimmed and eaten safely if the cheese was kept refrigerated.) Toxins produced by molds are called **mycotoxins** (MY koh tahk sin). **Aflatoxins** (AF lah tahk sin) are an especially dangerous group of mycotoxins that are produced by a common mold called *Aspergillus* (AS pur JIL us). Aflatoxins are usually found on moldy nuts or moldy grains. Thousands of farm animals have been killed from eating moldy grain. One type of aflatoxin is suspected of causing cancer.

In order to reduce the risk of food poisoning, use proper food-handling practices.

- Wash hands and implements before and after handling foods (i.e., when switching from making the hamburger patties to cutting the carrot sticks) to avoid cross-contamination. A disinfectant for cleaning cutting boards and implements can be made by mixing one tablespoon of household bleach with one quart of water. Anti-bacterial hand soap will help to insure sanitation when preparing food.
- Do not sneeze or cough over food; avoid food preparation when you are ill.
- Do not touch your hair or face while cooking. When cooking, keep hair confined.
- Use clean dishtowels and dishcloths. When handling raw poultry, use paper towels.
- Do not place cooked meat on the unwashed platter previously used to hold the raw meat.
- Store food either below 40 °F(4 °C) or above 140 °F(60 °C) to inhibit bacterial growth.
- Do not leave food at room temperature for more than two hours.

The United States Department of Agriculture (USDA) has a Meat and Poultry Hotline that operates between 10 A.M. and 4 P.M. (EST), Monday through Friday. **Dial 1-800-535-4555.**

If there is a chance that your food is spoiled or has been exposed to improper food handling procedures, it is best not to eat it. Most types of foodborne illnesses are just temporarily devastating, but some can be fatal.

Section Review

1. What are four ways that toxic substances can enter the body?

2. When it comes to taking drugs or medicine, what are three rules to remember?

3. Describe at least six substances that are normally not thought of as dangerous but are toxic.

4. Using the chart of common poisonous plants given in the chapter, make a list of plants with which you are unfamiliar.

Inhaled Poisons—Toxic vapors and fumes often provide increased danger because their presence may not be easily detected. For instance, carbon monoxide is a colorless, tasteless, odorless gas that can be deadly. Carbon monoxide is present when fuel is burned in a poorly ventilated area (exhaust from automotive engines, heaters, furnaces, or internal-combustion engines). It is very important to keep all chimneys, furnaces, stoves, and heaters in good repair and inspected regularly. Vents to water heaters, range ovens, or space heaters should not be covered. Be sure that stoves and heaters are properly exhausted to keep dangerous fumes out of the house. Beware of running the car engine in a garage for more than a minute. Never tune up a lawn mower, car, or motorcycle in an enclosed space. Dizziness, headache, nausea, fainting, and a cherry red color of the skin and lips are symptoms of carbon monoxide poisoning. Most of the fatal gas poisonings can be attributed to carbon monoxide.

Other gases may be more readily detected but are just as lethal. Cleaning agents are often the culprits in inhaled poisons. Chlorine bleach fumes and ammonia cleaner vapors can cause enough problems when inhaled by themselves. However, when accidentally mixed (such as spraying ammonia glass cleaner over chlorine cleaner), they can create a noxious gas. Never mix bleach with ammonia! In fact, do not mix any chemicals unless the label states that the combination is acceptable. Even using one product with vapors and immediately using another product with vapors can create problems when the chemicals mix in the air.

Do not mix bleach with any acidic substances since this will produce deadly chlorine gas. Remember that many common household cleaners

When using strong chemicals and cleaners, make sure the area is well ventilated.

and mildew fighters are made of bleachlike compounds. A noxious gas is formed if bleach is added to some dish detergents; so read the label before combining them.

Petroleum-based gases present problems when painting, using cleaning fluids, or working with liquid glues in a closed area that does not have adequate ventilation. Petroleum-based insecticides and aerosols can be lethal if inhaled; be careful!

Absorbed Poisons—Some chemicals can easily cause skin burns, rashes, itching, and blisters when they come into contact with skin. Many people have had the unfortunate experience of poisoning by poison ivy, poison oak, or poison sumac. The skin irritant is found in the sap of all three. The sap, which is found in the leaves, roots, stems, pollen, and flowers, is released whenever the plant is bruised. The offending substance can be spread by pets that brush against it, contaminated clothing, tools, sports equipment (golf clubs, baseballs, footballs), and even the smoke produced when the plants are burned. You should be familiar with each of these plants on sight so that you can avoid contact with them.

Some plants (buttercup, hot pepper, mango, cashew, Florida holly, wartweed, snow-on-the-mountain) have irritating sap that can cause injury. Other plants (parsnip, fig, lime, Queen Anne's lace, carrots) can cause the skin to react to the ultraviolet rays of the sun and produce a false or artificial sunburn.

The actual poison in poison ivy (a), poison sumac (b), and poison oak (c) is in the resin urushiol, which contains the allergin pentadecylcatechol.

Chemical burns can occur if the skin comes in contact with strong acids or alkalis (battery fluid, drain cleaners, oven cleaners, paint removers, metal cleaners, and disinfectants). Wear protective gloves, and use caution when working with chemicals so that they will not splash in your face or spill on you.

Injected Poisons—God created some plants with built-in protection from predators. Certain palms and plants have thorns, bristles, spines, or fibrous needles that can cause skin irritation. Although the cut or puncture may not be deep, infection from bacteria or detachable needles can cause added injury.

Poisons that are introduced to the body through skin punctures can cause serious reactions. Animal bites (by dogs, cats, squirrels) should always be examined by a doctor. Due to the danger of rabies or bacterial infection, the animal should be captured and turned over to the health department for observation.

Snake, insect, and marine bites and stings can be not only frightening but also, in some cases, fatal. Injection of foreign substances can cause some people to go into **anaphylactic** (AN uh fuh LAK tik) **shock**. Shock reactions can move quickly from cold, clammy extremities, swelling of the face and tongue, blueness of the lips, dizziness, rapid pulse, shortness of breath, wheezing, and falling blood pressure to unconsciousness or even death.

Approximately 1 million people in the world are bitten by snakes each year. About 30,000 to 40,000 of these bites result in death. Most of these snakebite deaths occur in tropical Africa and Asia. The deaths from snakebites in the United States usually average fifteen each year. Most of these bites occur when snakes are handled for various reasons. There are four kinds of poisonous snakes in the United States: rattlesnakes, copperheads, moccasins, and coral snakes. Unless you can readily identify snakes and have a good reason to disturb them, it is best to

Copperhead

Rattlesnake

Water moccasin

Coral snake

Snake Savvy

There are two major types of poisonous snakes: vipers (rattlesnakes, copperheads, and moccasins) and elapids (cobras, mambas, and coral snakes). Since cobras and mambas are not indigenous (naturally occurring) to America, they are not usually a problem. However, a variety of poisonous snakes are shipped to America where they are kept as pets, for display, or for research.

Most venoms of snakes found in America are slow-acting. Most nonpoisonous snakes leave only a horseshoe-shaped row of bites as opposed to the fanged puncture or punctures of a poisonous snake. If a person is bitten, the area should be moved as little as possible and kept below the level of the heart. Any stimulant which would increase the heart rate should be avoided. A snug (but not tight) band of cloth can be wrapped above the wound until medical attention is given. Whether the bite is poisonous or nonpoisonous, nervous shock may result. Make sure that the victim is resting, and keep him from getting chilled.

leave snakes alone. They provide a natural control for rat, mice, and other rodent populations in their area.

Insect toxins vary in type and application. Some people are allergic to stings of bees, yellow jackets, wasps, and hornets; these people must be cautious and prepared to treat stings immediately. Some insects have toxins that cause irritation when touched because they produce a chemical barrier (blister beetles), while others have stinging hairs or spines (saddleback caterpillars, puss-moth caterpillars, and larvae of the io, flannel, tussock, brown-tail, white, and buck moths). The sting of harvester ants or fire ants can deliver intense pain

and inflammation. Multiple stings or allergic reactions can result in death.

Other creatures to be wary of include spiders, scorpions, ticks, mites (chiggers), and centipedes. Although bites or stings from these animals may not always cause death, they usually cause a great deal of discomfort.

When people go diving, snorkeling, fishing, surfing, or swimming, they must be aware of possible marine toxins. Although the Portuguese man-of-war floats on the surface, it has stinging tentacles trailing underwater. Jellyfish, corals, long-spined tropical sea urchins, and even the bite of an octopus

Prime Precautions for Protection from Predatory Pests

It is amazing the power that one little bee can exert over a human being. Just let a single bee into the car, and almost simultaneously the screeching of brakes is accompanied by whoops and hollers and the immediate opening of doors and windows. In some cases, the hubbub is accompanied by a mass and rapid exodus from the premises. It is not that the presence of bees, wasps, or hornets should be taken lightly. Surprisingly, bee stings kill more Americans than snakebites. Most bees are

If provoked, these insects will swarm. If a person receives multiple stings or has an allergic reaction, he can die.

generally friendly unless they are bothered or threatened. Yellow jackets and bald-faced hornets can be very aggressive. The yellow jacket holds the record for being the most

common cause of sting allergies. The Polistes wasp, the bald-faced hornet, the bumblebee, and the honeybee follow in rank.

When you plan to go outside (gardening, ball games, hiking, fishing), make plans to protect yourself from pests. Note the following suggestions for avoiding insect stings:

- Wear white, tan, or green clothes.
- Avoid wearing bright colors or floral prints.
- Use insect repellent.
- Do not wear perfumed lotion, sprays, or powders.
- Avoid picking flowers.
- Stay away from insect hives or nests.
- Do not walk barefoot.
- Be aware that perspiration lures insects.

Due to the danger of contracting Lyme disease or Rocky Mountain spotted fever, it is important to know how to protect yourself from tick bites. When going through wooded or brushy areas, wear boots or socks and shoes. Tuck your pant legs into your boots or socks. When applying insect repellent, be sure to spray socks, shoes, and pant legs thoroughly to keep ticks, mites, chiggers, and spiders away. Wear a hat or head covering, and keep hair tucked in it. It is

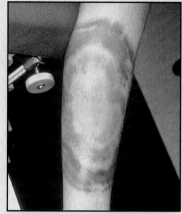

Recently, Lyme disease has become more prevalent. The deer tick is responsible for this very serious ailment.

wise to inspect the body and hair once or twice a day when in tick-infested areas. A complete inspection should be done when returning from a field trip. Clothes should be hung outdoors so any ticks clinging to them will remain outside.

To avoid the plight of the bumblebee and other such "friends," take time to consider the dangers and problems before starting. Be cautious when around bushes, tall grass, basements, attics, garages, boathouses, eaves, and garbage areas. Most insects attack because they have been disturbed and are simply defending themselves, their home, or their young.

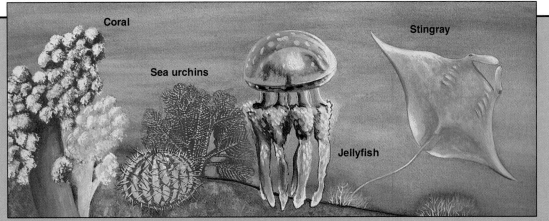

Coral

Sea urchins

Stingray

Jellyfish

Look, But Don't Touch!

The undersea world is fascinating and beautiful. However, it is filled with dangers that may not be deadly but can be painful. For instance, there are over 750 different types of corals; 9,000 species of jellyfish, sea anemones, sea nettles, and Portuguese man-of-wars; and 4,000 species of sea urchins and starfish. Many, but not all, of these species have poisonous nematocysts (stinging structures that penetrate and deliver toxins) or toxic spines that can cause human discomfort. Unless you can identify the various species, it is best to admire God's creatures without touching them.

can cause pain, infection, swelling, and numbness. Some of the fish whose venomous spines can introduce toxins are the spiny dogfish, ratfish, catfish, weaverfish, scorpion fish (zebra fish, waspfish, and stonefish), sturgeon, dragonfish, stargazers, and the stingrays. Use this knowledge of the dangers in the sea the next time you are in the open water.

Section Review

1. List three ways to prevent carbon monoxide poisoning.
2. Name at least five plants that can cause pain and irritation on contact.
3. What are five potential sources of injected poison?

ELECTRICAL SAFETY

One of the greatest achievements of modern science has been the discovery and use of electricity. Lights, microwave ovens, air conditioners, water heaters, hair dryers, irons, mixers, computers, and hundreds of other items are powered by it. You may not realize how much you depend on electricity until the power goes out and you have to live without it.

Hazards of Electricity

Although electricity is one of modern life's greatest assets, it also presents some unique dangers.

One danger is that electricity can cause fires. Electrical fires can be caused by frayed wires, defective appliances, appliances that are allowed to overheat, and overloaded circuits. An overloaded circuit may result from using appliances that require more current than the circuit is designed to handle. Using extension cords to allow you to plug several items into one electrical outlet is another common way of overloading a circuit.

If you blow a fuse or trip a circuit breaker, be sure to find out what caused the problem before replacing the fuse or flipping the breaker back on. Fuses should never be replaced with larger amp fuses, and never substitute a penny or foil-wrapped fuse.

Another danger related to the use of electricity is the danger that electric cords present for causing falls. Any electric cord that is lying across a place where people walk is a hazard. Be sure that cords are well secured and the excess cording neatly bundled out of the way.

Injury caused by the passage of an electrical current through the body is called electrical shock. Contact with exposed wires or faulty appliances and sticking an object into an electrical outlet are a couple things that can cause electrical shock. The electric current that makes your toaster work can be deadly if it runs through you instead of through your toaster. Many people suffer electrical shock from using hair dryers with wet hands or electrically powered tools while standing in wet grass or wearing damp shoes.

Frayed electric cords are fire hazards. Make an inspection of the appliances, lamps, and extension cords in your home. Replace or repair any that have frayed or exposed wires. Also make sure that electrical cords do not run under carpets and rugs since constant wear can result in fraying. In order to reduce the wear on electric cords, be sure to unplug them using the plug rather than jerk them by the cord from the socket. Never cut off or bend the grounding pin (the third prong) of a plug. It is also dangerous to file a polarized plug (with one side wider than the other) or try to make a polarized plug

reversible. It is better to develop good habits promoting safety rather than risk losing your home, possessions, or life to fire or electrocution.

Electrical Emergencies

There is a very real danger after a storm of electrical injuries because of downed power lines.

If a case of electrical shock is not handled properly, the situation can be deadly for both the victim and the rescuer. Electricity will travel from one person to any other person who touches him until it completes a circuit from the power source to the ground. If it is possible, *turn off the power source first.* Do not touch the victim until electrical contact is broken. If you cannot turn off the power, use extreme caution in attempting to separate the victim from the source of power. Stand at a safe distance on non-conducting material (*dry* rubber mat, thick board, thick stack of newspapers). Use a non-conducting material (*dry* wooden or bamboo pole, fiberglass fishing rod, or rope lasso) to knock the electrical line away or pull the victim from the electrical source. *Never touch a downed power line.* Call the power company and keep away from the live current. Because water is also a conductor of electricity, a rescuer must be careful not to stand in water or on moist ground. Do not even try to help if you or your equipment is wet.

Prevention of Hazards

Although you need to be prepared to help a victim of electrical shock if the occasion arises, it is much better to prevent such an accident whenever possible. Even a perfectly executed rescue cannot save every victim, but prevention can keep someone from ever becoming a victim. Below are some safety tips for avoiding electrically related injuries.

- Have frayed or faulty wires repaired or replaced.
- Never plug more electrical items into an electric outlet than the outlet was designed to handle.
- Use three-pronged plugs whenever possible, and never use a three-pronged plug that has the third prong broken off.
- Replace broken electric switch or outlet covers.
- Have broken appliances repaired by a qualified repairman.
- Instruct children to stay away from electrical outlets and not to stick foreign objects in them.
- Never use electrical appliances when you are wet or when you are standing on wet surfaces.

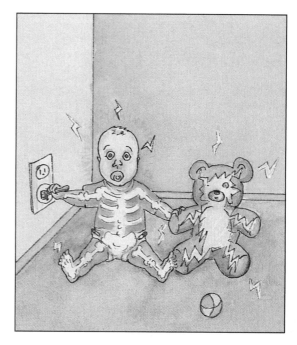

- Never store or use electrical appliances near water (such as the bathtub).
- Position electrical cords near walls and behind furniture where they will not cross places where people walk.
- Disconnect any electrical device if you feel a tingle when you touch it, if it gives a burning smell, or if you hear the crackle of electricity.

Section Review

1. What are three rules to remember about broken wires or appliances?

2. What are two major causes of circuit overloads?

3. In case of an electrical accident, what is the first step you should take in rescuing a victim?

PERSONAL SAFETY

Although God protects His children, He expects them to act wisely. If you are a Christian, remember that you are to be a testimony for Christ in a sinful and depraved world. Do not be so secure in your daily actions that you place yourself in dangerous situations. You are surrounded by an enemy who is intent on destroying you and your effectiveness for God. You must be on guard not only for spiritual attack but also for physical assault. An **assault** is an attack on a person by another. Never assume that you are an unlikely candidate for personal assault, or you will have made your first mistake.

Most of the time, common sense and precautionary actions can keep you out of jeopardy. For instance, do not walk in areas that are dark or isolated. If you must go walking in the dark, walk quickly with determination (as if you know where you are going), walk at a steady pace, and walk near the curb (away from bushes and hedges). Wear shoes that you can run in if you must. Let your family or trusted friends know where you are going and when you plan to return. If you think you are being followed, look for a safe retreat, such as a friend's or neighbor's house or a police or fire station. It is best not to go out alone at night, but if you must go, take a flashlight and walk quickly.

Shopping Safely

Many people make the mistake of thinking that mall or grocery store parking lots are perfectly safe; they are wrong. Parking lots often provide prime locations for assault. Keep the following guidelines in mind.

- Park as close to the entrance as possible. Seek a well-lit area.
- Do not park near bushes or near places that could provide hiding for a criminal.
- Be wary of people loitering in the area (sitting in cars or standing around).
- Do not leave valuables exposed in your car; put purchases in trunk.
- Lock all doors when you get out.
- Avoid walking through a parking lot alone, especially at night.
- Walk quickly and with confidence.
- Do not display large amounts of cash when in the parking lot or when shopping.
- If you feel uncomfortable, get a security guard to escort you to your car.
- Do not overload yourself with shopping bags.
- Have your keys in hand and ready to use before returning to your car.
- As you walk to your car, glance around and under it for potential attackers.
- Check the back seats and floor for possible intruders before getting in.
- Lock your doors as soon as you get in.
- If you think that anyone is following you, drive directly to the police or fire station.

Many people feel more confident taking a self-defense course; but, when it comes to self-defense, the best defense is not having to use it. Practice caution.

Even your home can be a location for assault. Never give personal information to strangers. Often teens unwittingly reveal that they are at home alone when people call and ask to speak to their parents. Much information is often passed in conversations with friends in stores or school that strangers can easily overhear. Initials rather than full names should be used on mail boxes and in telephone listings. Windows should be secured. Keep your doors locked, even during the day. Use a peephole and deadbolt lock for all outside doors. Delivery-men, repairmen, and even police should show valid identification. However, if your parents are not home, it is best to wait until you can get a neighbor, relative, or friend to come over before opening the door to a stranger. It is best not to let anyone into the house when you are alone, even if you know him.

It is also wise to vary your schedule or patterns of travel occasionally. Do not always walk home, to school, or to work the same way, at the same time, and do the same things. Always be aware of your surroundings. Notice if people are sitting in cars, loitering, or stalking the area. Do not enter an elevator with a person who makes you feel uneasy. Do not go to any secluded place or even to an interview alone; have a parent accompany you. You do not want to be constantly fearful, but you must be alert and careful.

Section Review

1. You are baby-sitting tonight. When you arrive at the house you will be working in, what are at least five precautionary measures you can take to help to safeguard the house from intruders?

2. It is 8:30 P.M. and you must run to the store to buy some paper for your report. What should you do?

TRANSPORTATION SAFETY

Getting from one place to another place can be a dangerous activity. There are more people killed in transportation-related accidents than any other type of accident. Traveling on a bicycle, in an

Concentration on a conversation, problem, or other things can often cause pedestrians to overlook basic safety rules.

automobile, or even walking pose the transportation dangers teen-agers face most often.

Pedestrian Safety

When you are walking from place to place, you are a **pedestrian,** or a person who travels on foot. Walking is an inexpensive means of transportation that also provides good exercise.

A pedestrian's greatest danger comes from the possibility of a collision when he is not watching where he is going. Pedestrians might walk into automobiles, bicycles, benches, mailboxes, other pedestrians, and thousands of other objects. Since a pedestrian has little protection when a collision occurs, it is important to use extra caution. You can avoid most collisions by watching where you are going and by being alert to the things around you.

There are a few other specific things you should do as a pedestrian to avoid accidents. First, if possible, you should always walk on the sidewalk instead of the road. If you must walk in the road, walk on the extreme left edge of the road, against the flow of traffic. Be careful to watch for cars that are turning corners, backing out of parking spaces,

or coming around a bus or truck. The driver may not see you in time to stop. Although the pedestrian may have the right of way, it is better to be cautious than to be dead.

Second, you should cross streets only at crosswalks or corners. This is important because motorists will be more aware of you and are more likely to see you at crosswalks. In many cities it is illegal to cross streets in the middle of a block. Crossing a street illegally is sometimes called **jaywalking.** Even when you use a crosswalk, look both ways before you cross; do not assume that a driver sees you.

Finally, you must use extra care if you are walking at night. Walking in the road is even more dangerous at night than it is during the day. Whenever you walk at night, you should wear light-colored clothing, carry a flashlight, and do everything you can to make certain that you are visible to others. Many pedestrians have been killed by drivers who did not see them until it was too late.

Bicycle Safety

Bicycles are another inexpensive form of transportation that can be an excellent means of exercise. Whether you travel by bicycle, moped, three-wheeler, or motorcycle, safety is important. The following safety steps can help keep cycling an enjoyable experience.

The first step to bicycle safety is to make certain the bicycle itself is safe. You should periodically check each part of your bike to make sure it is in good operating condition. The brakes should always work properly. (Brakes should be able to cause a skid when they are applied suddenly.) Your tires should be properly inflated and should be changed when the tread becomes excessively worn. The seat should be adjusted to the proper height. (When the seat is adjusted properly, you should be able to sit on the seat and place the balls of both feet on the ground. When you are pedaling, you should reach each pedal at its lowest position with your knee slightly bent.) Reflectors on your bicycle should be visible from the front, rear, and sides.

Second, realize that automobiles are your greatest danger, and always ride defensively. The safest approach as a cyclist is never to assume that you know what a driver is going to do. If you misjudge the driver and a collision occurs, you will lose. Even if the accident is not your fault, you will be the one more seriously injured.

Finally, there are some safety rules that you should practice.

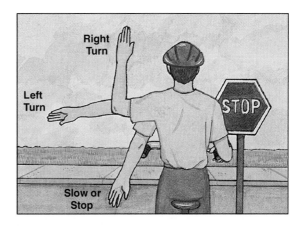

ny states require motorcyclists to wear helmets in an ·mpt to help prevent fatal injuries. Although helmets may be ·uired only for official cycling events, they are highly ·ommended for everyday bicycle riding.

- Obey all traffic regulations and signs.
- Signal all turns and stops.
- Ride on the right side of the road with the flow of traffic. (If there is a curb along the side of the road, you should avoid getting so close that your pedal can hit the curb and cause you to fall.)
- Beware of people opening the doors of parked cars.
- Ride single file if you are riding with others.
- Ride on a bike path whenever possible.
- Use a light if you ride at night.
- Always keep at least one hand on the handlebars.
- Never carry another rider unless your bicycle is designed for two.
- Never carry packages or other articles except in containers designed for use with bikes. The packages should not interfere with your control.
- Be alert for traffic and road hazards (such as rocks, sand, and potholes).

Section Review

1. What can a pedestrian do to decrease risk when walking? List three specific actions that can be taken.

2. What are three major guidelines for bicycle safety?

3. If your bicycle is not built for two and a friend wants to ride on your bike with you, what should you do?

Automobile Safety

Every year about 50,000 Americans are killed in traffic accidents. About one out of every three persons will be in a serious traffic accident sometime in his life, and almost half of those who die are under twenty-five years of age. Is there anything you can do to keep from becoming an accident statistic? The following information can help by preparing you to be a safe driver in the future and a safe rider today.

Driving Safely—Whether or not you have your driver's license, it is never too early to think about becoming a safe driver. Driving is a big responsibility. The safety of the people who travel in your car and of all those who share the highway with you, as well as your own safety, is in your hands. One mistake, one moment of recklessness, or one wrong decision can kill. Unfortunately, teen-age drivers cause more than their share of accidents.

Defensive Driving Techniques That Can Save Your Life

- Be alert for trouble ahead; know what is going on further than just one car ahead of you.
- Maintain an adequate space between your car and the car in front of you.
- If danger is detected, reduce your speed.
- Turn on your headlights (not just parking lights) in bad weather.
- Scan mirrors to determine the locations of cars around yours.
- Be aware of pedestrians and things along the side of the road (trees, telephone poles, ditches) that should be avoided in case you must swerve to the side of the road.
- Check blind spots and signal before you change lanes.
- Avoid sudden stops.
- Never assume that other motorists see you.

onsible actions and lack of attention can have tragic results.

How can you become a safe driver? Like many aspects of safety, becoming a safe driver takes work and thought. The most important ingredient for safe driving is the proper attitude. A safe driver obeys traffic laws and is courteous to other drivers. He is always alert and drives defensively. The key to defensive driving is watching out for potential problems created by the mistakes of others or by poor road conditions. Roads are especially hazardous during heavy rainstorms, in deep snow, on icy roads, or in times of poor visibility (fog, smog, sandstorms).

Driving a car is not a time to show off or to release your anger and frustrations. One of the reasons teen-age drivers have numerous accidents is that many do not have the proper attitude about driving. If you will maintain a safety-conscious attitude, you will increase your chances of being a safe driver. Reckless driving may be fun temporarily, but the consequences can be deadly.

Next, a safe driver will practice safe driving skills. A good way to develop safe driving skills is to take a driver education class. Many auto insurance companies give discounts to young drivers who take these classes. They have found that this additional training often produces better drivers.

Finally, a safe driver knows when not to drive. If you are sleepy or are taking any type of medication that can make you drowsy, you should not drive. Alcohol is a drug that causes many accidents. In fact, half of all traffic deaths are caused by drinking drivers. While alcohol is an ingredient in certain medications (such as cough remedies), most of the alcohol-related accidents are caused by people who drink alcohol for enjoyment. Drunk drivers are the greatest hazard on the highways. People should never drive while under the influence of alcohol.

The excuse "I drank only two beers" will never bring back those killed by drunk drivers. Alcohol acts like an anesthetic and causes one to make poor judgments. It also slows reaction time, causes a loss of concentration (drowsiness or passing out), and impairs the eyesight (blurred vision, double vision, or multiple vision). It takes the body one hour to eliminate the alcohol contained in one bottle of beer or one ounce of whiskey. Regardless of one's outward condition and regardless of his taking coffee, tea, or another stimulant, a person who has drunk alcohol will have impaired reflexes. He is a danger to himself and others if he attempts to drive.

Riding safely—Certainly, the driver is the most important influence on the safety of an automobile, but there are some things you can do as a passenger to be safer. The most important thing you can do is to use a safety belt whenever you ride in a car. Safety belts save lives. It is estimated that a lap belt can reduce death and injury resulting from auto accidents by almost one-third. A combination of a lap and shoulder belt is twice as effective as a lap belt alone. Although there may be little you can do as a passenger to avoid an accident, you can more than double your chances of surviving a traffic accident by wearing your safety belt.

Why are safety belts so effective? Research has shown that when an automobile collides with another object, there are actually two collisions. In the *first collision* the car hits the other object. In the *second collision* the person in the car is slammed into the interior of the car. The first collision causes the most damage to the car, but the second collision causes the most damage to the person in the car. Safety

Seat Belt Myths

Safety belts can trap people—Only one-half of one percent of car accidents end in a situation in which immediate escape from the car is necessary (fire or submersion). A safety belt is more likely to help keep a passenger conscious so that he can attempt an escape.

It is safer to be thrown out of a car—A person who is thrown out of a car is twenty-five times more likely to die.

Safety belts are not needed when traveling close to home—About seventy percent of traffic deaths occur within twenty-five miles of home.

Safety belts are not needed when driving slowly—Most accidents causing death and injury occur at speeds below forty miles per hour.

Safety belts are not important—Safety-belt use is credited with reducing motor vehicle deaths by forty to fifty percent.

Most car manufacturers have as a main priority the safety of the occupants using their vehicles. Engineers can test the effectiveness of their designs by using test dummies in a collision and then filming and studying the effects of the impact. Although a person in a car crash may see everything in slow motion, the actual crash sequence, like the one pictured, may take only a second. Improvements are sought in body design, material composition, restraint systems (safety belts with shoulder straps, air bags), interior design (collapsing steering assemblies, padding on dashboards, head and neck support on seats), and mechanical abilities (brake systems, maneuvering systems).

belts and air bags protect you from much of the damage caused by the second collision.

You may have heard of someone who was in a terrible accident and survived only because he was not wearing his safety belt. Although a few people may have survived accidents because they did not wear their safety belts, many more have died because they did not wear them. In almost any crash or circumstance, you are safer if you have your safety belt on. While wearing a safety belt may keep you alive if you are in a serious accident, you may avoid an accident by choosing whom you ride with. Teenage drivers are often more reckless when they are with other young people. Do not ride with people who you know drive recklessly. *Never* ride with anyone who is drinking alcohol or under the influence of drugs. If you are in a car and the driver starts driving foolishly, ask to be let out. Walking is slow and inconvenient, but it beats riding in a wheelchair the rest of your life.

Section Review

1. What are three characteristics found in a safe driver?

2. As a rider in a car, what is the main thing you can do to increase your safety?

3. In an accident, which collision causes most injuries to a passenger of a car?

4. Your cousin is supposed to pick you up and take you home. As you get into the car, you smell alcohol on his breath. What should you do?

RECREATIONAL SAFETY

Anyone interested in recreation? Boating (canoeing, sailing, water skiing), swimming, diving, playing ball (football, baseball, soccer, tennis, handball, racquetball), and hundreds of other sports and activities are available. Unfortunately, many people are injured each year while having fun, and injuries are never fun.

Any activity that involves movement increases your risk of injury, but the risk varies greatly from activity to activity. For instance, there are many more serious injuries in football than there are in volleyball. Climbing a mountain is usually more dangerous than roller-skating. However, roller-skating has more risks involved than walking in the mall. You should understand the risks of any activity you choose. Understanding the risks of an activity will help you to make better choices and may help you reduce possible risks. You can reduce the risks of many recreational activities by using

Christ should be evident in your life off and on the field or court. Sometimes you are the only Bible others will read. What kind of testimony does your life present during a game or competition?

proper equipment, obtaining proper training for the activity, and maintaining a proper attitude toward the activity.

Proper Equipment

Many activities require special equipment. Shoes, socks, helmets, bats, rackets, surfboards, and boats are some examples of equipment used for recreation. Whether it is big and expensive or small and inexpensive, you should make sure you have the right equipment for the activity.

When you choose your equipment, you should buy those articles that are safe and designed for the activity you are using them for. Any equipment you wear should fit properly. All equipment should be in good repair and replaced when necessary.

Proper Training

Most new activities must be learned. You can avoid many injuries by learning how to do a skill properly. Some of these injuries occur because the wrong technique puts too much strain on some part of the body. For example, if you stroke a tennis ball improperly, you can get tennis elbow. Even worse, a poorly performed tackle in a football game could result in a broken neck.

Other injuries occur because there has not been proper conditioning for the activity. Any time you choose a new activity or begin an activity you have not done for a while, you should work at getting "in shape" for that activity. Remember that your conditioning program should start slowly and progress gradually.

Another aspect of proper training is to learn the rules and safety tips for each activity. When rules are violated, an injury becomes more likely. When safety hints are not observed, an accident is almost certain. Can you think of some examples of how breaking a rule or ignoring a safety tip can cause injury?

Proper Attitude

The final thing you can do to reduce the risk of any activity is to keep the right attitude. Some players enter the playing field as if they are entering a war. They carry grudges onto the playing field and may even try to hurt their opponents. Some schools develop such intense rivalries with other schools that students talk about how much they "hate" the other team. These wrong attitudes can lead to violent behavior and unnecessary injuries.

The playing field is not a place to "get even." Playing with this type of attitude is unsafe and not Christ-like. Play for fun and not for blood. You should do your best but remember that it is just a game. Never make the outcome of a game or challenge more important than safety or your testimony.

Water Safety

Proper equipment, training, and attitude can prevent many injuries while mountain climbing or while playing basketball, for instance. They also help to prevent water-related accidents, but there

White water rafting (also called wild water racing in international competitions) is a popular sport in many areas of Europe and the United States. Whether you are on a raft or in a canoe, always wear the proper safety equipment.

Swimming Sensibly

Although learning to swim is the first step toward water safety, knowing how to swim will not always keep you from drowning. Most drowning victims know how to swim. After you learn to swim, the following safety precautions will help you to keep your head above water.

- Never swim alone. You should always swim with a friend. He may be able to help you or get help if you have trouble.

- Swim where lifeguards are on duty. Lifeguards are specially trained to keep you safe and assist you if you need help.

- Never show off or overestimate your swimming ability. Men are about ten times more likely to drown than women. This high ratio probably results from the fact that men often take more foolish chances.

- Know what is beneath the surface of the water and how deep the water is before you dive. Serious neck or head injuries may result.

- Get out of the water when storms or lightning threaten. Because water conducts electricity, it can be very dangerous to stay in the water during a thunderstorm.

are some additional considerations that may help you be safer in the water.

Because almost one-third of all drownings involve teen-agers and young adults, it is vital to learn about and to practice water safety. The most important step towards water safety is learning how to swim. Swimming is not a difficult skill to learn. Often the most difficult obstacle with swimming is overcoming the fear of the water. For this reason it is usually best to learn to swim at a young age. Some children learn to swim almost before they learn to walk. But it is never too late to learn to swim and to begin to practice water safety.

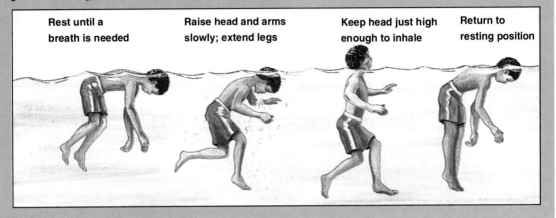

Drownproofing Techniques

Learn drownproofing techniques. **Drownproofing** is a method of staying afloat that requires little effort. Using drownproofing techniques, you may be able to stay afloat for hours if necessary. Almost any good swimming instructor can teach you drownproofing.

Rest until a breath is needed

Raise head and arms slowly; extend legs

Keep head just high enough to inhale

Return to resting position

Section Review

1. What are the three guidelines for recreational safety?

2. What is one hazard of swimming alone?

3. Jeff and Michael decided to go swimming at the lake. Michael noticed a thunderstorm heading their way and decided to go home. Jeff told Michael to go on home but that he wanted to stay and swim longer. What should Michael do?

SAFETY DURING NATURAL DISASTERS

Someday you may have to face the extra danger from some force of nature. Tornadoes, hurricanes, electrical storms, earthquakes, tsunamis, blizzards, and erupting volcanoes are examples of natural disasters. It is good to remember during these terrifying situations that God is in control. However, you still need to know how to react calmly and correctly.

Not all areas of the country face the same natural disasters. For instance, blizzards are usually not a danger to people who live in Florida, and hurricanes usually do not threaten Kansas. Wherever you live,

you should find out what types of natural disasters are common to your area and learn what to do if they occur.

The most important safety rule that applies to all natural disasters is to take the threat seriously. On May 18, 1980, dozens of people were killed when Mount St. Helens erupted violently. Most of those killed had been repeatedly warned to evacuate the area.

A similar tragedy occurred in August 1969. Over 300 people were killed by a powerful hurricane named Camille. Many of those who lost their

Hurricane Camille was one of the most powerful hurricanes ever (winds of 190 mph). In 1969 it moved from Louisiana to Virginia, causing over 250 deaths and $1.5 billion in damage.

lives had ignored instructions to evacuate the area, and some were actually having "hurricane parties." They never expected the storm to be as bad as it was. Anytime there is warning of a natural disaster, it should be taken seriously.

In order to be prepared for severe weather, stock up on food, bottled water, flashlights, batteries, candles, and needed medicines. It is good to have a battery-powered radio in order to listen to instructions given by the authorities.

When Lightning Strikes

Although thunderstorms may happen only occasionally in your area, there are about 44,000 thunderstorms on earth each day. Lightning flashes somewhere on earth about 100 times every second. Because lightning tends to strike at the highest or tallest place, during a storm it is best not to stand in an open field. It is best to crouch down and wait for the storm to subside. Do not stand under trees or next to wire fences, water pipes, electrical wires, large machinery (tractors, bulldozers), or goal posts since these objects tend to be struck by lightning. When storms threaten, stay away from boats and get out of the water. It is best to stay in a building protected by lightning rods or in a car. However, if you are in a car, stay away from the sides of the car.

When in a building, stay away from metal objects (pipes, ranges, refrigerators) and do not talk on the telephone. It is also wise to turn off and unplug appliances, stereos, and televisions.

Lightning kills about 150 people in the United States each year. Lightning is an electrical discharge occurring either between clouds, between a cloud and the air, or between a cloud and the ground. The temperature in a bolt of lightning can be around 60,000° F (33,000° C) and can discharge 10-100 million volts and 300,000 amperes of current.

When Floods or Hurricanes Threaten

Melting snow or severe rainstorms can cause flooding. If a hurricane warning has been given, you must evacuate the area. Do not plan to stay. As with most emergencies, listen for warnings and make your plans accordingly. If floods or hurricanes threaten your area, determine the safest area to evacuate to, inspect and collect emergency supplies, fill your car's tank with gas (filling stations may be closed for several days after a flood), bring in or tie down items that could float away, turn off your water and gas valves, unplug electrical appliances (or switch off electrical current at the fuse box), move items upstairs, and try to secure your house as well as possible (board windows and place sandbags in appropriate areas).

Never try to drive through water that covers the road. You may not know how deep the water actually is, and the water may cause the car to stall. Flood waters can also sweep the car downstream or erode sections of roads and bridges. If your car gets caught in flood waters, get out of the car and move to higher ground.

After a flood, do not drink water or eat food that has been touched by flood waters. Electricity should not be used until electrical equipment has been dried and checked. Before lighting matches or using lanterns, inspect the house for flammables that may have floated inside. Report broken utilities to the authorities, and stay tuned to your battery radio for instructions and information.

The following items are suggested emergency supplies to be kept in the car.

Flashlight
Packaged batteries
First aid kit
Blanket or sleeping bag
Booster cables
Rain gear and extra clothes
Bottled water
Canned food
Can opener
Candles and matches
ABC-type fire extinguisher
Necessary medication
Shovel
Snow or traction chains (depending on your area)

One of the dangers of floods occurs when flammable substances become dispersed in the water. Toxic substances, decayed debris, and pathogens are easily spread in flood-water conditions.

A blizzard is more than a heavy accumulation of snow. It also includes high winds, which explain why some refer to a blizzard as a blinding snowstorm.

When Blizzards Hit

If you live in an area that usually gets an abundance of snow, you are probably used to sitting through a blizzard. However, many people who are not used to snow may get trapped in their cars when traveling through snowy areas. If you will be traveling, check the weather forecast. If severe winter storms are predicted, avoid driving. If you are caught in a blizzard and your car gets stuck, stay in your car and wait for help (unless you see a definite haven where you can go for shelter and help). Turn the engine on occasionally to provide heat, but leave a window open slightly to avoid carbon monoxide poisoning. Keep the exhaust pipe free from snow. Move around occasionally and try not to stay in the same position for long. Leave the dome light on at night as a signal for rescuers. If two or more people are in the car, sleep in shifts.

In the snow, and even in wet, cold conditions, **hypothermia** (HIE poh THUR mee uh) can be a danger. Hypothermia results when the body temperature cools to a level that can cause death. In order to avoid hypothermia, make sure that you have maintained a good diet (dieters and thin people are more susceptible to hypothermia than others). If you plan to be out in the snow, take some high-calorie snacks

with you. In order to help prevent dehydration, which can reduce blood volume due to the loss of body fluids, drink extra fluids and take a hot beverage along. Dress warmly when chances for exposure are increased. The clothing rule of wearing light, loose, and layered clothes applies. Wear clothes that are windproof and water-resistant (repels water but still enables the body to "breathe"). Keep your head and neck covered, wear gloves, and put on warm, thick socks and water-resistant shoes. Whether you are going skiing or sledding, engaging in a snowball fight, or clearing the snow from the drive or walkways, keep warm and dry. Do not place yourself in danger of hypothermia.

If a blizzard strikes your area, do not leave your home, school, or business. It is good to have a source of alternative heat (kerosene heater, fireplace) in case the power lines are damaged. Stay warm by dressing warmly and bundling in layers of light-weight blankets. Use a blizzard as an opportunity to enjoy your family, sing songs, tell stories, share memories, and praise the Lord.

When Tornadoes Come

Although the authorities can often predict conditions that favor tornado appearances, tornadoes often come suddenly. They can whirl, skip, and

A tornado is the most destructive storm. It can rotate at more than 200 mph (320 kmph) and can vary in diameter from a few feet to over one and a half miles (2.4 km).

Historical Earthquakes in the United States

Because 503 people were killed as 500 city blocks were leveled, the San Francisco earthquake of 1906 was the deadliest in the United States. The largest earthquake occurring in the U.S. was the 1964 earthquake of southern Alaska, with a 9.2 magnitude. An earthquake televised around the world occurred in San Francisco in 1989, just prior to the World Series. Most of the deaths occurred when the second deck of Interstate 880 collapsed onto the first deck.

San Francisco, CA 1906

Anchorage, AK 1964

Alameda county, CA 1989

jump in unpredictable fashion causing chaos and destruction. Even though tornadoes usually occur in the central part of the United States during the spring, they can hit anywhere and at any time.

If a tornado *watch* has been issued for your area, keep listening to your local radio or television station and be alert for the appearance of funnel-shaped clouds. If a tornado *warning* has been given, a tornado has been sighted, and you should seek shelter immediately. If you are at home, open your windows on the side opposite the approaching storm, seek an underground shelter (basement), and go to the corner nearest the storm. If you can see the tornado coming, do not stop to open windows, but go quickly to your shelter. If you do not have access to a basement, get into the smallest room with strong walls on the lowest level of your house or under a heavy table or bench. Stay away from windows! If you are in a mobile home, trailer, or car, get out immediately. A ditch, a ravine, or even the undergirders of an overpass can provide safety if you are outdoors; cover your head with your arms.

When Earthquakes Occur

It is amazing how suddenly and quickly an earthquake can create havoc and destruction. Although the San Andreas Fault in California is one of the most famous faults (break or fracture in the earth's crust), numerous faults transverse the United States. Some areas are more prone to having earthquakes than others, but earthquakes can occur in almost any part of the country.

If you are in a building when an earthquake occurs, get under a heavy piece of furniture or sit against an inside wall away from windows, mirrors, shelves, and furniture that could fall. Cover your head with your arms, clasping your hands behind your neck. If you are in a kitchen or laboratory, try to turn off all burners before taking cover. If you are in a car, stop but stay in the car. However, do not stop under a bridge or overpass or park near utility wires or tall buildings. If you are outside, move to an open space away from buildings or power lines. Lie down or crouch down and keep alert for danger.

When the shaking ceases, avoid driving on bridges in case they have been damaged. Inspect your home for damage that could have weakened the structure. Also check the house and area for any broken gas lines before igniting a flame. If you smell gas, turn off the main gas valve, call the gas company, and leave the house. If electrical appliances are wet, turn off the main power switch, disconnect them, and allow them to dry before reconnecting them and switching back to electrical power.

A TIME FOR SAFETY

No matter what the emergency, keep calm. Focus on what you need to do and remember that God is in control. "They cry unto the Lord in their trouble, and he bringeth them out of their distresses. He maketh the storm a calm, so that the waves thereof are still. Then are they glad because they be quiet; so he bringeth them unto their desired haven" (Ps. 107:28-30).

Your teen-age years are a time of growth and excitement, but they are also the years that you are most likely to be injured in an accident. Do not presume on God's power by living recklessly. Do not expect your parents or your friends to be responsible for your safety. Your safety is your responsibility. Today is the best time to begin practicing safe behavior. Tomorrow may be too late.

Section Review

1. What is the most important rule to remember when it comes to natural disasters?

2. What is hypothermia? Explain how you can protect yourself from hypothermia.

3. During which natural disasters are you to leave your home?

4. What is the difference between a tornado watch and a tornado warning?

CHAPTER REVIEW

Terms

presumption

risks

accident

hazards

flammable

flash point

evacuation

ingestion

inhalation

absorption

injection

botulism

anaerobic

salmonella

mycotoxins

aflatoxins

anaphylactic shock

assault

pedestrian

jaywalking

drownproofing

hypothermia

Content Questions

1. Explain why a Christian should not place himself at risk on purpose.

2. Describe five ways to prevent fires in the kitchen.

3. If you were to explain the dangers of gasoline and flammable substances to a group, what points of importance would you be sure to cover?

4. *Fire! Fire!* If your home were engulfed in flames right now, how should you react? List at least five things you should do.

5. When handling firearms, what are seven rules to remember?

6. Your little sister wants to learn to cook. Explain at least ten rules for her to know in order for her to avoid poisoning the family.

7. Explain at least three substances or combinations of substances that can actually "take your breath away."

8. Because water is an excellent conductor of electricity, what two rules should you remember when using or storing electrical appliances?

9. List at least ten guidelines to remember to help prevent assault?

10. When should a driver not drive and a rider not ride?

11. What hazards can cause electrical fires or electrocution at home?

12. Give at least two pedestrian rules and bicycling rules that are similar.

13. List the rules of water safety that you must remember in order to make safe water recreation decisions.

14. During which of the natural disasters should you remain in your car?

Application Questions

1. How can you help to inform others about poisonous hazards? Make a poster that warns of poisonous possibilities. Your poster should clearly point out potential hazards included under each of the four ways of being poisoned.

2. Granny is moving in; she is eighty-eight years old and not very stable on her feet. What are at least three precautionary safeguards that should be installed or fixed before she arrives?

3. In order for this story to end "happily ever after," how should Nathan respond when Jesse begins to open his dad's gun cabinet in order to show him a pistol?

4. You are driving on the interstate and you notice a tornado coming toward you. What should you do?

5. If you were in charge of planning a neighborhood bicycle rally, how would you do it? Plan a bicycle safety conference, including a short object lesson, devotional, rules for the ride, and a bicycle trail for your neighborhood children. Also be sure to indicate safety measures that must be included (blocking off certain areas, adult supervision, etc.).

IN SERVICE

Emergency Medical Technicians

Job Description: Emergency medical technicians are trained professionals who provide emergency care for sick and injured people. Depending on their training, an emergency medical technician (EMT) may be called on to treat shock, open airways, restore breathing, control bleeding, administer oxygen, immobilize fractures, bandage wounds, assist in childbirth, treat and resuscitate heart attack victims, and give initial care to burn or poison victims.

Job Location: Emergency technicians usually work in teams of two. They are called on to respond in all types of weather and may be exposed to all types of danger (violence from drug-overdosed victims, mobs, riots, and shoot-outs; emergencies caused by storms, radiation, explosions, downed electrical lines, and gas leaks). There is a great deal of kneeling, lifting, bending, and standing involved in this occupation. Because emergency medical technicians deal with life-or-death situations, there is great stress placed on them; there is not much room for error.

Training Required: Emergency medical technicians must successfully complete a 117-hour course designed by the United States Department of Transportation to train EMT-Ambulance (EMT-A) workers in basic life support techniques. This is a nondegree course which enables a person to become an entry-level worker (EMT-A or basic EMT). More training will enable a worker to become an EMT-Intermediate (capable of treating patients with intravenous fluids and with antishock garments and airway management techniques) or an EMT-Paramedic. EMT-Paramedics are trained in advanced life support skills (administering drugs orally and intravenously, interpreting EKG's by using complex equipment such as monitors, defibrillators, or external pacemakers) and, when in radio communication, can work under the direction of a physician.

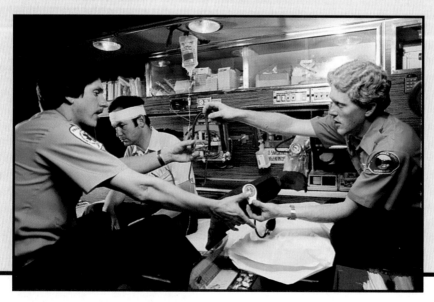

FIRST AID

Not all accidents can be avoided; therefore, it is important for you to know what to do when an accident occurs. Although you may never experience a tornado or a hurricane, you probably will encounter a car accident or come across a friend who has fallen and broken a bone. For these and other such emergencies, it is vital to know how to render first aid until help arrives.

CHAPTER 8

"When he saw him, he had compassion on him. And went to him, and bound up his wounds."
Luke 10:33-34

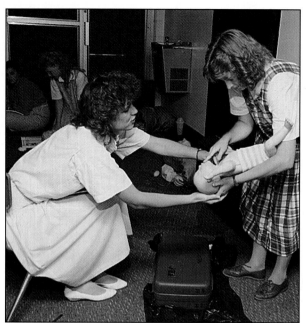

Knowing basic first aid skills can help you as you baby-sit, help in Sunday school, or coach a Little League team.

KNOWING FIRST AID PROCEDURES

Treatment that is given immediately or until professional medical help arrives is called **first aid.** If everyone knew basic first aid techniques, thousands of lives could be saved each year. Do you know how to stop bleeding? What would your reaction be if a loved one suddenly began to choke on some food? What would you do if a child accidentally swallowed a poisonous substance? A standard first aid course can teach you what to do in these circumstances and in many others.

Why Learn First Aid?

It is important to remember that first aid is only temporary care. However, this initial assistance can sometimes make the difference between temporary and permanent disability or even between life and death. Knowledge and practice of first aid techniques can enable you to help in an emergency. First aid training can increase your confidence in an emergency and encourage a calm reaction. Training in first aid procedures also reemphasizes the importance of practicing safety and prevention.

Many first aid techniques are easily accomplished. Most teen-agers show little hesitation in cooling a person with heat exhaustion or removing a splinter. Doing what needs to be done is usually easy as long as you know what needs to be done. However, **cardiopulmonary** (KAR dee oh PUHL moh NER ee) **resuscitation (CPR)** should not be applied unless special training has been given. CPR is a lifesaving technique that is used when respiratory failure (cessation of breathing) is combined with cardiac arrest (heart ceases to beat). CPR training teaches a person how to use rescue breathing and external chest compression to keep the victim alive until medical help arrives or until the heart and lungs begin to function. You can register for training at your local Red Cross organization or check about instruction given by your local hospital for training in CPR. *You should not attempt CPR unless you have completed a specific course in it.*

This chapter will provide useful information and recommendations for first aid. *Please note that studying this chapter does not equal certified first aid training.* Reading about what to do and actually training how to do it are not the same. There is no substitute for actual first aid training.

There is no substitute for training to know how to help someo during an emergency.

What Are the Laws?

Citizens are not obligated to administer first aid, but if you begin to administer first aid, you must continue until professional help arrives. You cannot abandon the victim. Many states provide legal protection to rescuers in the form of "Good Samaritan" laws. These laws protect the first aid providers who act in good faith and are not guilty of gross negligence or willful misconduct. Because states have different protection laws and ranges of protection, it is wise to check on your state's laws.

It is important to get the victim's consent before administering first aid. If a child is seriously hurt and there is no parent or guardian available, you may give aid without consent. If the person is unconscious, the law assumes that consent would be given. If a person refuses help, however, try to document his decision or get his or a witness's signature on a statement stating his refusal of help.

What Do You Do in an Emergency?

If you do not know what to do, get additional help immediately. Always let the most qualified person take charge of the situation. Keep calm and try to keep others that are around calm and out of the way. If the victim is not in any danger where he is, do not move him. Do your best to provide protection and warmth (protect a victim from injuring himself further, cover him with a blanket, keep him from exposure to wind and rain). Stay with the injured person until professional medical care arrives.

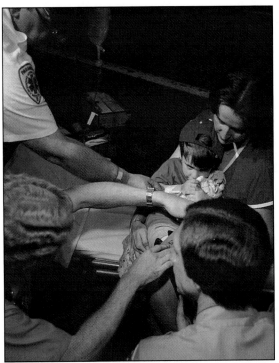

Calm, immediate action can be of great service to the victim and the emergency response team.

Do not place yourself in danger. If you can safely provide help, do so. Quickly determine whether the scene is safe, what happened, how many are injured, and if bystanders can help. If there is more than one victim, treat the most seriously injured first. Be sure that you know your first aid limits; when in doubt, quickly get someone who knows what to do.

Section Review

1. What is first aid?

2. What are three reasons a person should be trained to give first aid?

3. If a person is unconscious, should a person wait for him to revive and give his consent for help before beginning to administer first aid?

4. If a person has fallen off a ladder and is lying unconscious on the driveway, should he be moved to a grassy area where the ground is softer?

Check

Suppose you are working in the yard when a car suddenly careens down your street and slams head-on into the pole of a power line. You are the first bystander to notice the accident. What should you do? Yell for help? Try to pull the driver out of the car? Run into the house and dial 911?

As soon as you realize that an accident has occurred, quickly survey the scene. Do not place yourself in danger. Look around for fire hazards, electrical hazards, toxic hazards, and other hazards. You cannot be of any service if you become a victim yourself.

If you can safely approach the accident site, determine what happened, how many people are involved, and see if any bystanders can help. Look directly at the victim and ask, "Are you all right?" If the victim is conscious, you may be able to question him. For instance, perhaps the car accident you witnessed occurred because the mother noticed that her toddler had gotten out of his car seat and

When checking on a victim, do not move him unless leaving him where he is further endangers him.

safety harness. You may on first glance notice only the mother in the car accident, but after hearing her story, notice the small child trapped on the floorboard behind her seat.

Remember that if the victim needs first aid and is conscious, you must obtain permission first. If you are trained in first aid, tell the victim that you are trained in first aid and would like to help him. Ask him if you can help until the ambulance arrives. This should help to reassure him as well as give you the consent that you need to proceed.

If the victim is unconscious, look for clues. A door hanging open may indicate that more than one person was in the crash. Look on the victim to see if he is wearing a medical alert tag on his neck or wrist. Does the victim have diabetes? Epilepsy? A heart condition? Is there a diaper bag in the car? Then perhaps a baby is also in the car. Are the victim's arms or legs in a strange position? They may be broken.

Unless you need to move the victim for safety, leave him where he is. If the victim's life is endangered by remaining where he is, then carefully move him to safety, trying not to cause neck or spinal injury. Remember, though, it is best not to move the victim at all.

You should also find out whether there are any bystanders who can help. Ask them to call *Emergency Medical Services (EMS)*, give first aid, flag down the EMS or police, keep the victim calm, and keep other bystanders calm and out of the way.

Key Emergency Information

WHO?

WHAT?

HOW?

MAIN ST. | E

WHERE?

Call

When an accident occurs, shout for help as you approach the accident site. In an emergency, every minute is important. When people are injured, minutes can mean the difference between life and death.

It is a good idea to memorize the phone numbers of the police department, the fire department, and the emergency medical service in your area. In some places you can reach any of these agencies by dialing one emergency number (in many areas this emergency number is 911; in most areas you can dial 0 to get an operator who can assist you). Anytime you call an emergency number be sure to give complete and accurate information. Clearly and quickly describe *what* happened, *who* was involved, *how* the victim is doing, and *where* the accident occurred.

All information should be stated clearly and concisely. Do not talk excitedly or rapidly. Be calm and deliberate when speaking. State what the emergency is (car accident? car accident with fire? car accident with victim trapped? car accident with

victim trapped and danger of fire?). Give vital statistics (approximate age of the victim? gender of the victim? breathing? pulse? CPR being given?). Give easy and clear directions to the accident site. Do not hang up until the dispatcher tells you to do so.

If you are giving first aid to the victim, tell a specific person to call the emergency response team. Do not just yell, "Call 911!" because everyone standing around may think you are talking to someone else and no one may make the call. Instead, tell a specific person to call and have him report to you after the call has been made. Send someone to wait for the help to arrive. He may need to direct the medical help to the correct area and give them permission to enter.

Care

Check the victim's **ABCs.** Does he have an open *airway?* Is he *breathing?* Is his blood *circulating?* Is he bleeding severely? These vital signs must be noted immediately. It should take only a few seconds to note if his airway is blocked, if he is breathing on his own, and if he has a pulse.

Check for consciousness, call EMS, gently roll the victim on his back, and check for an open airway. In order to check for a clear airway, place your hand on the victim's forehead, gently tilt his head back, and lift his chin. This head-tilt, chin-lift should open the airway.

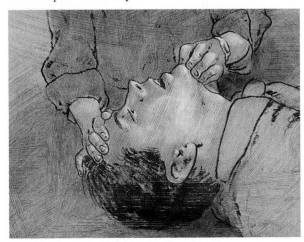

The head-tilt, chin-lift is used to open the airway.

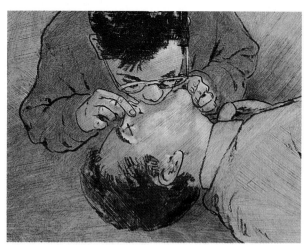
When administering rescue breathing, be sure that the victim's airway is clear, his nose is pinched shut, and his mouth is properly sealed.

Check whether the victim is breathing. *Look* for the chest to rise and fall with breathing, *listen* for the sound of breathing, *feel* for breathing for about five seconds. If there is no breath, proceed to administer **rescue breathing.** Pinch his nose shut, and administer two breaths (lasting one to one and one-half seconds).

Make sure that the victim's heart is beating. Take his pulse at the side of his neck (at the carotid artery). If there is no pulse, CPR is needed. If you are not trained to give CPR, try to find someone who is qualified. If the victim has a pulse but is not breathing, continue to give one breath every five seconds (with each lasting one to one and one-half seconds). Check the victim's pulse every minute (about every twelve breaths). If no one has called EMS for help, quickly run and do so after the first minute of giving first aid. Quickly return and continue rescue breathing.

WAITING FOR HELP

After the victim's breathing and pulse have been stabilized, use the time to get important information. If possible, either you or a bystander should write the information down so that it can be given to the EMS personnel when they arrive.

Find out the victim's name and ask him if he has any medical problems, allergies, or is on any medications. Ask him if he is in pain. If so, where? How much pain? Is the pain consistent? If the victim is unconscious, stay by his head so that you can easily check his ABCs (airway, breathing, circulation). Ask bystanders what they know about the victim and the accident.

Check the victim's vital signs every five minutes. Remember that this information should be noted on paper if possible. Normal *pulse* is between sixty to eighty beats per minute. Normal *breathing* is between twelve to twenty breaths per minute. His skin should be warm (not hot or cold), not moist or dry, and normal in color.

Write It Down!

An easy way to remember what to ask the victim is to think "Do I have AMPLE information?"

A **Allergies**

M **Medications**

P **Previous illness**

L **Last meal or drink**

E **Events preceding the illness or injury**

If the victim's pulse or breathing becomes very fast or slow and his skin becomes cool, moist, and pale or bluish, he may be going into **shock.** Shock can kill a person. If you notice these symptoms, have the victim lie down, cover him with blankets or coats, and, if there is no head or back injury, elevate his feet eight to twelve inches. If the ground is cold, place blankets or coats beneath him too. Do not let him get too warm, but try to keep him from being chilled. Because the loss of blood can cause shock, control all visible bleeding. As you wait for help to arrive, monitor the victim's ABCs and vital signs. Do not give him anything to eat or drink.

Keep the victim still as you quickly inquire about injuries. Check for wounds, bumps, broken bones, or areas of pain from head to foot. Inspect the ears, nose, and mouth for blood or fluids. Be sure to note the size of the victim's pupils when examining his eyes. Are they larger than normal (dilated)? Smaller than normal (constricted)? Unequal in size? Continue your examination for injuries in a methodical fashion, noting any problems. After your initial exam, you can proceed to give first aid to the most serious injuries first or at least help the victim cope until qualified help arrives.

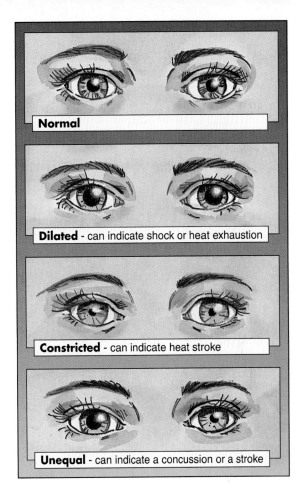

Normal

Dilated - can indicate shock or heat exhaustion

Constricted - can indicate heat stroke

Unequal - can indicate a concussion or a stroke

Section Review

1. Put the following emergency procedures in the correct order.

   Remove any risks to your safety.

   Ask victim if he is OK.

   Look for clues as to what happened and be wary of danger.

2. Put the following emergency procedures in the order you should do them if the victim does *not* answer.

   Call EMS for help.

   Give necessary care. Proceed with rescue breathing if necessary. Do not give CPR unless trained to do so.

   Yell for a neighbor or bystander to help.

   Check the scene for safety and victims.

3. Put the following emergency procedures in the correct order if the victim does answer.

   Call EMS for help.

   Care for severe injuries with basic first aid procedures.

   Get the victim's consent to give first aid.

   Ask him what happened and ask about any medical problems, allergies, or medications and check him from head to foot for wounds, broken bones, and injuries.

4. What information can be noted while waiting for the Emergency Medical Services (EMS) to arrive?

GIVING FIRST AID

Not all accidents require the attention of professional medical help. Nevertheless, many seemingly minor incidents may be worse than they appear. For instance, a slip and fall may seem to be of little consequence, but a hairline fracture or a concussion may have occurred. It is best to call EMS or see the doctor if you are unsure of what to do.

Never underestimate the seriousness of a fall. Just because a wound is not visible does not mean that everything is all right.

The type of medical help to call will depend on the incident. It is usually not necessary to call EMS to remove a speck of a splinter in the finger. A medium-sized splinter, however, should probably be removed and tended to by a doctor. In such a case, the victim can usually be easily transported to a hospital, clinic, or local doctor's office. However, if a large stick is embedded in a person's arm, it would be better to call EMS to transport the victim to the doctor since problems of shock, bleeding, and infection may need to be addressed.

The following sections will give you basic procedures to follow in applying first aid. Remember that a quick and proper reaction is best applied with a calm approach.

BLEEDING, WOUNDS, AND SHOCK

Although exterior portions of the body are protected by skin, all body openings are protected by mucous membranes, which form a protective barrier from bacteria and injury. A **wound** is a break in the skin or mucous membrane. Bleeding and infection are the main problems to be avoided. Infection is often indicated by redness, swelling, pain, pus, and sometimes fever.

There are four types of open wounds: abrasions, cuts, avulsions, and punctures. An **abrasion** is a break on the surface of the skin, a scrape with little bleeding. A **cut** can be described as being either an incision or a laceration. An *incision* is an even cut that can cause damage to muscles, tendons, and nerves. A *laceration* is a

Instant Index: Rapid Reference For Emergencies

rip or tear of the tissues that forms irregular edges. An **avulsion** is the partial or complete separation of a portion of skin or other body tissue. If a portion of the body has been completely avulsed, it is termed an *amputation*. A **puncture** is a wound that penetrates causing a hole in body tissue. Many times a puncture can be misleading. Because there may be little bleeding on the surface, the extent of internal damage may not be apparent; it may be worse than it looks.

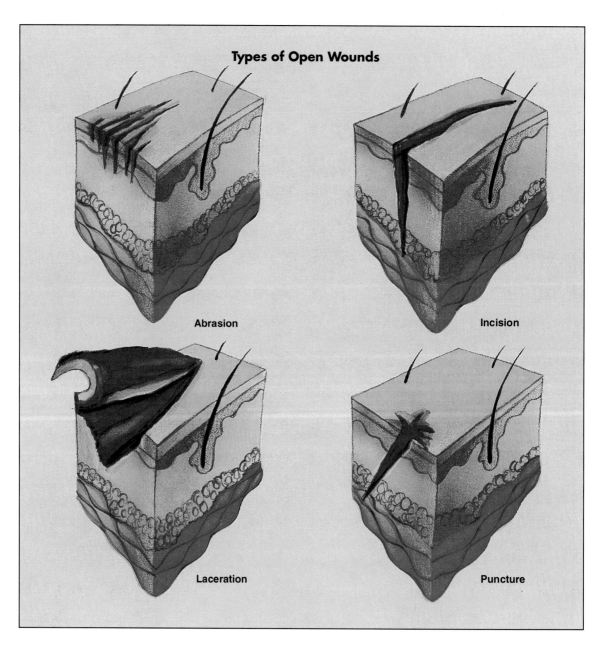

Types of Open Wounds

Abrasion

Incision

Laceration

Puncture

Stop It! Stop that Bleeding Right Now!

The rapid loss of ten percent of one's blood volume can be extremely dangerous. Weakness, shock, and even death can result from excessive bleeding. Because a person can bleed to death within a minute, it is essential to know how to stop severe bleeding. There are three main methods used to control bleeding: direct pressure, elevation, and pressure point.

Because of the danger of being exposed to the HIV virus and other contaminants, you should be careful when helping a bleeding person. If you also have a cut or nick in your skin, it would probably be best to let another qualified person help. If no one else is available, try to place some sort of barrier (protective plastic, rubber gloves, or even plastic wrap) between yourself and the victim's body fluids.

When using *direct pressure,* place a clean dressing or covering over the wound and press firmly. A bandage will aid in protecting the wound, absorbing the blood, and helping the blood to clot. If the dressing becomes saturated, *do not remove it.* Instead, add another layer of gauze on top and continue to apply pressure.

If you are sure that there is not a fracture in the area and no object is impaled, continue to apply direct pressure as you *elevate* the wound above the level of the heart. This should help reduce the flow of blood to the injured area. If the person is unconscious or may have a broken neck

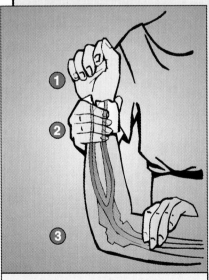

In order to stop a bleeding wound, you can 1) elevate the area, 2) apply direct pressure, and 3) supply pressure to a pressure point.

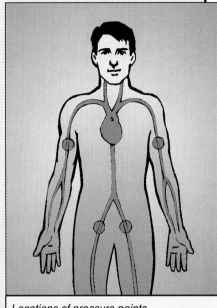

Locations of pressure points

or back injury, do not move him.

Some arteries are located close to the skin surface and also pass near a bone. Placing pressure on these *pressure points* can be used to slow down the rate of bleeding. Using pressure points will help to control bleeding but usually cannot stop bleeding. Bleeding can usually be controlled until emergency medical help arrives by applying direct pressure while elevating the injured area and putting pressure on pressure points if necessary.

≡RAPID⊕RESPONSE

Minor Wounds

Small Cuts

1. *Stop* the bleeding.
2. *Wash* the wound. Use soap and water to remove all traces of embedded material.
3. *Rinse* and pat dry.
4. *Cover* with a sterile dressing. You may desire to apply an over-the-counter antibiotic ointment to the wound first.
5. *Watch* for any signs of infection.
6. *Check* to see whether a tetanus shot will be necessary.

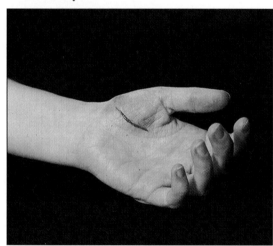

Even small cuts can lead to infection.

Blisters (not from burns)

1. *Protect* an unbroken blister. An ice cube placed on a blister that is forming will help to lessen the pain and the amount of fluid within. Cover with petroleum jelly and a bandage until it heals or breaks.
2. *Wash* a punctured blister with soap and water.
3. *Press* fluid out with sterile gauze.
4. *Cover* with a sterile dressing. You may desire to apply an over-the-counter antibiotic ointment to the wound first.
5. *Watch* for any signs of infection.

Bruises (closed wound)

1. *Apply ice* or cold compresses.
2. *Elevate* and rest the wounded area.
3. *See* the doctor if the pain is severe, if it is large, or if blood accumulates underneath a nail and pressure must be released.

Eye Injuries

1. *Look* for loose objects in the victim's eye. Gently pull the lower lid down and have the victim look up.
2. *Flush* any loose object from the eye with water.
3. *Roll* the upper lid up. Have the victim look down as you gently pull outward and up.
4. *Flush* any loose object still remaining from the eye with water.
5. *Bandage both* eyes and take the victim to the doctor if an object is embedded in the eye, if pain persists, if blood is visible in the eye, or if there is a sudden change in eyesight.
6. *Reassure* a victim who must have his eyes bandaged.

Loose objects and chemicals should be flushed out of the eye with water.

In case of chemical burns to the eye:
1. *Wash* the eye with flowing water for 15 to 30 minutes.
2. *Wrap* both eyes and take the victim to the doctor.

If a large object is embedded in the eye:
1. *Secure* an inverted paper cup over the object to keep it from being knocked or moved until the doctor can remove it.
2. *Bandage* both eyes since movement by the uninjured eye will cause the injured eye to move too.

Splinters
1. *Sterilize* a needle or tweezers over a flame, in boiling water, or with rubbing alcohol.
2. *Wash* the area around the splinter.
3. *Numb* the area with ice.
4. *Remove* the splinter by pulling in the same angle that the splinter went in.
5. *Wash* the area again.
6. *Cover* with a sterile dressing. You may desire to apply an over-the-counter antibiotic ointment to the wound first.
7. *Watch* for any signs of infection.

In the case of fishhooks:
1. *Back* the hook out gently if it has only slightly penetrated the skin.
2. *Seek* medical attention if the hook is imbedded deeply or if it is barbed.

For a nosebleed, pinching the nostrils together is not enough. The head should be tilted forward to prevent blood from going down the throat into the stomach.

Nosebleeds
1. *Sit* the victim down with his head forward.
2. *Pinch* the nostrils together.
3. *Quiet* the victim; keep him from laughing, walking, talking, and blowing his nose.
4. *Apply* a cold pack over the bridge of the nose.
5. *Avoid* trying to control the nosebleed in the case of head, neck, or back injury. Stopping the blood flow could increase internal pressure and cause more harm to the victim.

Major Wounds

Amputations
1. *Stop* the bleeding.
2. *Cover* the wound with a dry, sterile dressing.
3. *Treat* the victim, if necessary, for shock.
4. *Find* the amputated body part.
5. *Wrap* the amputated part in wet, sterile gauze.
6. *Place* the amputated part in a plastic bag.
7. *Cool* the amputated part in a cool container (a plastic bag of ice water or a cooler) to be transported with the victim. The amputated part should not be allowed to freeze.

Internal Injuries

1. *Watch* for signs of internal bleeding (blood excreted in vomit, urine, or stool) following a fall, hard hit, or automobile accident.
2. *Roll* the victim on his side if there are not head or back injuries.
3. *Cover* the victim and keep him warm.
4. *Do not give* the victim anything to eat or drink.
5. *Get help* immediately.

Shock Reviewed

1. *Get* medical help.
2. *Check* the victim's ABCs.
3. *Control* severe bleeding.
4. *Position* the victim correctly.
   a. Usual position (no head or neck injuries, no fractures)—victim lying on back with legs elevated 8 to 12 inches.
   b. Possible head or neck injury—victim lying flat on back.
   c. Victim vomiting—victim lying on side.
   d. Difficulty breathing—victim lying on back and propped up.
5. *Maintain* normal body temperature by lightly covering the victim with a blanket (over as well as under if necessary). Do not let him get too hot.

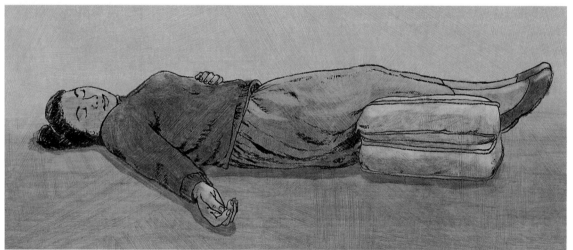

The type of injury determines how a person should be placed. This shock victim has been placed in the usual position (victim lying on his back with his legs elevated 8 to 12 inches).

Section Review

1. What are the four major types of open wounds, and how do they differ from each other?

2. List four symptoms that may indicate infection.

3. Your sister has sliced off the tip of her finger. List, in correct order, what you should do.

4. Little Brittany has a nosebleed. What should you do?

5. After being hit by a car, Justin's coloring looks pale, his skin feels cool and clammy, his pupils are dilated, and his breathing seems almost like gasping. He begins to throw up. How should you respond if first aid were totally up to you?

BREATHING PROBLEMS AND CHOKING

Thousands of Americans die each year from choking. In many of the cases, the victims were simply laughing or talking while eating. If a person has food trapped in his throat or mucus blocking his airway, he can die of **asphyxiation** (as FIK see ay shun), death caused by the lack of oxygen, within minutes. A person can suffer permanent brain damage if he cannot get oxygen in four to six minutes. *All breathing problems should be taken seriously.*

A twentieth-century American surgeon, Henry J. Heimlich, developed a method of using abdominal thrusts to remove objects caught in the throat. This is often referred to as the **Heimlich** (HIME LIK) **maneuver** or abdominal thrust maneuver. This life-saving technique is administered by the rescuer

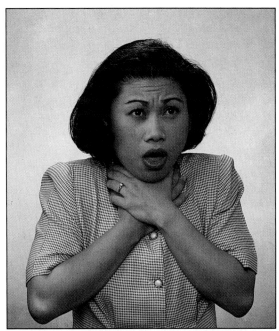

If a person is choking, he may give the universal signal for choking. Other symptoms of choking include ineffective coughing; wheezing or breathing difficulty; sudden collapse; hands, face, or neck turning blue in color; and unconsciousness.

standing behind the victim and placing his hand in a fist (thumb against the victim's abdomen) just above the navel and well below the lower tip of the breastbone. The rescuer covers his fist with his other hand and presses inward and upward with a quick thrusting motion. This maneuver uses air in the lungs to force the object out.

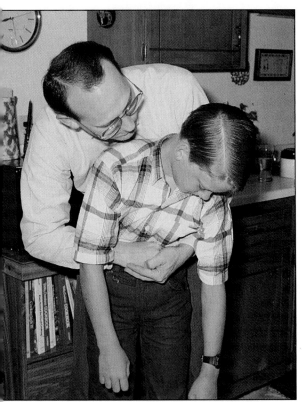

e Heimlich maneuver is a life-saving procedure used to bel obstructions from a choking person's airway. Quick vard and upward thrusts are given to the abdomen just ove the navel until the airway is cleared.

≡RAPID≡RESP⊕NSE

Asthma, Croup, and Breathing Difficulty

1. *Calm* the person down as much as possible.
2. *Get* his medication and help him take it.
3. *Provide* warm, moist air.
4. *Keep* the victim in an upright or comfortable position.
5. *Get* medical assistance if necessary.

Hyperventilation (Fast Breathing)

1. *Calm* the person down as much as possible.
2. *Get* medical assistance if the victim's breathing does not slow down.

Choking

1. *Recognize* the universal signal for choking (see the picture on page 217).
2. *Ask* if he is choking and if you can help him. He should nod yes. If he is coughing forcefully, encourage him to cough. Have someone call 911.
3. *Stand* behind the choking person.
4. *Place* your fist with thumb side against the middle of his abdomen, above his navel. Your other hand should grasp your fist.
5. *Thrust* inward and upward quickly, keeping your elbows out.
6. *Repeat* until the obstruction is expelled, or until the victim is unconscious.

If the victim becomes unconscious:

1. *Place* him on his back.
2. *Straddle* the victim.
3. *Use* the heel of one hand with the other hand clasped above it and placed above the navel to administer rapid inward and upward thrusts (up to 5 thrusts).

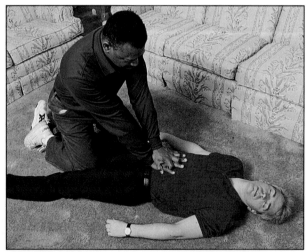

If the victim becomes unconscious, the rescuer should straddle him and continue abdominal thrusts.

If the victim is obese or in the late stages of pregnancy and is standing or sitting:

1. *Stand* behind the choking victim.
2. *Encircle* the victim under the armpits with your arms and give chest thrusts straight back toward the spine.

As soon as possible, call the Emergency Medical Services (EMS) since you may not know how long the victim has not been breathing.

Rescue Breathing Reviewed

1. *Tell* someone to call EMS. If you are alone, give one minute of care to the victim first, and then run and call EMS.
2. *Roll* the victim on his back.
3. *Open* the airway by placing your hand on the victim's forehead, gently tilting his head back, and lifting his chin.
4. *Check* to see whether the victim is breathing.
   a. *Look* for the chest to rise and fall.
   b. *Listen* for the sound of breathing.
   c. *Feel* for breathing for about five seconds.

If the victim has a pulse but is not breathing:

5. **Pinch** his nose shut. For an infant, cover the mouth and nose with your mouth.

6. **Administer** two breaths (each breath lasting one to one and one-half seconds) by sealing your lips tightly around the outside of the victim's mouth.

7. **Check** for pulse on the side of his neck.

8. **Continue** rescue breathing, giving an adult 1 breath every 5 seconds (1 min.=about 12 breaths) and a child or infant 1 breath every 3 seconds (1 min.=about 20 breaths). Check the pulse every minute.

If there is an obstruction when you try the first two breaths:

9. **Retilt** the victim's head and give two full breaths.

10. **Give** up to five abdominal thrusts to try to dislodge any obstructions.

11. **Lift** the jaw and tongue to check for obstructions and sweep out the mouth with your finger.

12. **Tilt** the head back and give two breaths. (If the airway clears, continue from Step 7. If the airway is still blocked, repeat Steps 10, 11, and 12.)

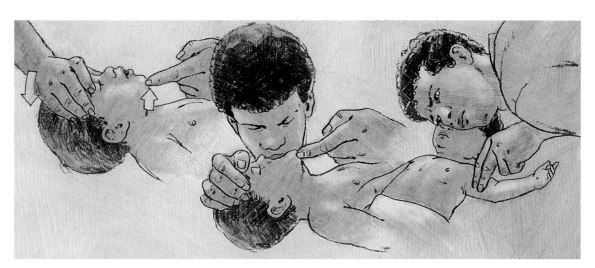

When giving rescue breathing to a baby, the rescuer should cover and seal both the infant's nose and mouth with his mouth. One breath is given every three seconds (approximately 20 breaths per minute).

Section Review

1. Describe the universal signal for choking.

2. How and where are your hands placed when administering abdominal thrusts (the Heimlich maneuver) for a person sitting or standing up? For a person who is lying on the ground? For a woman in the late stages of pregnancy?

3. Tosha got so scared about the close basketball game that she started breathing rapidly and could not seem to take in enough air. She starts complaining that her hands and feet feel numb and tingly. What can you do to help her? She is beginning to get hysterical and dizzy.

BROKEN BONES, DISLOCATIONS, SPRAINS, AND STRAINS

The term **fracture** is used to describe a bone that is broken or cracked. Fractures are named for their location, type, or special features. The main types of fractures are closed (or simple), open (or compound), partial, and complete. A **closed fracture** describes a bone that is cracked or broken under the skin. An **open fracture** is indicated by the bone's actual protrusion through the skin. A **partial fracture** describes a break that is incomplete and does not go through the bone. A **complete fracture** indicates that the break goes completely across the bone.

A broken bone can often be indicated by an audible cracking or snapping sound. Some fractures, such as partial fractures, may not always produce a sound when the bone is cracked. Pain, tenderness, swelling, bruising, a grating or rubbing sensation, numbness, an abnormal shape, or the inability to move the injured area may be indicators of a fracture. If you suspect a fracture, the area should be kept from moving or *immobilized*. The victim should be taken to the doctor for necessary x-rays and treatment as soon as possible.

In order to immobilize the area, a **splint** is used. A splint serves many purposes. It is mainly used to keep the injured area from being moved, and in doing so, helps to reduce pain. Splinting also helps to prevent simple fractures from becoming open fractures and reduces the risks of having serious bleeding and circulation problems. When an injury is splinted, it makes it easier to move the victim and transport him to the doctor.

A splint should be used only if you must move the victim and if applying one does not increase the victim's pain. A victim should not be moved without a splint unless he is in danger where he is. Any open wounds should be covered with a sterile dressing, and the victim's circulation should be checked before a splint is applied. When a splint is applied, the injured area should be moved as little

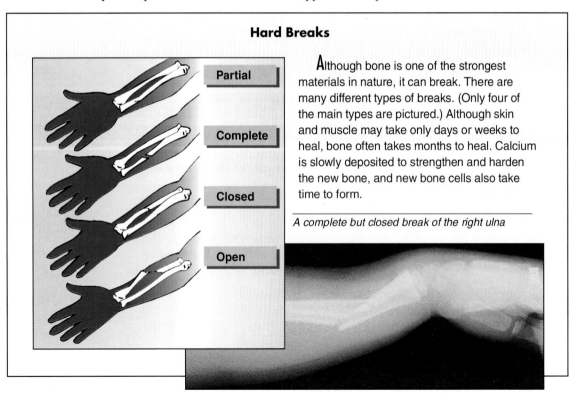

Hard Breaks

Partial

Complete

Closed

Open

Although bone is one of the strongest materials in nature, it can break. There are many different types of breaks. (Only four of the main types are pictured.) Although skin and muscle may take only days or weeks to heal, bone often takes months to heal. Calcium is slowly deposited to strengthen and harden the new bone, and new bone cells also take time to form.

A complete but closed break of the right ulna

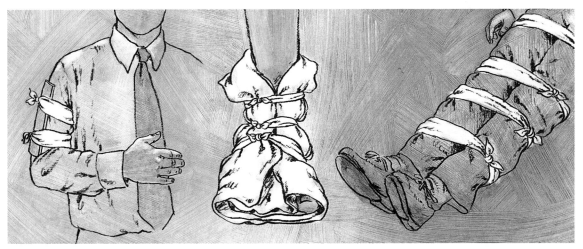

Splints are usually applied by the EMS; however, there may be occasions (camping, hiking) when emergency first aid requires one to make a splint from materials available in order to transport a victim, alleviate pain, keep the potential fracture from damaging surrounding tissue, and restrict bleeding.

as possible. For instance, if a broken limb is bent at an odd angle, do not try to align it. Secure it in the position that it is in as well as possible. If you can, pad the splint to make it more comfortable. When applying a splint, immobilize the bone and joints above and below the fracture. After the splint is in place, check the victim's circulation to make sure that the bindings are not too tight. Always be monitoring the victim's breathing and pulse and looking for signs of shock.

A dislocated joint or a sprain can also cause great pain. A **dislocation** occurs when the bone end

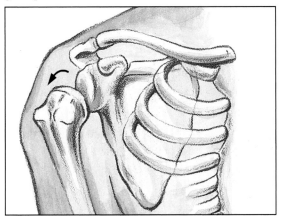

When a bone has moved from its normal location, the tendons and ligaments surrounding the area also suffer damage.

is moved and locked into a displaced position. If the area appears to have a marked deformity at the joint area, swelling and tenderness at the joint, pain, and an inability to move at the joint, then a dislocation may be the problem.

A **sprain** is a joint injury that occurs when a joint is twisted or pulled to the point that the surrounding tendons and ligaments are stretched or torn. A sprain can range from a slight injury to one in which even blood vessels and nerves are damaged. Some sprains can cause just as much pain and damage as a dislocation. Sprains are usually indicated by tenderness over the area, swelling, discoloration, and inability to use the area normally. Because it is difficult to distinguish between a fracture and a sprain, a severe sprain should be treated like a fracture.

A **strain** is a wrenching or pulling of a muscle. Strains can be caused by the sudden and forceful stretching of a muscle or by exerting too much stress on a poorly conditioned muscle. This is one reason a warm-up session with stretching exercises is recommended prior to intense exercise or aerobic activity. Overexertion of the muscles can cause the tissues to become sore, tender, and even swollen. If the area becomes severely swollen or painful, medical attention should be given.

Fractures

1. **Do not move** the victim unless you must for reasons of safety.
2. **Get** medical help if necessary.
3. **Stop** any bleeding wounds and cover with a sterile dressing.
4. **Check** the circulation below the injured area.
5. **Do not realign** the limb. Leave it in the position it is in and move it as little as possible.
6. **Immobilize** the area by applying a splint. Pad the splint if possible before sliding it under the injured area.
7. **Secure** the splint, being sure to immobilize the bone and joints above and below the fracture.
8. **Recheck** the circulation below the injured area.
9. **Apply** a cold pack to a simple fracture, but do not do so for a compound fracture.
10. **Watch** for signs of shock and monitor ABCs.

Dislocations

1. **Do not move** the joint or try to correct the deformity.
2. **Splint** the area and immobilize the joint.
3. **Support** the splint with a sling or elevate it.
4. **Avoid** placing pressure or weight on the area.
5. **Get** medical care immediately.

Sprains

1. **Treat** severe sprains like a fracture (see fractures).
2. **Rest** the area and use it as little as possible for at least one day.
3. **Ice** packs (cold packs) should be applied for 30 minutes (do not immerse in ice water or pack the area in ice). Ice packs should be shifted every five minutes.
4. **Compress** the area by *loosely* wrapping the area with an elastic bandage. Leave the bandage on for 30 minutes, remove for 15 minutes, and then rewrap for 30 minutes.

5. **Elevate** the area for at least 30 minutes.
6. **Get** medical attention if pain and swelling continue.

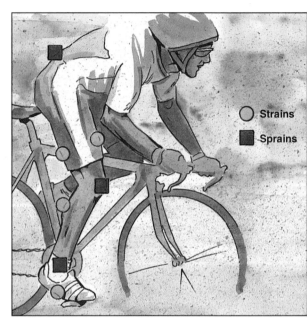

When treating sprains and strains, think of the acronym **RICE:** **R**est the area, apply **I**ce packs, **C**ompress the area loosely with a bandage, and **E**levate it for at least 30 minutes.

Strains and Muscle Tears

1. **Rest** the area and use it as little as possible for at least one day.
2. **Ice** packs should be applied for 30 minutes (do not immerse in ice water or pack the area in ice). Ice packs should be shifted every five minutes.
3. **Compress** the area by *loosely* wrapping the area with an elastic bandage. Leave the bandage on for 30 minutes, remove for 15 minutes, and then rewrap for 30 minutes.
4. **Elevate** the injured area for at least 30 minutes.
5. **Get** medical attention if pain and swelling continue.

Muscle Cramps

1. *Stretch* the cramped muscle gently.
2. *Massage* the knotted muscle area with the heel of the hand.
3. *Flex* the muscle repeatedly until the muscle spasms end.
4. *Apply* heat with a heating pad, a hot water bottle wrapped in a towel, or by taking a warm bath.

Section Review

1. What makes a partial fracture different from a complete fracture? How can you tell the difference between a simple fracture and a compound fracture?

2. Lance twisted his leg while playing soccer. It is beginning to swell and is very painful. The coach begins to put a splint on the area. Why is this a good idea? How would the splint help? What should the coach remember to do when applying the splint?

3. Jonathan fell from a tree. His shoulder looks misshapen, and he is in great pain. What should you do?

BURNS AND ELECTRIC SHOCK

God created man with a protective covering of skin. When the skin is burned, the nerve endings in

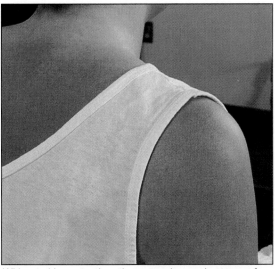

Without skin protection, there may be a price to pay for "fun in the sun." A temporary sunburn may result in permanent cell damage to the skin. Tanning is the main cause of skin cancer.

the skin relay messages of pain. Even seemingly light sunburns can cause great discomfort. Burns are divided into three categories: first-degree burns, second-degree burns, and third-degree burns.

First-degree burns affect the upper layer of the skin. Sunburns, burns from spilled hot soup or beverage, or surface burns from chemicals or light electrical burns are examples. The skin is usually red and tender and may swell. **Second-degree burns** occur when the burn extends deeper into the skin. In second-degree burns, the lower layers of the skin are damaged and cause more pain, swelling, and blistering. **Third-degree burns** destroy all the layers of the skin, nerve endings, and blood vessels. The area appears charred (white, brown, or blackened), dry, and leathery. The tissue beneath the skin is exposed. Although the destruction of the nerve endings means that the burned tissue does not relay messages of pain to the mind, the surrounding areas that are less severely burned may be extremely painful. The greatest danger in third-degree burns is infection.

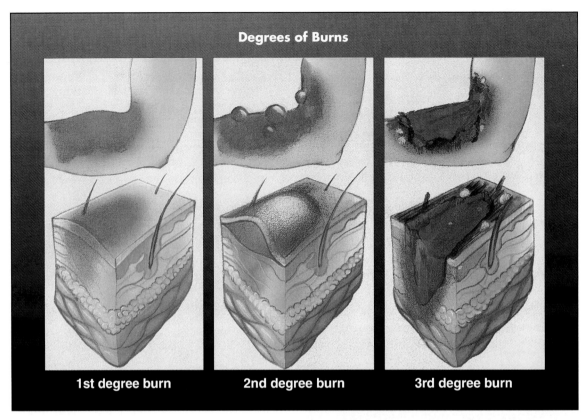

Degrees of Burns

1st degree burn   2nd degree burn   3rd degree burn

Minor burns, in which the surface of the skin is not broken, can be treated by applying cold water and moist dressings. Do not place ointments, butter, or petroleum jelly on a burn. Applying lotions and creams to the unbroken skin burn may actually cause the heat to be retained in the skin. In the cases of second-degree burns when the blisters are open or third-degree burns, it is important to guard against infection. Use dry, sterile dressings and get medical attention immediately.

Chemical burns require extra attention. The chemical should be removed by running water over the area immediately. Clothing and jewelry covering the burn site should be removed *as water is used to flood the affected area.* The injured area should be flooded with water for fifteen to thirty minutes. If the chemical is in the eye, the eyelids must be held open as water is used to flush the chemical out. If a dry chemical is involved, briskly and carefully brush as much of it off as possible before flushing

When flushing chemicals off of the skin or out of the eye, be sure that you do not contaminate areas not originally affected by the chemical.

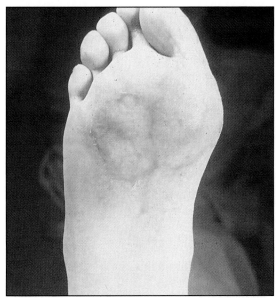
Electrical burns are usually worse than they look since severe tissue damage may have resulted deeper in the wound. Electrical burns have a burn at the point of entry and another (usually more extensive) wound at the point of exit.

the area with water. Be careful not to get chemicals on the rest of the body.

An electrical current can flow from one person to another. Because of this, rescuing a victim of electric shock can be dangerous for the rescuer. Before attempting to help someone who is a victim of electric shock, make sure that he is no longer connected to the electrical power source. Turn off the electricity. *Never touch the victim until you are certain he is no longer in contact with the electric current.* Failure to do this can result in two victims instead of one.

High voltage current can cause the victim's breathing and heart to stop. After he has been removed from the power source, immediately monitor his ABCs. After the victim has been stabilized, check for burns. Electrical burns can be deceiving. The entry wound may be small, but the exit wound or internal damage may be extensive. Electric shock victims should be seen by a doctor.

Another form of electrical injury is caused when lightning strikes a person. The major danger of lightning injuries is usually not the burns on the person but irregular heart rhythms, injuries to the nervous system, and even fracturing of the spine and skeletal system. A person who has been struck by lightning should not be moved without a spine board and should have his airway, breathing, and circulation monitored immediately. The victim may suffer temporary paralysis, blindness, inability to hear, or inability to speak.

RAPID RESPONSE

Minor Burns
1. **Place** the injured area in cold water (not ice water). You may need to apply cold soaks or ice packs at intervals for an hour.
2. **Pat** the injured area dry.
3. **Apply** a moist, sterile dressing over the area.
4. **Do not break** any blisters that have formed.
5. **Get** medical attention if a large area has been burned, if the face has been burned, or if it is a child, an elderly person, or an ill person that has been burned.

Major Burns
1. **Get** medical attention immediately.
2. **Remove** burned clothing that does not stick to the burned area.
3. **Cover** with a *dry,* sterile dressing (or a clean sheet if necessary).
4. **Keep** burned limbs propped above heart level.
5. **Monitor** breathing and pulse; watch for symptoms of shock.

Chemical Burns
1. **Get** medical attention.
2. **Brush** any dry chemical residue off first.
3. **Flush** the affected area with water for 15 to 30 minutes. If the eyes are burned, you must hold the eyelids open when running the water.
4. **Remove** contaminated clothing and jewelry while the water is running over the victim.
5. **Cover** burns with a dry, sterile dressing.
6. **Monitor** for shock.

Electric Shock

1. *Disconnect* the power source.
2. *Call* for help.
3. *Monitor* the victim's ABCs immediately.
4. *Cover* burned areas (check points of electrical entry and exit) with dry sterile dressings. Bandage the areas.
5. *Watch* for symptoms of shock. Keep the victim lying on his back and elevate his feet 8 to 12 inches. Cover him with a blanket if necessary to maintain body temperature.

Lightning Injuries

1. *Call* for help.
2. *Monitor* the victim's ABCs.
3. *Do not move* the victim. There may be spinal injuries.
4. *Continually monitor* the victim's ABCs.

Section Review

1. Just by looking at the victim, how can you tell whether he has a first-, second-, or third-degree burn?

2. What should you place on a burn?

3. How do treatments for electric shock and shock from lightning differ? How are treatments for both similar?

CONVULSIONS AND UNCONSCIOUSNESS

It can be very frightening to witness a person having a seizure or a convulsion, or going unconscious. It is important to react calmly and correctly in these situations. The victim must have your assistance since he is totally unable to call for help.

Epilepsy is the term used to describe the symptoms resulting from many different conditions; it is not a disease. Epilepsy is a much more common disorder than you might have thought. One out of every two hundred people suffers from epilepsy. Epilepsy is characterized by recurring episodes of seizures. Seizures usually result from abnormal electrical activity in the brain. This can be caused by head injury, brain injury, a brain tumor, a block of blood flow to the brain, infection, fever, insulin shock, reaction to medicine, or genetic predisposition. Not all epileptic seizures result in convulsions. Some seizures result in the person's simply blacking out for a period of time.

Convulsions can result in the person's falling to the ground while having muscular contractions and spasms. Convulsions can be caused by several different things: an epileptic seizure, a head injury, or a high temperature. During a convulsion, the victim may suffer loss of bladder and bowel control. The victim's jaw muscles usually contract tightly. He will not swallow his tongue, but he may bite his tongue, lips, or inner cheeks. Never place your fingers or any other object in the mouth of a person having convulsions. The major role of first aid during convulsions is to keep the victim from hurting himself by moving furniture or equipment out of the way, loosening his clothing, and rolling him on his side if he vomits. Do not try to hold him or restrain him unless he is in a dangerous area.

Fainting is a form of unconsciousness that usually does not indicate a serious problem. It is caused by too little circulation of blood to the brain resulting from a variety of reasons (standing too long, being in pain, seeing something frightful, giving blood, receiving bad news). Falling and hitting something is the main danger of fainting. If someone is feeling faint (feeling nauseated, getting lightheaded, becoming pale, perspiring suddenly, feeling

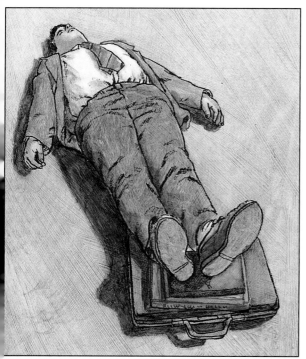
A person who feels faint should lie down to prevent hitting an object if he does faint. Elevating his feet and loosening tight clothing also help.

cold and numb), get the person to lie down. Then loosen any tight clothing and sponge the victim's face with cool water. If the victim does not return to consciousness after a short time, he needs medical attention.

A person may lose consciousness or become unconscious for a variety of reasons (injury, disease, stroke, electric shock, poisoning, drowning, heat stroke, hypothermia, diabetic coma, or insulin shock). After stabilizing the victim's ABCs, it is important to check for and to treat any severe injuries. Try to determine the reason for his becoming unconscious. Perhaps he is a diabetic. Diabetics may lose consciousness when their sugar and insulin levels are imbalanced. If you do not know whether a person needs insulin (slipping into a diabetic coma) or sugar (slipping into insulin shock), *give sugar.* However, never give an unconscious person something to eat or drink. The food

or drink may be taken into the lungs and may block respiration. The victim may be clutching a bottle of nitroglycerin tablets, which would indicate that he has had previous heart problems. Look for clues, medical alert tags, or ask his companions for any background information that can be of help. This information can help you to give proper first aid and be of service to the emergency medical team.

RAPID RESPONSE

Fainting
1. **Prevent** the victim from falling or being injured in a fall.
2. **Get** the victim to lie down with feet elevated.
3. **Loosen** any tight clothing.
4. **Sponge** his face with cool water.
5. **Maintain** body temperature by covering him with a blanket if necessary (do not overheat).
6. **Keep** the victim down for a little while after consciousness returns.
7. **Get** medical attention if the victim does not regain consciousness in a few minutes.

Convulsions and Seizures
1. **Remove** objects that can be of danger to the victim.
2. **Do not place** anything in his mouth.
3. **Loosen** clothing.
4. **Roll** him on his side if he vomits.
5. **Check** the victim's ABCs following the seizure.
6. **Get** medical attention.

If convulsions are caused by a high fever:
1. **Lower** the victim's body temperature.
   a. *Give* him a sponge bath.
   b. *Place* towels soaked in tepid water under and over him.
2. **Do not place** the victim in icy or cold water; he may go into shock.

Many diabetics and people with other life-threatening diseases wear medical alert bracelets to inform others of what to do in case of an emergency.

Unconsciousness

1. *Tap* the victim on the shoulder to confirm that he is unconscious.
2. *Call* for medical help.
3. *Check* the victim's ABCs.
4. *Cover* the victim and position him correctly to prevent shock.
5. *Check* for other injuries.
6. *Talk* to bystanders to gather helpful medical information.
7. *Continue* monitoring the victim's ABCs until medical help arrives.

HEAD INJURIES AND CONCUSSIONS

Head injuries can vary from a slight bump on the head to severe brain injury. If emergency care is given promptly and properly, most victims can survive even severe head injuries. Sometimes head wounds appear worse than they are because they tend to bleed heavily. Some head injuries may be worse than they seem; a light bump on the head may mask a **concussion** (injury to the brain). Any fluid loss from the ears, nose, or mouth; loss of consciousness; loss of memory; slurred speech; vomiting; drowsiness; pupils of

unequal size; or paralysis following a blow to the head are indicators of trouble. Watch for signs of head injury for the next twenty-four to forty-eight hours after the injury. If any symptoms occur, medical attention should be given immediately.

Many head injuries are accompanied by spine or neck injuries. Treat head injuries as though a spine or neck injury is present: do not move the victim unless he is in danger where he is, do not move his head, and stabilize him in the position he is in (have someone place their hands on each side of his head or place folded blankets or coats around his shoulders and head if there is no other help). If a spinal injury is present, moving the victim's head just a fraction of an inch can cause major spinal cord injury. Monitor the victim's ABCs and make sure that any severe bleeding is stopped.

≡RAPID≡RESP✚NSE

Minor Scalp Wounds

1. *Get* medical attention.
2. *Replace* any loose skin back over the wound.
3. *Apply* direct pressure using a dry, sterile dressing. If the dressing becomes saturated, place additional dressings on top of the saturated one.

A person suffering from a head injury may require a CAT scan. The abbreviated term CAT scan *means computerized axial tomographic scanning.*

4. *Do not clean* the wound.
5. *Elevate* the head and shoulders about six inches by placing a pillow, folded blanket, or folded coat underneath. If there is a possibility of neck or spine injury, do not move the victim.
6. *Monitor* the victim's ABCs.
7. *Watch* for symptoms of shock.

Concussions
1. *Keep* the victim lying down.
2. *Get* medical attention.
3. *Monitor* the victim's ABCs.
4. *Stabilize* the victim's head and neck. Do *not* move him unless he is in danger where he is.
5. *Note* the time of the injury.
6. *Do not give* food or drink to the victim.

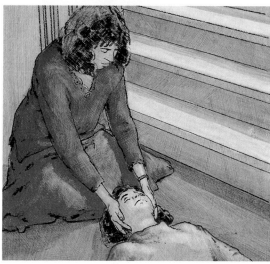

When stabilizing the head, place each hand around the base of the victim's skull. The index and long fingers are used to support the lower jaw, and the thumbs and palms should be placed right above the ears.

Section Review

1. Your cousin's wedding is just about to begin. You are part of the wedding party when you notice that the bride has grown very pale. She says that she feels nauseated and lightheaded. What is wrong? What should you do?

2. You are in the library when the man at the next table falls to the ground and begins to have convulsions. He begins to vomit. What should you do?

3. Why is it important to seek clues for the reason a person has become unconscious?

HEART ATTACK AND STROKE

Blood is used to carry life-sustaining oxygen and nutrients to the heart by the coronary arteries. A **heart attack** is caused when a coronary artery is blocked. This can cause the death of a portion of the heart muscle or even the death of the person. Symptoms of a heart attack include the following.
- Prolonged squeezing sensation or pressure felt in the center of the chest, arms, shoulder, upper jaw, or back
- Nausea
- Cold sweating
- Dizziness
- Shortness of breath
- Feeling of dread
- Weakness
- Pale or bluish skin or lips
- Irregular pulse

If a person shows these symptoms, try to calm him and get him to sit down, loosen any tight clothing, keep him warm, call for medical help, and help him to take any necessary medicine if he is conscious.

The importance of being trained to administer CPR cannot be overly emphasized. Two-thirds of all heart attack victims die before they reach the hospital. Many of those lives could be saved if bystanders would give them CPR. If you do not know CPR and you witness someone having a heart attack or stroke, the best thing you can do is to find someone with CPR training to come and help the victim. CPR is necessary if the heart stops beating.

A **stroke** is caused by the interruption of blood flow to the brain to the point that it causes brain damage. If blood flow is interrupted for more than six minutes, permanent brain damage occurs. The extent of damage depends on *why* the stroke occurred (clotting of the artery? breaking of the artery? clot from elsewhere in the body traveling to clot the artery?), *where* it occurred (which portion of the brain is affected?), and *how long* it lasted. Symptoms of a stroke may include the following:

- Headache
- Confusion
- Dizziness
- Ringing in the ears
- Memory changes
- Difficulty in speaking

- Weakness or paralysis in an arm or leg
- Difficulty in breathing and swallowing
- Pupils of eyes unequal in size
- Loss of facial expression
- Convulsions
- Unconsciousness

Because a person may have difficulty in swallowing, do not give him anything to eat or drink. Place him on his side so that he will not choke on his saliva. If the victim experiences paralysis, he should be placed with the paralyzed side down. Monitor his ABCs until medical help arrives.

RAPID+RESPONSE

Heart Attack
1. *Call* for medical assistance immediately.
2. *Calm* the victim and reassure him.
3. *Position* the victim in a well-supported and comfortable sitting position.

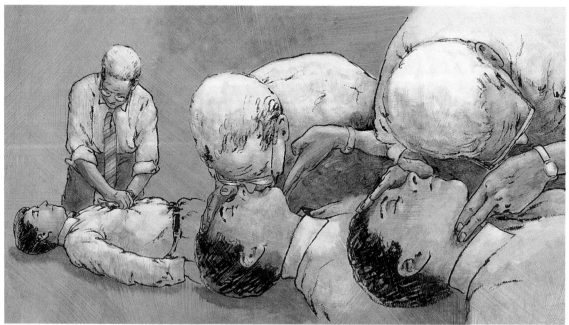

Before you administer CPR, get certified training. A few hours of training may mean the difference between another person's life or death.

4. *Loosen* any tight clothing.
5. *Cover* the victim lightly to retain warmth.
6. *Monitor* the victim's ABCs.
7. *Give* him his medicine if he has some and if he is conscious.

Stroke

1. *Get* medical attention.
2. *Cover* the victim lightly.
3. *Monitor* his ABCs.
4. *Place* the victim on his side.
5. *Do not give* him anything to eat or drink.

HYPOTHERMIA AND HEAT EXHAUSTION

The normal body temperature is 98.6° F (37° C). God made the human body capable of sustaining varied temperature changes and extremes. If the body becomes too cold, hypothermia can occur. If it becomes too hot, heat exhaustion can take place. The severity of the problem depends on what the body's **core temperature** is. The core temperature is the temperature that the heart, lungs, brain, and vital organs register.

The symptoms of hypothermia vary as the body temperature decreases. Note the following decrease in core temperatures and the resulting symptoms.

Although an extremely hypothermic person may seem to be lifeless, he may still be able to be revived. The adage in these cases is, "No one is dead unless he is warm dead." Never assume that a cold, pulseless victim is dead.

In giving first aid to a hypothermic person, always remember that the major objective is to gradually warm the victim back to normal. Moving the victim to a warm shelter, removing wet clothing, and covering him with dry blankets are helpful ways to combat the cold. Do not give the victim something warm to eat or drink unless he is fully conscious.

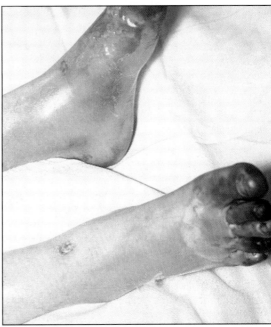

Rewarming and refreezing frostbitten tissue can result in gangrene and the need for amputation. Blackened tissue indicates that the cells have already died in the area.

Declining Body Temperatures

98.6° F (37° C) Normal
95° F (35° C) Shivering; foot stamping
90° F (32.2° C) Loss of coordination
85° F (29.4° C) Lethargy; slow pulse
80° F (26.6° C) Coma; decreased pulse and respiration
78° F (25.5° C) Apparent death; cardiac arrest

Frostbite can occur when body parts get so cold that ice crystals form in the body tissue. The nose, ears, chin, cheeks, fingers, and toes are very susceptible to frostbite. Frostbite begins with the area appearing slightly flushed and progresses to a state where the skin appears dead-white or grayish-yellow. Early pain, tingling, burning, and itching sensations result in numbness. *Do not rub* the area.

Heat exhaustion is caused by profuse sweating that lowers the blood pressure, causing the body to enter a state of shock. Before engaging in sports or recreation, prehydrate and then rehydrate afterwards.

Rubbing will cause more damage as the sharp ice crystals cut into the body cells. It is best to immerse the area in warm (not hot) water. The water temperature should not be warmer than 112° F (44.4° C).

Too much warmth may cause heat exhaustion. **Heat exhaustion** occurs when the victim gets too hot and sweats profusely. The water loss causes the blood flow to decrease to the point that the victim enters a mild form of shock since the blood pressure is lowered. Sweat or perspiration is one way the body uses to cool itself. If it is very humid, or if the victim is wearing too many layers of clothing, evaporation of body perspiration and resulting cooling of the body may not occur. Symptoms include heavy sweating, moist and pale skin, dilated pupils, nausea, dizziness, and vomiting. Although the body temperature may remain near normal, one's blood pressure can still drop to a dangerous level.

Heat cramps can be a symptom of heat exhaustion. Heat cramps occur when muscles have painful spasms because of overexertion. It is thought that heat cramps are caused by the loss of water and salt from heavy sweating.

The most life-threatening heat emergency is **heat stroke.** Unlike heat exhaustion and heat cramps in which the body temperature is almost normal, heat stroke results when the body is totally unable to cool itself and the body temperature rises. Brain damage and death could result from heat stroke. Small children, the elderly, the sick, or overweight people are more susceptible to heat stroke. Locations that are hot, humid, poorly ventilated, or closed up may produce heat stroke problems. Remaining in a non-air-conditioned room with poor ventilation or sitting in a hot car on a humid day may result in heat stroke. Body temperature may rise to 105° F (40.5° C) or higher; the skin will be dry, hot, and red; the pupils will be constricted; the pulse will be rapid and weakening; and the victim may become unconscious. Cool the body immediately. Get the victim out of the heat into a cool or air-conditioned environment, remove most of his clothing, sponge him with water, and fan him. Take a person with heat stroke to the doctor immediately.

≡RAPID≡RESPØNSE

Hypothermia
1. *Move* the victim into a warm place.
2. *Monitor* his ABCs.
3. *Remove* wet, frozen, or constricting clothing.
4. *Wrap* with warm, dry blankets.
5. *Give* warm drink (nonalcoholic, no caffeine) to victim only if he is fully conscious.
6. *Do not rub* any frostbitten areas.
7. *Get* medical attention immediately.

Heat Exhaustion and Heat Cramps
1. *Move* the victim into a cool place.
2. *Monitor* his ABCs.
3. *Elevate* his feet.
4. *Remove* some of his clothing.
5. *Fan* while applying cold packs or wet towels.

6. *Give* half a glass of water every 15 minutes for one hour if the victim is conscious.

7. *Watch* for symptoms of shock or heat stroke.

8. *Get* medical attention if the symptoms do not decrease, if the victim begins to vomit, if he refuses water, or if he becomes unconscious.

Heat Stroke

1. *Get* medical attention immediately.
2. *Move* the victim to a cool place.
3. *Check* his ABCs.
4. *Remove* most of his clothing.
5. *Sponge* the victim with water and fan him.

Section Review

1. What is the difference between a heart attack and a stroke?

2. Make a chart comparing the symptoms of a heart attack and a stroke.

3. Why is it dangerous to rub a frostbitten area?

4. Of the heat emergencies covered in the text, which is the most dangerous?

POISONS, BITES, AND STINGS

As discussed in the previous chapter, poisons can enter the body in four major ways: ingestion, inhalation, absorption, and injection. Poisonous substances react in varied ways, and the antidotes for them are diverse. For instance, not all cases of ingested poisons require the victim to vomit the substance out. It is best to dilute rather than vomit ingested acids, alkalis, or petroleum products. These substances burn body tissues as they are swallowed and would cause additional harm if they were regurgitated. Because of the many types of chemicals and poisons, it is best to contact the Poison Control Center in your area. You should have this important number memorized.

There are some basic rules for responding to poisonings. First, do not place yourself in danger in order to help the victim. If he is trapped in a building where there are gas fumes, call for help but do not enter unless you can do so safely. If possible, identify the exact source of the poison. If a poison or food was ingested, prepare the bottle or a portion of the food for transport with the victim to the doctor.

When calling the Poison Control Center, have the container which held the toxin in your hand so that you can accurately define which chemicals are in the poison. If a snake, marine animal, or insect is responsible for biting or stinging the victim, capture it only if you can do so safely. Call the police to capture an animal that has bitten a person (snake, squirrel, dog, cat, or raccoon); do not try to restrain the animal by yourself. If the animal cannot be secured, get an accurate description so that the animal toxin can be identified.

Basic first aid rules also apply. Always monitor the victim's ABCs. Watch for and prevent shock. Roll a person who is vomiting on his side so that the vomitus will not reenter the food or breathing passages. Never try to give a person who is unconscious or having convulsions something to eat or drink. Keep the victim calm until professional medical help can be given.

≡RAPID≡RESPONSE

Ingested Poisons

1. *Call* EMS and the Poison Control Center. Have the container or labels of the poison in your hand if possible.
2. *Follow* the directions given by the Poison Control Center.
3. *Find* the container that held the poison and a sample of the food, poison, or any vomitus expelled by the victim for examination by the EMS.
4. *Remove* any poisonous residue left in the victim's mouth or on his skin.
5. *Roll* the victim on his side if he is vomiting.
6. *Monitor* his ABCs.
7. *Watch* for and prevent shock.

Inhaled Poisons

1. *Move* the victim away from toxic fumes if you can do so without endangering yourself.
2. *Place* the victim where he can get fresh air.
3. *Call* EMS and the Poison Control Center; follow their instructions.

4. *Elevate* the head and chest if the person is conscious to ease breathing. Loosen tight clothing.
5. *Check* the victim's ABCs.
6. *Watch* for shock.

Absorbed Poisons

1. *Remove* contaminated clothing.
2. *Wash* the area with soap and water.
3. *Rinse* with water (about five minutes of flushing the area with water).
4. *Apply* calamine or soothing skin lotion if the rash or burn is mild.
5. *Get* medical help if the reaction is severe.

Injected Poisons

Animal Bites/Human Bites

1. *Wash* the area with soap and water. Rinse with water for five minutes.
2. *Control* any bleeding.
3. *Apply* sterile gauze.
4. *Get* medical help for animal bites and if possible determine when the victim had his last tetanus shot.

Insect, Tick, and Spider Bites and Stings

1. *Get* medical help immediately if the victim has a history of allergic reactions to insect bites. If he has an anaphylactic shock kit available, quickly help administer the medication. Monitor his ABCs.

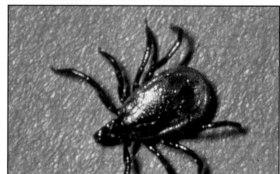

Because ticks are often vectors of Lyme disease, they should be removed as soon as possible.

2. **Remove** the stinger by scraping it out (using a tweezer will squeeze more venom into the skin). In case of a tick bite, place any type of oil (salad oil, machine oil, mineral oil) on top of the tick to close its breathing pores. The tick should release its hold within half an hour if not immediately. Then use tweezers to carefully remove the tick.
3. **Wash** the area with soap and water.
4. **Apply** cold packs and calamine or a soothing lotion to the area.
5. **Get** medical help as soon as possible if the victim develops a fever or if the wound becomes infected.

Snakebites
1. **Keep** the victim still with the bitten area immobile and resting below heart level.
2. **Get** medical attention immediately.
3. **Monitor** the victim's ABCs.

BEING READY

Many people are more than willing to help or give first aid to an injured person. However, not knowing what to do in an emergency can endanger the victim. It is important to be willing to help, to be trained to help, and to use your training to be of aid. You never know when you will be called upon to use first aid techniques. Be a prepared servant who is ready to help others.

Section Review

1. What is the telephone number of the Poison Control Center in your area?

2. Your grandfather accidentally drank some paint thinner. Your grandmother is running around trying to find something to make him vomit. Explain to her why it is best not to make him vomit. What course of action should you take?

3. While waiting in the car for you and your mother to grocery shop, your older brother left the car running so that he could keep warm. You return to find him slumped over the steering wheel with his skin and lips looking cherry red in color. What should you do?

CHAPTER REVIEW

Terms

first aid	fracture	third-degree burn
cardiopulmonary resuscitation (CPR)	closed fracture	epilepsy
ABCs	open fracture	convulsions
rescue breathing	partial fracture	concussion
shock	complete fracture	heart attack
wound	splint	stroke
abrasion	dislocation	core temperature
cut	sprain	frostbite
avulsion	strain	heat exhaustion
puncture	first-degree burn	heat cramp
asphyxiation	second-degree burn	heat stroke
Heimlich maneuver		

Content Questions

1. Make a two-column list. In one column write a basic outline of things to do if you are not trained in first aid. In the second column list things to do if you are trained in first aid.

2. What are the vital statistics that should be noted on paper (if possible) while waiting for the EMS to arrive? What are the normal ranges for each?

3. How can the acrostic AMPLE help you to treat a victim? What do the letters stand for?

4. What are some of the symptoms of shock and what should you do to treat a person with these symptoms?

5. The size of the pupils of a person with a concussion will be

   a. normal.   b. dilated.   c. constricted.   d. unequal.

6. What is the universal signal for choking? What should your response be?

7. Explain the procedure for giving rescue breathing (mouth-to-mouth ventilation).

8. Michael Paul got sand in his eye while you were riding your bikes. You are a block away from home on a dirt road. How can you help him?

9. Why would the method used to treat strains and sprains also be referred to as RICE?

10. Why should you always use a cold pack and not just ice on the skin? How often must the cold pack be moved? List six of the seven situations mentioned in your text in which a cold pack should be applied.

11. Why should contaminated clothing and jewelry be removed from a person with a chemical burn? Should this be done before rinsing the victim off with water?

12. What is the difference between epilepsy and a seizure?

13. In which ways is caring for a scalp wound similar to taking care of a major wound? In which ways does first aid care differ?

14. What are the three major techniques used to stop bleeding?

15. Why should one never attempt to give an unconscious person something to eat or drink?

16. Why would a body's core temperature be an important factor in hypothermia?

17. How can you tell the difference between heat exhaustion, heat cramps, and heat stroke?

18. Why is it important to obtain the container that contained the poison or a sample of the food and any vomitus for the EMS?

Application Questions

1. You are visiting your grandfather when he accidentally falls down the stairs. Your father tells you to call the EMS. Your grandfather is breathing and has a regular pulse. What number do you call? What do you say?

2. You are baby-sitting five-year-old Nathan. You notice that he is lying very still under the tree in the back yard. You quickly run to check on him. Assuming that a serious accident occurred (broken leg, broken arm, concussion, convulsions), list the correct emergency procedures of first aid you should use in proper order in the case of no response and in the case of getting a response from Nathan.

3. Why would it be important to take an infant, an elderly person, or an ill person who has a first-degree burn or minor burn to the doctor?

4. Research and find out what is meant by the "Rule of Nines?" How would this information be used by the EMS?

5. In which occupations would people be highly susceptible to incur heat exhaustion? What could these people do to avoid heat exhaustion?

6. Would aspirin be an appropriate way to combat heat exhaustion?

Radiologic Technologists

Job Description: Radiologic technology is a diverse and expanding field. Radiology is not only necessary when getting x-rays for a broken arm but also useful in diagnosing and treating some illnesses. Actually, the term *diagnostic imaging* is more appropriate than *radiology*. Radiologic technologists may obtain training in using more forms of imaging than just x-ray machines. They may use ultrasound machines (using sound waves), magnetic resonance scanners (using radio waves), positron emission scanners (using electrons), and various kinds of computer-enhanced equipment to produce visual images.

There is a difference between a radiologist and a radiologic technologist. A radiologist is a physician who specializes in interpreting the data. Radiologic technologists (also called radiographers or x-ray technicians) take x-ray films and help in fluoroscopic examinations (which allow doctors to watch a patient's internal organs on a screen or monitor). Other components of this field include sonography (ultrasound), the use of sound waves to form a visual image of areas in a patient's body, and radiation therapy, the use of radiation to help treat cancer patients.

Job Location: Most radiologic technologists are employed by hospitals. However, some specialized centers, clinics, or physicians also hire trained technologists. The job requires the technologist to stand on his feet a great deal. The radiologic technologist often needs to assist the patient to get into the proper position or help lift and turn a patient who is unable to move. Of course radiation is the greatest hazard of this occupation, but the use of shielding devices usually keeps exposure to radiation at a minimum.

This occupation also requires precision and accuracy. The technologist must precisely follow the instructions given by the doctor. It is especially important for a radiation therapy technologist to position the patient with absolute accuracy in order to expose only the necessary body parts to radiation. Because the patient may be very sick, nauseated, or excited, a radiologic technologist should also exhibit sympathy and understanding.

Training Required: The amount of education required for this career depends on the job to be done. Programs range from a one-year certificate to an associate's degree or a bachelor's degree. Most technologists go through a two-year program at a technical school, medical center, hospital, or university. High school courses in mathematics, physics, chemistry, and biology are helpful in preparing to enter this field.

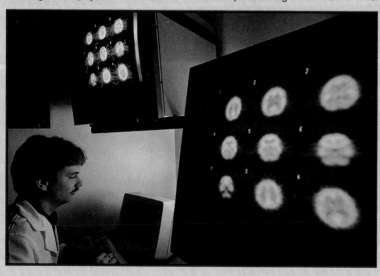

DISEASES

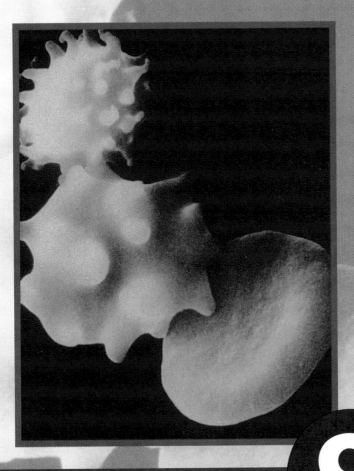

Plague! Typhoid! Cholera! These words have struck fear into the hearts of men throughout the centuries. What do these diseases have to do with you? After all, most of them are not common in the United States. However, some diseases once thought to be eradicated in America have returned. You should also consider that the Lord may call you to a future career (soldier, missionary, teacher) involving traveling in countries where disease is prevalent.

CHAPTER 9

"If thou wilt diligently hearken to the voice of the Lord thy God, . . . I will put none of these diseases upon thee."

Exodus 15:26

Of Epidemic Proportions

An epidemic is declared when the number of cases of a disease rises significantly above the normal number in an area, state, or country. A pandemic is an epidemic that covers wide geographic areas throughout the world. Influenza periodically produces epidemics that lead to pandemics. This picture shows how a university gym was used as an infirmary during the flu epidemic of 1918.

Disease is a mysterious and feared enemy that can strike anyone at any time. Some diseases strike suddenly and kill quickly; others disable and disfigure slowly and painfully; yet others merely cause discomfort and frustration, such as missing your classes, activities, or well-planned outings. Since the fall of man in the Garden of Eden, disease has been a threat to man's health. It is a constant reminder of his weakness and sin. This chapter will acquaint you with some of the more common diseases of today and suggest ways you can prevent them.

MAN'S LIMITED POWER

Only recently has man begun to understand the causes of many of the diseases that afflict him. Medical science has leaped forward in the last century. Great progress has been made in detecting, preventing, and treating many diseases, yet all the great technology available cannot conquer them.

Fortunately, doctors are available to help fight disease. It takes the teamwork of doctors and patients to fight the battle. As a part of a team, you should know your responsibilities and have a general idea of your doctor's responsibilities.

The Doctor's Role

Can you imagine what your basketball team would be like if you could hire a professional player to play on your team? Although you cannot do this for your basketball team, you can do this for your health team. Your doctor brings years of experience and training to your aid.

There are at least two things that your physician is trained to do for your health team when you are sick. First, your physician is trained to **diagnose** (identify) your illness. While you may have a good idea about the nature of some illnesses, you do not have the training or the equipment to diagnose most serious illnesses.

There are many members in a health team, but you and your doctor are the prime members.

Secondly, your doctor is trained to order medical treatment. Ordering medical treatment is sometimes called **prescribing** treatment. Your doctor might prescribe a certain diet, an exercise program, some type of medication, or a change in habits.

Beware of combining over-the-counter drugs. Dangerous interactions can occur when some nonprescription drugs are combined with certain drugs, foods, sunlight, or medical conditions. Read the warnings printed on the drugs or additional information supplied by the pharmacist. Many times people get so used to seeing warnings that they ignore them.

Medicine prescribed by your doctor is called a *prescription.* Drugs that can be ordered only by a doctor are called **prescription drugs;** drugs that can be purchased legally without a prescription are called **nonprescription drugs** or *over-the-counter drugs.*

Usually your doctor will ask about your symptoms so that he can properly diagnose and treat your illness. A **symptom** is any change from the way you look, feel, or function when you are well. For example, a common symptom of an infection is a fever. If you develop a fever, write down the time and your temperature each time you check it. You can then accurately and completely inform your doctor of changes you noticed and when they occurred.

Doctors are qualified to diagnose illness and prescribe treatment. Does this mean that your doctor will always be right? Not necessarily. If you do not think your doctor is treating you properly, you can go to another doctor. This is called getting a

second opinion. Before approving recommended surgery, many insurance companies require a second opinion. Most companies are willing to pay for a second opinion because eliminating unnecessary surgery will save them money.

The Patient's Role

You are the *patient* in your health team. A patient is anyone under a doctor's care. You do not have to be in the hospital to be a patient. Since you and your doctor are a team, you are his patient even when you are well. Your doctor is always ready to help you with your health needs.

Although your doctor is an important member of your health team, you are the captain of your team. Since you are such an important member, you should know what your responsibilities are. Your first responsibility is to do what you can to stay well. Staying well is much better than trying to get well. The chapters on exercise, diet, and safety have given you some tips on doing this.

Next, you must know when to go to the doctor. The greatest basketball player in the world cannot help your team if you never put him in the game. Likewise, the best doctor in the world cannot help you if you refuse to see him. You must keep your doctor an active member of your team by having regular physical examinations and by seeking his help when you are sick.

This does not mean that you must rush to the doctor every time you sneeze or have a slight headache. Since your parents probably decide when you are sick enough to go to the doctor, you should let them know whenever you feel bad. Sometimes it is difficult to know whether you need medical treatment. If you and your parents are uncertain about whether to go to the doctor, call your school nurse or call your doctor.

You must have confidence in your doctor, be able to openly communicate with him, and be willing to follow his directions. When you visit the doctor, be sure to give details concerning your symptoms (Did you have a rash just on your arm or did it extend to your back? Was the rash raised or just under the skin? Did you have a fever? If so, how high? When did you notice the fever or take your temperature?). Talk to your doctor and make sure that you understand what he says to you. Do not leave wondering about the nature of or treatment for your sickness. Your doctor should explain your illness and the procedure for treating it in simple but clear terms so that you will understand what to do.

Finally, you should follow your doctor's advice. If he says to rest, you should rest. If he prescribes a medication, you should take it exactly as he prescribed it. Many people make the mistake of stopping medication too soon. For example, if a patient decides to stop taking the antibiotic that his doctor prescribed because he feels better, there is great danger of a relapse. The patient may feel better even though harmful bacteria remain in his body. When the medication is stopped, these bacteria can begin multiplying again and in some cases become resistant to further medication. It is senseless to spend money to see a doctor and then ignore his advice.

You cannot prevent all disease. Your doctor cannot cure all disease. But together as a health team, you can win many more battles than either of you could win alone.

Someday God will end disease and death forever. Revelation 21:4 says, "And God shall wipe away all tears from their eyes; and there shall be no more death, neither sorrow, nor crying, neither shall there be any more pain: for the former things are passed away." Until that day, you should do your part to protect your temple from disease. God has allowed man to learn many facts about disease, and He expects you to use these facts wisely.

GOD'S LIMITLESS POWER

Disease has never been a mystery to God. When the children of Israel came out of Egypt, God gave them many promises. One of those promises was that if they would listen to Him and obey His law, He would deliver them from the diseases that plagued the Egyptians. Some of the regulations seemed unusual. The Israelites were forbidden to eat certain harmful foods. They were required to isolate those who had certain illnesses. There were specific laws regulating cleanliness and sanitation. And there were instructions for handling the dead. Long before man discovered that disease could be spread by "germs," God was protecting His people.

The law that God gave to the Israelites was quite different from the laws of the people who surrounded them. The Israelites probably wondered why God's law contained so many strange instructions. They had to obey by faith. Man cannot always

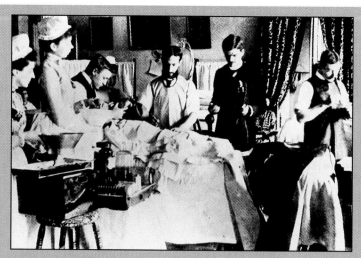

Before the Clean Cut

Early surgical practices did not include cleanliness. Notice the lack of masks or gloves by the surgeons and nurses and the presence of bacteria-collecting objects such as curtains and picture frames. It was not until 1865 that Louis Pasteur introduced the concept of the germ theory of disease. Joseph Lister did not develop antiseptic surgical procedures until 1867.

Medical Mayhem—Trails of the Trials of Medical Discovery

The medical skills and practices used today did not come without immense exploration, misconception, and agony. Superstition often waylaid knowledge, and the lack of basic facts and equipment hindered medical discovery. In order to appreciate the medical benefits enjoyed now, consider some of the pioneers and practices in medical history.

Ancient skulls have been found with holes bored into them which indicate the earliest use of "surgery." This process, called trephining (or trepanning), was used to provide an exit for the "demons" or "evil spirits" that caused disease. Some primitive tribes still practice this form of "medicine" today.

Signs and seals of Babylonian physicians dating to 3000 B.C. have been found. The fact that the Code of Hammurabi included laws relating to medical practice and established severe penalties for malpractice (e.g., "if the doctor, in opening an abscess, shall kill the patient, his hands shall be cut off") is thought to have discouraged explorations in medicine in Mesopotamia.

The history of Chinese medical practices goes back before written records were kept of it. According to legend, though, medical care began around 2953 B.C. with the work of Fu Hsi. During the reign of the Yellow Emperor, Huang Ti, in 2598 B.C. the standard for internal medicine called the *Nei Ching* was written. Much of the ancient Chinese practices hinged on their occult belief in the dualistic cosmic theory of *yin* and *yang* as well as the mystical belief that the body was made of five elements (wood, fire, earth, metal, and water), and that there were five planets, five atmospheres, five colors, and five tones. Chinese medicine tried to control the balance of these groups in order to insure good health.

In Egypt the study of medicine goes back to 2560 B.C. when the famed architect and physician Imhotep lived. Apparently, the steps toward becoming a physician were clearly organized from a general education in reading and writing to the study of medicine. The Egyptian practice of medicine was a mixture of science and mysticism. In the mid-1800s Edwin Smith found an Egyptian manuscript (now referred to as the Edwin Smith Papyrus) which contains an essay on the heart, forty-eight clinical observations on surgical cases (including a description, diagnosis, prognosis, and treatment of each), and a series of magic spells for removing evil spirits.

Medicine in India was practiced as early as 2000 B.C., but much of the practice for curing disease consisted of spiritism and charms to expel the demons of disease. Sometime between 800 B.C. and the seventh century A.D., two collections of medical treatments were written. These works were used for centuries as a guide for the examination of patients, prognosis of disease, treatment of disease, and surgical techniques. The early Hindus had astonishing expertise in the field of surgery. They used instruments of steel to perform surgery and used alcohol to numb during the operation. The Hindus also introduced the practice of cosmetic surgery.

Early Greek and Roman medical techniques did much both to help and to hinder medical discovery. For instance, Plato (c. 428-348 B.C.) thought that the brain was the seat of reasoning simply because it was spherical in shape and a sphere was considered to be the ideal shape. Needless to say, although the conclusion was correct, his explanation was wrong. A scientific investigation was later conducted by Herophilus (c. 300 B.C.). He dissected brains of dead criminals and animals and began the idea that it was the brain which controlled the functions of the body.

It is interesting to note that the ancient Greeks and Romans used the electric shock of the electric ray, or numbfish, to treat gout and chronic headaches. (In fact the word *narcotic* comes from the Greek word also used for the numbing effect of the electric ray, *narke*.)

Hippocrates, the Greek physician, is often called the "Father of Medicine." He established a code of principles for health care; looked for possible natural causes of disease; noted the effect of food, occupation, and climate on disease; and encouraged the use of medicine and diet as treatments for disease. An adaptation of his principles for medical conduct is often used in medical school graduation ceremonies; the following is an excerpt from one version of the Hippocratic oath.

The regimen I adopt shall be for the benefit of my patients according to my ability and judgment, and not for their hurt or for any wrong. I will give no deadly drug to any, though it be asked of me, nor will I counsel such, and especially I will not aid a woman to procure abortion. Whatsoever house I enter, there will I go for the benefit of the sick, refraining from all wrong doing or corruption. . . . Whatsoever things I see or hear concerning the life of men, in my attendance on the sick or even apart therefrom, which ought not to be noised abroad, I will keep silence thereon, counting such things to be as sacred secrets.

Another fallacy that hindered medical advancement for years was the belief that the harmony of the four bodily humors, (blood; phlegm; choler, or yellow bile; and melancholy, or black bile) was necessary to maintain health. This belief was instrumental in the development of bloodletting to remove excess humors. As a thirteenth-century Latin manuscript translated into English stated:

By bleeding, to the marrow
commeth heat,
It maketh cleane your
braine, relieves your eye,
It mends your appetite,
restoreth sleepe,
Correcting humours that do
waking keepe:
All inward parts and senses
also clearing,
It mends the voyce, touch,
smell & tast, & hearing.

In A.D. 164 a Greek physician, Galen, began to practice medicine in Rome. Although he continued to stress the humoral theory, he also did much to increase knowledge in the realm of anatomy. Although he refuted the 400-year-old belief that blood vessels were filled with air and noted that blood filled the arteries of the body, he failed to understand the circulatory system. Instead, he held that blood was formed in the liver and that the blood was then able to flow from the liver to the outer portions of the body where it was then transformed into flesh. The teachings of Galen influenced medical thought for more than 1,400 years.

Because of the religious restrictions of the time, Galen's explorations were limited to observations made while working with wounded gladiators and by dissecting animals. It was a physician from Brussels in 1540 by the name of Andreas Vesalius who took the study of the human body to a more accurate level. Not satisfied with the accepted Galenic theories of anatomy, Vesalius began his own study by dissecting human cadavers. He then had his findings drawn and printed. His work resulted in a seven-volume study of the the human body, called *Fabrica.*

The early pioneers of medicine had to face great scorn and skepticism. After all, who would believe that there were imperceptible "microbes" in the air? Why should a surgeon wash his hands between patients and operations or wear a mask while operating? What good did it do to pasteurize products? How could mold be beneficial to man? How can the brain and not the liver or heart control body functions? The superstitions and unsanitary medical practices of the past seem ridiculous to modern man. Yet one must marvel at the determination and intellect that the ancients displayed in their step-by-step progress away from mysticism and ignorance.

It is important to remember that scientific knowledge is changing almost constantly. The best information known today may be obsolete tomorrow. The treatment and prevention of disease is an area where changes are often rapid and radical. Health education should be constantly updated.

understand why God directs His people to do certain things. It is not for a Christian to understand, but to obey.

God showed His power over disease during Christ's ministry. Although Christ was often surrounded by those who were sick and dying, He was never confronted by a disease that He could not heal. In fact, His power over disease was so complete that even those who touched his clothes were healed.

God still heals today. Sometimes He heals miraculously, but more often He heals through medical knowledge He has allowed man to acquire. There are also times when God does not heal. In II Corinthians 12:7, Paul speaks of a thorn in his flesh. Apparently, this was a physical ailment that caused Paul great distress. Paul asked the Lord three times for healing. Although Paul had been used by God to heal others, God did not choose to heal Paul. Instead, He promised to give Paul the grace to accept his illness. There are times when God is glorified more by sickness than by healing.

Section Review

1. What are the two main duties of a doctor?
2. What are your responsibilities in the health team?
3. Describe ways God has exhibited His power over disease.

TYPES OF DISEASE

If you have had a cold, a stomach virus, or a dental cavity, you have been a victim of disease. Scientists have identified thousands of different diseases. Some diseases were first described hundreds of years ago, while others have just been recently discovered. A **disease** occurs when a part of your body fails to function properly. Diseases are often divided into two groups: infectious (microbial) diseases and noninfectious (nonmicrobial) diseases.

An **infectious disease** is any disease caused by organisms or viral particles that can be spread from one person or animal to another, either directly or indirectly. A **noninfectious disease** is any disease that does not have a microbial cause. However, diseases like botulism and tetanus, caused by microbes, are noncommunicable. You cannot catch a noninfectious disease from another person.

Infectious Disease Information

Have you ever caught a cold? You may have felt fine the day before, but you suddenly began to feel sick. Even though your friend was sneezing and coughing, you had tried to keep your distance. What happened? How could you have avoided getting sick?

The Enemies—In the definition of infectious disease you learned that infectious diseases are caused by organisms or viral particles. These organisms and viral particles that cause disease are called **pathogens** (PATH uh juhn). Most pathogens are very small; some can be seen only with the aid of an electron microscope. A virus can be from 10 to 250 nanometers long (a nanometer is one billionth of a meter). When these pathogens get inside your body and begin to multiply, they cause you to get

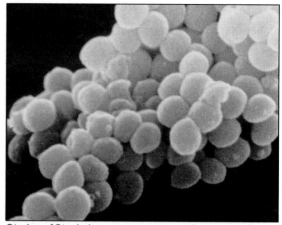

Strains of Staphylococcus aureus, *as these magnified 24,000 times, can cause human ailments such as food poisoning, impetigo, and toxic shock syndrome.*

sick. Although there are six major types of organisms that can cause illness, most types of infectious diseases are caused by either bacteria or viruses.

Bacteria are unicellular (single-celled) microorganisms. Bacteria can grow almost everywhere, and they multiply quickly. There are many different species of bacteria of which most are harmless, some are helpful, and some are harmful. Bacteria can cause disease and also produce toxins which cause disease; they are probably the most common cause of infectious disease. Bubonic plague, tetanus, tuberculosis, syphilis, and strep throat are a few of the diseases caused by bacteria.

Viruses are the other major cause of infectious diseases. A virus is composed of a nucleic acid wrapped in protein. Viruses multiply only inside living cells. They can enter the body's cells where they then cause the cells to reproduce the virus. Fortunately, viruses are very specific in their ability to attack host cells. A virus must have specific proteins available in a host cell before it can reproduce itself. Host cells must provide an appropriate site before the virus can enter and multiply.

Viruses can be multiplied in a cell by the hundreds in as little as thirty minutes, which is why some viral diseases produce such sudden symptoms and sickness. However, after initially infecting the cells of the body, some viruses are reactivated

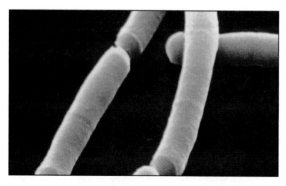

Minute pathogens such as these rod-shaped bacteria Bacillus cereus *may cause great, though temporary, distress.* Bacillus cereus *can produce food poisoning, resulting in inflammation of the stomach and intestines.*

Pathogen Panorama

Pathogen	Description	Sample of Diseases	Example
Viruses (10 - 250 nanometers)	Non-living particles of DNA or RNA surrounded by a protein coat	AIDS, colds, chicken pox, influenza, polio, rabies, red measles, rubella, hepatitis	polio
Rickettsia (less than 1 micrometer)	Bacterial organisms that require a host's living cells for growth; always associated with insects and other arthropods	Rocky Mountain spotted fever	rickettsia
Bacteria (1 - 10 micrometers)	Unicellular microorganisms; some secrete disease-causing toxins; rod (bacilli), spiral (spirilla), or spherical-shaped (cocci)	Boils, pneumonia, diphtheria, food poisoning, meningitis, scarlet fever, strep throat, tuberculosis, Lyme disease	cocci
Fungi (a few micrometers to several inches)	Spore-producing parasites; molds and yeasts; release enzymes that digest cells	Athlete's foot, candidiasis, ringworm	ringworm
Protozoa (3 - 250 micrometers)	Unicellular animal-like organisms; release enzymes and toxins that destroy cells or interfere with their normal functions	African sleeping sickness, amebic dysentery, malaria	plasmodia
Parasitic worms (1/32 inch to 30 feet)	Multicellular animals; tapeworms, leeches, pinworms, and round worms	Abnominal pain, anemia, trichinosis	tapeworm

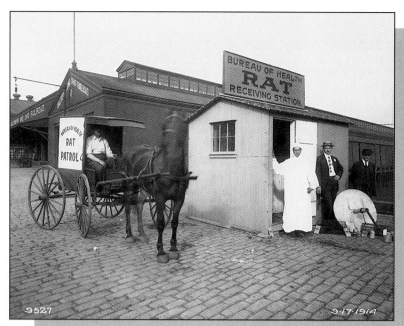

as they are stimulated (by ultraviolet light, burns, chemicals, etc.) into action. Chicken pox, polio, influenza, warts, and cold sores are a few of the diseases that are caused by viruses.

The Attack—Any time you face an enemy, you stand a better chance of defeating him if you know how or where he will attack. During World War II, the Japanese seriously defeated the Americans at Pearl Harbor because the Japanese caught the Americans by surprise. Today, you are surrounded by many enemies potentially dangerous to your health. You may be better equipped to defeat them if you know how they attack.

Pathogens are spread in many ways. Some pathogens are transferred through direct contact (impetigo, ringworm). Others are spread by droplets in the air initiated by a sneeze or a cough (colds,

pneumonia). Food and objects (dishes, silverware, glassware) can be vehicles that carry pathogens into the body (food poisoning, trichinosis).

Vectors (animal carriers of pathogens) also help to disperse disease. Examples of some vectors are *Anopheles* mosquitoes (vectors of pathogens causing malaria), *Aedes* mosquitoes (vectors carrying

Methods of Transmitting Infectious Diseases

Contact   Airborne   Vehicle   Vector

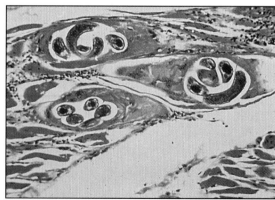

Trichinosis (TRIH kuh NOH sis) is a potentially lethal disease caused by ingesting cysts of the trichina worm Trichinella spiralis. *The larvae in the cysts can live in muscle tissue for years. When the cyst is eaten by a host, the larvae make their way to the intestinal tract where they mature and mate. This is why it is so important to cook meat thoroughly since cooking is the only known means of killing the encysted larvae.*

pathogens for yellow fever, encephalitis, and filariasis), tsetse flies (vectors of the pathogens for African sleeping sickness), rat fleas (vectors of pathogens resulting in bubonic plague or epidemic typhus), and common house flies (vectors for the pathogens causing typhus, bacillary dysentery, and amoebic dysentery).

As you can see, most pathogens enter your body through your food, your drink, the air you breathe, or the things you come in contact with. If you never had to eat, drink, breathe, or touch anything, you might be able to completely eliminate the threat of infectious disease, but this is obviously not feasible. Fortunately, God designed you with an elaborate defense system to assist in the fight.

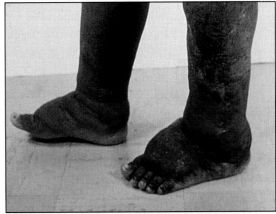

The tropical disease elephantiasis is caused by adult filarial worms that live in the lymph passages of the body. They block the flow of lymph, causing enormous enlargement of those body parts. The larval microfilariae are pathogens transmitted by mosquitoes.

Section Review

1. What is the difference between the terms *pathogen* and *vector?* What is the difference between *bacteria* and *virus?*

2. Distinguish between infectious diseases and noninfectious diseases.

3. List four major ways that pathogens are spread.

The Defense—Most of the pathogens that threaten you are harmless as long as they remain outside your body; they can make you sick only if they can enter. God has created your body with several natural defenses. For instance, your skin is a barrier for most bacteria and viruses. Body oils and perspiration also help to inhibit pathogens. There is special danger, however, when the skin barrier is broken. Pathogens may enter through a wound and cause serious problems. That is why it is important to thoroughly wash and medicate any wound. Washing the wound helps to remove harmful organisms, and applying a disinfectant and antibiotic ointment to the wound helps to kill pathogens.

Although your skin can be an effective barrier, it does not cover your entire body. Obviously, there are places such as your mouth and nose that pathogens can enter without penetrating the skin. However, these areas are designed by God with various types of protection to keep pathogens out. For example, the hairs in your nose help to screen out foreign particles which could enter your respiratory system. **Mucous membranes** (layers of cells that secrete mucus) line the entries to the body to trap microorganisms and particles. Tiny hairlike structures, **cilia,** also line areas of the respiratory tract (nose, trachea, lungs) to move mucus containing trapped pathogens back to the throat so they can be swallowed and taken to the stomach (where highly acidic digestive juices can destroy the invaders).

Even the most careful person will have some pathogens that penetrate these structural defenses. God made other lines of defense to protect from the destructive force of pathogens. Whenever a foreign organism invades your body, the body can respond dramatically. For instance, your body can increase the blood supply to the area of infection, causing your body temperature to rise. If the temperature of a localized area rises, it is called **inflammation.** If the temperature of the entire body is raised, it results in **fever.** Medical evidence suggests that fever may be more than an uncomfortable side effect in the body's fight against infection. Many pathogens live and reproduce in a narrow temperature range. Fever can elevate the body temperature enough to help fight against certain pathogens. Some medical authorities now question the value of taking medication to fight moderate fever. Of course if fever becomes too high, it must be treated because the fever itself may begin to cause body cells (especially brain cells) to die.

When your body comes under the attack of a pathogen, your body will rush white blood cells, leukocytes, to the area. Some of these white blood cells attempt to engulf and digest the intruders. Other white blood cells produce **antibodies.** Antibodies are protein substances that attack invading organisms or foreign substances. The action of antibodies is very specific. Each antibody that is produced only protects you from the specific organism or foreign substance that it was designed to attack.

The antibodies your body produces may stay in your body for the rest of your life. They will protect

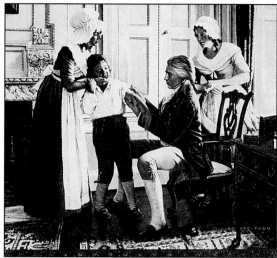

Edward Jenner used cowpox scrapings to produce an immunity against smallpox. The term vaccine (Latin vaccinus, of cows) is used to describe preparations of weakened pathogens for producing immunity.

you from the organisms if they attack again. This resistance to attack is called **immunity.** For example, most people get chicken pox only once in their lives. When you get chicken pox, your body produces antibodies that may make you immune to further attacks from the chicken pox virus.

God has allowed man to use this natural defense of his body in a marvelous way. It was discovered that injecting the body with weak or dead organisms will produce antibodies that will protect from future attacks. This process is called **vaccination.** You have probably already been vaccinated against such diseases as polio, tetanus, diphtheria, measles, rubella, and mumps. These vaccines have saved millions of lives.

The following general guidelines will help to reduce the number of pathogens that you are exposed to.

- Keep your skin clean (wash your hands frequently; bathe often).
- Make certain that the food that you eat was properly stored and prepared.
- Never drink water that may be contaminated or tainted, such as water from a stream.
- Use clean dishes, glassware, and silverware.

Donated blood is usually separated into plasma and platelets. Plasma that is to be used in humans must be frozen within eight hours. It can be stored in an ultra-low temperature freezer (–28 ° F [–33 ° C]). The platelets are stored at room temperature and expire after five days.

- Use extra care whenever you are around someone who is ill. Remember that pathogens can be transmitted through food, objects, or direct contact as well as through droplets in the air. Even if your sick friend does not sneeze on you, you expose yourself to his illness if you come into contact with a contaminated area or articles.
- Be sure to keep your room and home clean and tidy in order to discourage vectors.
- Make sure that your vaccinations are updated.

The Battle—Not all attacks result in instant illness. Once an infectious disease enters the human body, it follows a pattern.

- **Exposure**—At this stage, the pathogen is transmitted to the host.
- **Incubation**—This is the time that passes between exposure to the pathogen and the appearance of the disease symptoms.

Recommended Vaccinations

Age	Type of Immunization
2 months	Diphtheria-tetanus-pertussis (whooping cough) vaccine (DTP), trivalent oral polio vaccine (TOPV), haemophilus influenza type b vaccine (Hib), hepatitis b vaccine (HB)
4 months	DTP, TOPV, Hib, HB
6 months	DTP, TOPV, Hib, HB
12 - 15 months	DTP, Hib, tuberculin test, measles-mumps-rubella vaccine (MMR)
18 months	DTP, TOPV
4 - 6 years	DTP, TOPV, MMR
14 - 16 years	Tetanus-diphtheria
Every 10 years	Tetanus-diphtheria booster
When recommended	Pneumococcus

Although a person may not feel sick, the pathogen is actively reproducing in the body.

- **Outbreak**—During this time, the symptoms of the disease appear. This is usually a highly contagious stage for many diseases.
- **Convalescence**—This is the time between the outbreak and renewed health. If a person tries to resume normal activities too soon, he may not recover, but suffer a relapse of the disease instead.

The Allies—During a war there are often times when you need some help. If you are fighting a strong enemy, you may be more successful if you enlist others to help you. These people become your allies. An ally is someone who helps you fight against a common foe.

In the war against disease you have some powerful allies that can help you. Medicines can be valuable allies when you are sick. Your doctor is best qualified to recruit the proper allies for you in these battles. Remember not to expect your doctor to dispense some miracle drug that will cure you instantly. There are no miracle cures found in a bottle. Some patients often misunderstand the limitations of medicine. For instance, antibiotics are useful drugs, but they are mainly used against bacterial infections. Many patients feel their doctor is negligent when he does not prescribe an antibiotic for their viral infections. They fail to understand that antibiotics are useless against viruses. Your doctor will choose the medicine, if there is one, that will best aid your recovery.

Other allies that will help to combat disease are proper nutrition, water, and rest. Many times people who are ill do not feel like eating at all. Sometimes it is best to serve small portions of food frequently. For instance, you can serve a feverish person some clear broth (made from boiling meat and vegetables, straining the fluids, and removing excess fat) and fruit juices every hour or two rather than making him eat three big meals as usual.

Depending on the symptoms of the disease, a patient's diet should be planned to provide wholesome nutrients in an attractive and appealing manner. The food can be garnished, colorful in combination, or accented in presentation. Always consider the patient, (his age, hobbies, tastes) and the ailment when making plans. Mom would probably like her meal served on china with a flower, but Dad would probably like a soup mug and a sports magazine or crossword puzzle.

Of course, water will help keep a person from dehydrating and also aid in moving waste products (remains from the battle) out of the body. Water is vital in helping to cool the body when fever is present. Although fruit juices will also help to provide nutrients, provide plenty of plain cold water.

When a person is sick, rest and sleep help the body rejuvenate. Illness has been associated with an increased need for sleep. Sometimes this condition is caused by the medications taken. Sleep plays a part in tissue regeneration; while the body is resting, much repair of tissue damage is done. Remember, however, that moderate exercise and movement of muscles is also necessary for a sick person. After twenty-four hours of total bed rest, body muscles can stiffen from disuse.

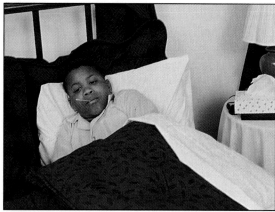

Many doctors do not recommend giving children medicines to reduce fever unless the temperature is over 103° F (39.4° C). Because of the risk that children and teen-agers may develop Reye's syndrome (a potentially fatal illness following one to three days after a viral infection), most doctors now question the use of aspirin.

Plenty of nutritious food, water, and rest will help the body to fight infection effectively. When these allies are supported by needed medicine, your body's defenses will be well supported in the battle toward restored health.

Section Review

1. What are the lines of defense with which God has equipped the human body for battle against pathogens?

2. You are a television health commentator. You have a five-minute segment of time in which to describe ways to prevent exposure to pathogens and the spread of disease. Write an interesting, informative script.

3. Develop a diagram that outlines the stages an infectious disease follows when it enters the human body.

4. How can you help your body to combat infection and to heal?

COMMON INFECTIOUS DISEASES

You have probably heard of many different infectious diseases. In fact, there are far more diseases than can be discussed in any health book. The next five sections in this chapter will examine some common infectious diseases, their causes, and the cures for them.

The Common Cold

You wake up one morning and you feel a little sick. You are not sure what is wrong but you seem to ache all over, and your throat feels dry and scratchy. Soon you are coughing and your nose gets stuffy. You have just become another victim of the common cold.

Actually, there are over a hundred different viruses that cause symptoms of the common cold. The symptoms include sneezing, chills, sore throat, coughing, stuffy nose, and head and body aches. A person with a cold is infectious for two or three days after the appearance of the symptoms. In order to keep the virus from infecting others, frequent hand washing is highly recommended for the sick person as well as those with whom he comes in contact. If you have a cold, avoid sharing towels, eating utensils, or drinking glasses. It is also best to cover coughs and sneezes in order to minimize the airborne spread of the virus.

Currently, there is no proven method for curing the common cold. A vaccine is not practical because there are so many different viruses capable of causing colds. Antibiotics are not helpful because colds are caused by viruses and not bacteria. Although vitamin C has been recommended by some for

During a sneeze, saliva and mucous filled with microorganisms can be propelled at more than 200 mph (100 m/sec.). Some microorganisms attach to dust particles in the air (and continue to be airborne) or settle on objects.

preventing colds, there is no consistent evidence that vitamin C prevents or cures colds.

Because there is no medical cure for colds, you must let your body cure itself. Getting plenty of rest and drinking a lot of liquids (especially fruit juices and water) are two ways of helping your body fight the cold. Although cold medicines do not cure colds, they may help you feel better by reducing your symptoms. There are many different cold medications that treat a variety of symptoms. The pharmacist at your local drug store can help you choose a cold medication that meets your needs.

Colds are a common illness, but they seldom cause serious problems. Although colds are not usually a serious threat, they can result in bacterial infections that may require the attention of a physician. Colds may last from seven to fourteen days. If your cold lasts longer than this; if your symptoms are severe; or if you develop a fever, pain in the chest, ears, or glands in the neck, shortness of breath, or wheezing; you should see your doctor.

Influenza

Another common infectious disease is influenza or the flu. Like the common cold, influenza is caused by viruses. There are three major groups of influenza viruses.

- Type A (is the most lethal type and strikes the general population every year)
- Type B (strikes every two to three years)

Contrary to popular belief, colds are not caused by exposure to drafts but by a virus. Hand-to-hand contact spreads colds as well as sneezing or coughing. It is possible to catch a cold by grasping a doorknob even 72 hours after it was touched by an infected person.

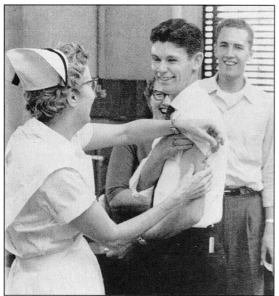

In the past, many students were required to have a flu shot. Today, it is available but not mandatory. Since some influenza vaccines are cultivated in chicken embryos, those who are allergic to eggs, feathers, or chickens should not take influenza immunizations.

One of the major problems with influenza viruses is that they have the ability to change their antigens. This means that vaccines made for one type of influenza and antibodies present in the general population may be ineffective against the new strain that may appear the next year.

The flu is much more dangerous than the common cold and can be fatal. The catastrophic pandemic of influenza in 1918 caused 20 million deaths. Other pandemics occurred in 1957 and 1968 when the Asian influenza and then the Hong Kong influenza swept across the globe. The elderly and those who are weak from other diseases are the most common victims.

Many flu symptoms are similar to those of the common cold except they are more severe. In addition to head and body aches, chills, extreme fatigue, sneezing, and coughing, the flu usually causes a high fever (rarely present in colds). The incubation period of influenza is one to two days. The symptoms usually last from three to five days, after which they begin to subside. However, coughing and weakness may continue. If the fever lasts longer than three to five days, complications (pneumonia, bacterial infection, etc.) may have set in. At this point, it is best to see the doctor.

While there is no cure for influenza, there are vaccines available to prevent some types of flu. Although children, teen-agers, and people over forty are more likely to get influenza, it is the elderly that are highly encouraged to get vaccinated. Doctors may also urge people with a history of asthma, cardiac, or respiratory problems to get the yearly vaccine. Remember, though, that a vaccine does not guarantee immunity. Vaccines are made from inactivated viruses; however, the influenza virus alters its structure every year.

Hepatitis

One of the most reported infectious diseases in America is **hepatitis.** Hepatitis is an inflammation of the liver that can be caused by one of several different viruses. Each type not only varies according to the virus causing it but also in the way it is transmitted, the incubation period, and the duration (some infections continue for a prolonged time and are considered to be chronic).

Type of Hepatitis	Transmission	Incubation and Duration
Hepatitis A (infectious hepatitis, HAV)	Ingestion of contaminated food or water	2 - 6 weeks; not chronic
Hepatitis B (serum hepatitis, HBV)	Infection by contaminated blood or body fluids	4 - 26 weeks; chronic liver disease
Other hepatitis viruses (similar symptoms to HBV but has negative test for both HAV and HBV)	Some by contaminated blood or body fluids; some by contaminated food or water	2 - 24 weeks; may or may not be chronic

Tuberculosis is a very contagious disease that is caused by a bacterium. Because it is transmitted through the air (by coughing, singing, sneezing), people with tuberculosis could inadvertently spread the disease to those with whom they come in contact. Because the symptoms may not appear for a period of time, many people in the United States are unaware that they have been exposed to tuberculosis. Teachers, health care workers, food handlers, and those who live or work in institutions where they may be exposed to a variety of people should be tested periodically for tuberculosis.

Tuberculosis bacteria have proved to be more resistant than most bacteria to drying, sunlight, and many antiseptics and disinfectants. One of the growing concerns about this disease is the rise in multiple drug-resistant strains of tuberculosis. These bacteria are no longer susceptible to many drugs used for treating this disease.

Symptoms of tuberculosis include fever, fatigue, coughing with a show of blood, night sweats, and weight loss. The disease causes the formation of hard nodules (tubercles) in the lung and may result in death.

Symptoms of hepatitis may include fever, fatigue, headache, and **jaundice** (the yellow coloring of body tissues). Jaundice is not a disease but a symptom of problems with the flow of bile (a yellow compound essential in the digestion of fat). Jaundice can often be detected by seeing if the whites of the eyes are yellow in appearance.

Streptococcal Infections

Streptococci are bacteria that are spherical in shape. Members of this group of bacteria cause various familiar diseases (strep throat, impetigo, pneumococcal pneumonia, scarlet fever, and rheumatic fever). Streptococcal bacteria can be spread in many different ways: sneezing, coughing, direct contact, and even from swimming in a crowded, poorly chlorinated pool.

Strep throat is a common disease. In fact, strep throat accounts for many bacterial sore throats. Humans can serve as **carriers,** (organisms that harbor a pathogen without exhibiting signs of illness) of streptococci. Doctors will sometimes test the entire household for carriers of infection if strep throat continually recurs in a home.

The incubation period for strep throat is one to five days. Symptoms include a sudden onset of sore and red throat (sometimes swollen tonsils); fever; swollen, tender glands under the base of the jaw; headache; and nausea or vomiting. Because a strep throat infection may lead to scarlet fever or rheumatic fever, it is important to begin treatment as soon as possible. Antibiotics are usually an effective cure for strep throat, but they must be taken for the entire prescribed period. A person with strep throat should be kept in isolation from others for 24 hours after beginning to take an antibiotic.

Rheumatic fever is a very dangerous complication characteristically following a strep infection such as a sore throat. This disease can produce fever, joint pain, and rashes, and can result in damage to the heart. Sometimes rheumatic fever can strike just a few days after a person has strep throat, or it can even occur up to six weeks after a person has been inadequately treated for strep throat. It is very important to take the entire antibiotic prescription for strep throat; do not stop taking the medication just because you feel better.

Sexually Transmitted Diseases

Sexually transmitted diseases or **STDs** are a large group of diseases that are usually spread by sexual contact. These diseases are also called *venereal diseases*. Because of the immoral lifestyle of many people today, STDs are a widespread problem.

The symptoms and problems that are caused by STDs vary greatly. For example, syphilis can cause blindness, mental illness, and death if it is left untreated for years. Other STDs can cause **sterility** (the inability to reproduce). Many STDs can seriously damage newborn children who are infected by their mothers. Most cause painful irritation to those who are infected.

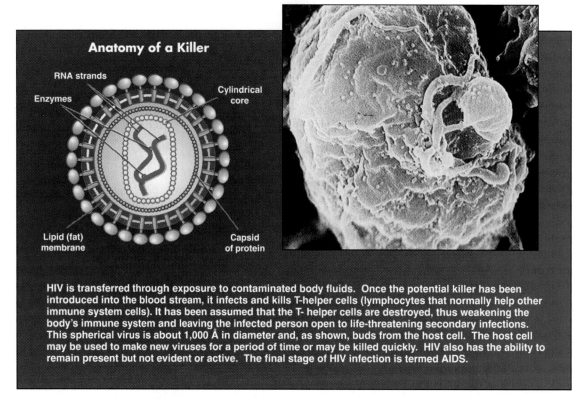

Anatomy of a Killer

RNA strands

Enzymes

Cylindrical core

Lipid (fat) membrane

Capsid of protein

HIV is transferred through exposure to contaminated body fluids. Once the potential killer has been introduced into the blood stream, it infects and kills T-helper cells (lymphocytes that normally help other immune system cells). It has been assumed that the T- helper cells are destroyed, thus weakening the body's immune system and leaving the infected person open to life-threatening secondary infections. This spherical virus is about 1,000 Å in diameter and, as shown, buds from the host cell. The host cell may be used to make new viruses for a period of time or may be killed quickly. HIV also has the ability to remain present but not evident or active. The final stage of HIV infection is termed AIDS.

Antibiotics are usually effective in treating those STDs that are caused by bacteria such as gonorrhea (GON uh REE uh) and syphilis (SIF uh lis). However, there are some new strains of these diseases that are resistant to many antibiotics. There are other STDs such as genital herpes and AIDS that have no known cure.

Though there are cures for some STDs, the God-ordained method for avoiding these diseases is clearly stated in His Word. God forbids sexual contact between those who are not married. The Bible calls sexual contact between those who are not married fornication. Fornication is a sin condemned by God. The book of Proverbs contains many warnings about the dangers of sexual immorality. First Corinthians 6:18 points out that fornication is a unique sin against the temple of God. It says, "Flee fornication. Every sin that a man doeth is without the body; but he that committeth fornication sinneth against his own body." Obeying God's commands is the best way to avoid infection with STDs.

Section Review

1. What causes the common cold?

2. Why is influenza so difficult to control from year to year?

3. Make a table with three columns: colds, influenza, and strep throat. Now list symptoms found in each so as to compare differences and similarities.

4. What difference is there between infectious hepatitis and serum hepatitis?

5. What is God's plan in order to prevent contamination from STDs and AIDS?

NONINFECTIOUS DISEASE

Noninfectious diseases (previously termed chronic diseases) are a great threat to people in the United States. Two chronic diseases, heart disease and cancer, are the greatest killers of Americans today.

The specific causes for many noninfectious diseases are uncertain. One reason for this is that some diseases may result from a variety of factors rather than any single cause such as a specific pathogen. Most of the factors that appear to contribute to chronic disease are the result of either heredity, lifestyle, environment, or a combination of these factors.

Because noninfectious diseases often take years to develop, many people do little to prevent them. It is often the case that when the symptoms of chronic disease become evident, little can be done to prevent further illness. To prevent noninfectious disease you must become aware of the factors which appear to contribute to their development and begin changing them today. The following section will help you become familiar with the causes and prevention of some of the most important noninfectious diseases.

Cardiovascular Disease

Since 1940, more Americans have died from **cardiovascular disease** than from any other cause (cardiovascular refers to the heart and the blood vessels). Over half of the deaths in the United States today result from some type of cardiovascular disease. While the percentage of deaths from cardiovascular disease in your age group is much lower (about five percent), there is evidence that your present lifestyle contributes to your risk of future heart disease.

One group of cardiovascular diseases that are not acquired are **congenital** (kun JEN ih tl) **heart diseases.** Congenital heart disease is responsible for about two percent of all cardiovascular diseases. These problems are caused by a malformed heart or large blood vessels having structural damage. A congenital defect is a problem that is present at birth. The damage occurs during the formation of the cardiovascular system while the fetus is developing. The Lord has enabled modern technology to help many born with congenital defects to survive and lead normally active lives.

Atherosclerosis (ATH uh roh skluh ROH sis) is a main cause of cardiovascular disease. Do not confuse atherosclerosis with arteriosclerosis (ar TEHR ee oh skluh ROH sis). Arteriosclerosis refers to the thickening and hardening of arterial walls (also called hardening of the arteries). Atherosclerosis refers to the most common form of arteriosclerosis in which fat deposits build up on the walls of blood vessels. These deposits decrease the size of the vessel openings, making it difficult for the blood to pass through. As recommended in Chapter 5, it is wise to have a low intake of cholesterol and saturated fats and to exercise regularly in order to help fight atherosclerosis.

Congenital defects may not be obvious to the casual observer. One baby in every 100 has a malformed heart at birth. Some defects are life-threatening while others may never be detected throughout one's lifetime.

Atherosclerosis is particularly dangerous when it affects the arteries that supply blood to the heart muscle (the coronary arteries). The heart muscle must have a constant source of oxygenated blood to stay alive. A temporary lack of oxygen can cause the feeling of gripping pain in the chest and the feeling of suffocation called **angina pectoris.** Attacks of angina can occur during times of stress or physical exertion. Angina is a symptom of heart problems and is not a disease. Suffering from angina indicates some blockage in the coronary arteries but does not mean that a person is having a heart attack.

A heart attack can occur when the narrowed openings in the coronary arteries are blocked. A heart attack is the death of a portion of heart muscle because it is deprived of oxygen. If a major artery is blocked, then the person may die. However, if a small artery is blocked, then the heart may continue to beat and the chances of recovery are increased.

Heart failure is another danger of cardiovascular disease. Heart failure occurs when the heart is no longer able to pump a normal amount of blood. Weakening of the heart can be caused by a heart attack, heart damage due to atherosclerosis, heart defects, rheumatic fever, or high blood pressure. Heart failure may occur on one or both sides of the

The calcium deposits on the inside of these water pipes illustrate the fat buildup in arterial walls. As the deposits in the pipes hinder water flow, atherosclerotic buildup in arteries hinders blood flow.

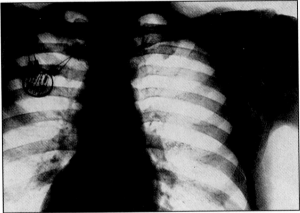

An artificial pacemaker helps to correct irregular heart rhythms. With a pulse generator of battery cells, wire lead, and an electrode to deliver an electrical charge to the heart, an artificial pacemaker cannot compare with the God-made pacemaker, the sinoatrial node, which discharges about 75 times each minute.

heart. Because the heart lacks the ability to pump blood efficiently, blood can collect in the veins (causing swelling especially in the arms and legs), and fluid can collect in the lungs (causing breathing difficulty). Heart failure can be fatal.

Another danger of cardiovascular disease occurs when the heart rhythm is altered. This is called an **arrhythmia** (uh RITH mee uh). Arrhythmias can cause the heart to beat in an unusually slow but regular manner or in a rapid but regular manner. However, if the heart begins to beat rapidly in an irregular and uncoordinated manner it is called **fibrillation.** Fibrillation can affect the pumping action of the heart. If the heart is unable to keep the blood pressure throughout the body, a person may go into shock and die.

Strokes are caused by the interruption of blood flow to the brain. Strokes can occur if the arteries leading to the brain are blocked by a clot formed in the artery (**thrombus**) or by a clot from another part of the body (**embolus**). Damaged or brittle arteries of the brain that burst can cause a third type of stroke called **cerebral hemorrhage.** A weakened area of an artery that balloons out is called an **aneurysm** (AN yuh RIZ um). The fourth type of stroke occurs if an aneurysm in the brain bursts (**cerebral aneurysm**).

There are certain factors that seem to contribute to heart disease. These are called *risk factors.* There are ten major risk factors for heart disease. Of these ten, however, there are three that are more crucial than the others: smoking tobacco, high levels of cholesterol in the blood, and high blood pressure. Because of the strong link between these risk factors and heart disease, they are sometimes called *primary risk factors.*

Primary risk factors

• **Smoking**—Many people are aware that smoking can cause lung disease. Fewer people realize that smoking also raises your risk of heart disease. Smokers have about twice as many fatal heart attacks as nonsmokers. The more a person smokes, the greater this risk becomes.

• **High Levels of Cholesterol in the Blood**—In Chapter 5 you learned that cholesterol is a fat-related substance that is transported in your blood. Cholesterol is produced by your body and is taken into your body in the foods you eat. High levels of cholesterol in your bloodstream appear to contribute to atherosclerosis. If there is a high level of LDL

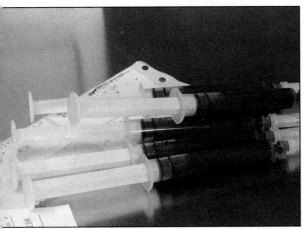

Not all people know their blood cholesterol levels. The next time you have a check-up, ask your doctor to check yours.

in your blood, you have a great danger of developing heart disease.

• **High Blood Pressure**—**Blood pressure** is the force that blood exerts against the walls of the arteries. This pressure pushes your blood through the many miles of arteries and veins in your body. It is vital for this pressure to stay high enough to move blood throughout your body. If your blood pressure gets too low, you can go into shock and die. However, if a person has consistently high blood pressure readings, he may be diagnosed as having high blood pressure, which is also known as **hypertension.** Hypertension may be a result of atherosclerosis. The blood pressure rises because the blood is forced into arteries that are narrower than usual. High blood pressure can harm many of the organs in the body. It is sometimes called the "silent killer," because its victims often do not know they are sick.

Risk factors you cannot control

• **Age**—Heart disease is a chronic disease. It often takes many years to develop. As you get older your risk of heart disease increases.

• **Gender**—Heart disease is about six times as common in young men as it is in young women. Therefore, if you are male, your risk is much greater. After middle age this difference between males and females is greatly reduced.

• **Family History**—Heart disease seems to be more common among certain families. If you have close relatives that suffer from heart disease, your risk is about twice as great as someone with no family history of heart disease.

Other risk factors

• **Stress**—Stress can be harmful to your health. If you are under a lot of stress and you do not handle it properly, you will have a greater risk of heart disease. Some scientists believe that people who are always pushing themselves have a greater danger of heart disease than those who "take it easy."

• **Diabetes**—People who have diabetes have a greater risk of heart disease. In Chapter 2 you learned that the pancreas secretes a hormone called insulin. Diabetes is a disease caused by a

Healthy Pressure

contracts again. This blood pressure is called *diastolic* (DIE uh STOL ik) blood pressure. Your systolic blood pressure is higher than your diastolic pressure.

Blood pressure is usually written like a fraction with the systolic pressure as the numerator and the diastolic pressure as the denominator. Although the average blood pressure for a healthy young adult might be about 120/80, recent studies have shown that blood pressure readings less than 110/70 are best for long-term health.

Your blood pressure varies every time your heart beats. When your heart contracts, it pushes more blood into your arteries and the pressure rises. This pressure can be measured with a **sphygmomanometer** (SFIG moh muh NOM ih tur). You have probably had your blood pressure checked with one when you went to the doctor.

When your heart contracts, the muscle fibers constrict or draw together. This is called **systole** (SIS tuh lee). At this time the blood pressure in your arteries is called *systolic* (sis TAHL ik) blood pressure.

After your heart contracts, there is a resting phase of the heart cycle, called **diastole** (die AS tuh lee). During this phase the pressure in your arteries falls rapidly until your heart

The Cardiac Cycle

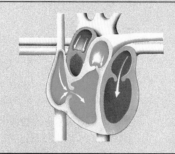

Atrial systole (contraction)

Ventricular diastole (relaxation)

Blood pumped into ventricles

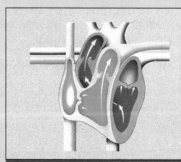

Atrial diastole (relaxation)

Ventricular systole (contraction)

Blood pumped into arteries

The entire heart does not contract as a unit. The atria contract and relax simultaneously, and then the ventricles contract and relax simultaneously. Blood pressure is measured by noting the rise and fall of pressure in the arteries. This is caused by the systolic and diastolic pressures of the left ventricle, which pumps the blood from the heart through the body.

malfunction of this process. You will learn more about diabetes later in this chapter.

• **Obesity**—Many of the victims of heart disease are overweight. Some researchers think that extra body fat makes the heart work harder and this contributes to heart disease. Others believe that people who are overweight have more heart disease because they are more likely to have other risk factors such as high levels of cholesterol in the blood, high blood pressure, or diabetes.

• **Lack of Exercise**—After studying Chapter 6 you are already aware of some of the ways exercise affects your heart. Exercise makes your heart stronger. It may also increase the blood supply available to the heart muscle. Exercise also may change other risk factors. It may help lower blood pressure in some people and reduce the effects of stress.

Multiple risk factors—While each risk factor is harmful, having many risk factors is even more dangerous. Combinations of risk factors can increase the risk of cardiovascular disease. The more risk factors you have, the more important it is for you to begin reducing them immediately.

Reducing the risk—Although heart disease is a great killer, you can keep its effect on your life to a minimum by reducing the risks. Because you have

already studied weight control, stress, exercise, and diet, you should have a good start toward changing these risk factors. The best way to handle the risk factor of smoking is never to start. It is far easier to avoid smoking altogether than it is to quit smoking after it has become a habit. Your doctor may be able to help you with some of the other risk factors such as diabetes and high blood pressure. There are medications available that can help control both of these problems.

Section Review

1. What major factors appear to contribute to chronic disease?

2. List at least four cardiovascular diseases.

3. What are four types of strokes?

4. Which risk factors for cardiovascular disease cannot be controlled? Which risk factors can be controlled? Underline or highlight the top three risk factors.

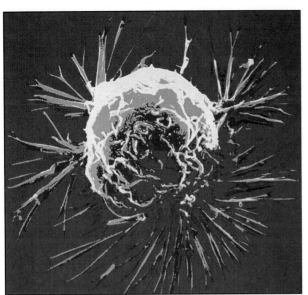

Cancer is not just one disease. Like the cancer cell pictured above, each of the more than 100 different types of cells in the human body can malfunction to cause its own type of cancer.

Cancer

Cancer may be the most feared noninfectious disease in America today. Many people think that cancer means a slow and certain death, but this is not true. Although cancer may kill, it does not always kill. New treatments are being tried every day. Every year more and more people are successfully treated. If you are diagnosed as having cancer today, your chances of surviving and living a normal life are better than ever.

What is cancer?—**Cancer** is a group of diseases in which abnormal cells multiply and spread uncontrollably. As these abnormal cells multiply, they interfere with the function of normal cells. If the cancer is not stopped, the cancer victim will die. Cancer is second only to cardiovascular disease in causing death in the United States.

Cells are normally manufactured by the body to replace old or damaged cells. Sometimes cells are altered, begin to multiply, and form a tissue mass called a **tumor.** If the tumor is not in danger of spreading, it is termed a **benign** (beh NINE) **tumor.** Benign tumors are usually harmless unless they press against a vital organ. Surgery may then be required to remove the benign tumor.

If the cells in the tumor display uncontrolled growth, the tumor is considered to be cancerous and is called a **malignant tumor.** Cancer cells deprive the normal, functional cells of nourishment and can cause them to die. A tumor can also extend to the point that it causes pressure and damage to surrounding tissue. Another danger of a malignant tumor is the ability of the cancerous cells to spread throughout the body. Cancer can spread via the blood stream or the lymphatic system, or be accidentally transplanted from one site to another during surgery. When cancer cells invade distant tissues in the body it is called **metastasis** (meh TAS tuh sis).

What causes cancer?—Some people think that "almost everything causes cancer." This is not true. A chemical or type of radiation that causes a malignant change of cells is called a **carcinogen** (kar SIN uh jun). While food additives, radiation, and other factors may cause cancer, scientists believe that many cancers are caused by the use of tobacco. Some studies indicate that an unbalanced, high fat, low fiber diet may increase cancer risks. Excessive exposure to the sun's ultraviolet rays and the consumption of too much alcohol are two other factors that are linked to cancer. Clearly, your lifestyle can increase or reduce your risk of getting cancer.

Preventing cancer—One of the best ways to prevent cancer is to reduce the number of cancer-causing factors in your life. Most cancers are caused by factors you can control. By changing your lifestyle, you can reduce your cancer risk.

There is also evidence that some foods may give extra help in preventing cancer. For instance, foods from the cabbage family of vegetables and foods rich in vitamins A and C seem to lower the risk of cancer. Diets that are high in fiber provided by whole grain cereals, fruits, and vegetables may reduce the risk of colon cancer. Avoiding foods cured with salt, smoke, or nitrite (found in some types of bacon and hot dogs) may also prevent cancer. Diets high in fat not only promote obesity but may increase the risk of certain cancers.

Avoiding tobacco products is another way to prevent cancer. Lung cancer is one of the most common and deadly types of cancer. It is rare in nonsmokers. Research also indicates that exposure to secondary smoke (smoke in the air surrounding a person who is smoking) can be hazardous to your health. Notice that all tobacco products should be avoided. Smokeless tobacco (chewing tobacco, snuff) may cause oral cancer.

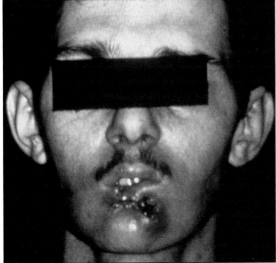

Chewing tobacco can cause oral cancer as pictured. Plastic surgery is sometimes used to fix areas destroyed after cancer has been removed.

A variety of other practices may help you avoid cancer. Avoiding too much sunlight or alcohol are a couple of them. These practices will not prevent all cancers but they may prevent many of them.

Detecting cancer—Many cancers can be cured. The key to curing cancer is to find it before it spreads. Unfortunately, many people never know they have cancer until it has spread through their bodies. Once cancer has spread, it is difficult to treat.

While there is no test that will detect all cancers, there are tests that can detect many of them. Your doctor may give you some of these tests. If you see

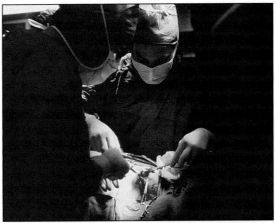

Biopsies are often done to determine the specific type of cancer present in the patient.

your doctor regularly, he will probably let you know of any tests that you should have done.

There are other signals that you can detect on your own. The American Cancer Society has come up with a list of seven warning signals that *may* indicate cancer. If you have a warning signal, it does not mean that you have cancer. It only means that you should see your doctor. The seven warning signals are given below.

Cancer's Warning Signals

C Change in bowel or bladder habits

A A sore that does not heal

U Unusual bleeding or discharge

T Thickening or lump in breast or elsewhere

I Indigestion or difficulty in swallowing

O Obvious change in wart or mole

N Nagging cough or hoarseness

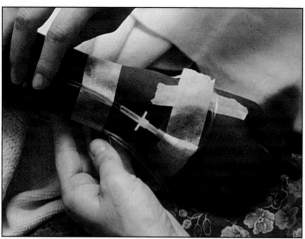
Chemotherapy is often used to destroy cancer cells. Unfortunately, side effects such as nausea, hair loss, weight loss, and fatigue may also accompany the treatment.

Treatment of cancer—There are many experimental methods of treating cancer that are being tried today. Some of these look promising for the treatment of certain cancers. However, the four types of treatment that are used most often are surgery (to cut out the tumor), radiation (to kill the cancer cells), chemotherapy (to kill cancer cells using chemicals), and immunotherapy (to enhance the body's immune system to control cancer).

Fear of cancer—You learned earlier that cancer is one of the most feared diseases in America today. Unfortunately, this fear keeps many people from seeking the medical treatment that can save their lives. These people die from cancer that could have been cured if they had sought treatment when they first suspected that something was wrong. Early detection is the best way to fight cancer in the body. If you ever suspect that you have cancer, do not let fear keep you from getting the help you need.

Section Review

1. Define the term *cancer.*

2. What is the difference between a benign tumor, malignant tumor, and metastasis? Which is the most dangerous?

3. Which of the following factors may increase your chance of developing cancer?

   a) A high-fat diet

   b) Too much exercise

   c) Not enough exposure to the sun

   d) Using tobacco

4. List the seven warning signals of cancer.

5. What is the key to fighting cancer already present in the body?

Diabetes

What did Thomas Edison and Nikita Krushchev have in common? They both had **diabetes.** Diabetes is a group of potentially fatal, noninfectious diseases that afflict an estimated 100 million people worldwide, including 12 million Americans. Diabetes is caused by an inability of the body to produce or respond properly to the hormone insulin. Normally, insulin is released by the pancreas to control the utilization of sugars and starches in the body to produce energy.

Before man had the ability to identify the cause of diabetes or to treat it, people called this mysterious

Many diabetics use a blood glucose monitor to determine their insulin needs. The blood test is usually taken prior to eating and at bedtime.

affliction a "wasting away disease." Following is a description of the horror of diabetes without treatment.

"Moreover, life is disgusting and painful; thirst unquenchable; excessive drinking, which however, is disproportionate to the large quantity of urine, for more urine is passed; and one cannot stop them either from drinking or making water. Or if for a time they abstain from drinking, their mouths become parched and their bodies dry; the viscera seem as if scorched up; they are affected with nausea, restlessness, and a burning thirst; and at no distant term they expire" (Artetaeus of Cappadocia, c. A.D. 150).

Diabetes is not a single disease. In fact, it is a group of disorders of abnormal sugar usage. There are two major types of diabetes. Type I diabetes is also known as insulin-dependent diabetes mellitus (IDDM) and has been called juvenile diabetes. It is not restricted to striking only the young, although it chiefly attacks during childhood. This type of diabetes can be genetic or acquired and causes the body to lose its ability to produce insulin. It affects about ten percent of the diabetic population.

Type II diabetes is now known as non-insulin dependent diabetes mellitus (NIDDM) and was previously known as adult-onset diabetes. This type of diabetes is experienced by over eighty percent of the diabetic population. In people with Type II diabetes, the body can produce insulin but not in sufficient quantities. Scientists have observed that ninety percent of the people suffering from Type II diabetes are obese and are middle-aged or older.

Fortunately, most people today who have diabetes can be successfully treated. Living with diabetes has improved as technology has been sharpened. Insulin used to be derived from the pancreas glands of cows or pigs. However, genetic engineering and research have helped improve the quality of insulin. Insulin pumps and home-monitoring kits are helping diabetics to control their blood-sugar levels more precisely. Diet and nutrition have also been added to the treatment of diabetes. Exercise is also encouraged.

Although daily living with diabetes has been improved, diabetics face the risk of many health complications. Blindness because of retina and lens damage; increased risk of atherosclerosis, heart attack, or stroke; kidney failure; destruction of nerve cells; infection due to slow healing of damaged tissue; poor circulation; and congenital defects

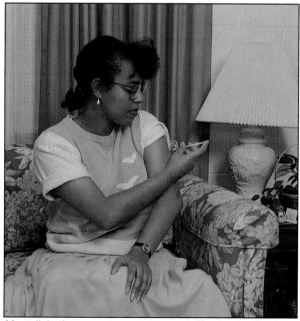

Most diabetic teen-agers can live normal and active lives as long as they are careful to monitor their blood sugar levels, medications, and diets.

Could You Be a Diabetic or Be at Risk?

- Have you experienced a sudden loss in weight?
- Are you constantly thirsty?
- Are you eating more food?
- Do you need to urinate frequently?
- Do you seem to tire easily?
- Do wounds seem to heal slowly?
- Have you experienced a change in your vision?

- Do you have a craving for sweets?
- Does diabetes occur in your family history?
- Are you overweight?

WARNING!

If your answers are **yes**, see your doctor for testing.

in their children are some of the possible problems threatening a diabetic. However, even the complications can be somewhat eased by laser surgery to help save eyesight; bypass surgery to salvage hearts; and dialysis machines and organ transplants to help in cases of non-functioning kidneys. When a diabetic does not follow the balanced lifestyle prescribed by the physician, he puts himself at high risk for these complications.

Insulin-dependent diabetics have to keep a constant balance between the level of blood sugar and the level of insulin in their bodies. Too much physical activity, illness, or excitement can cause their body to use too much blood sugar. Eating too little, waiting too long between eating, or injecting too much insulin can also cause an imbalance since

there is too little sugar and too much insulin in the body. This can lead to insulin shock. In order to establish a balanced level, a conscious person in insulin shock should be given fruit juice or a candy bar. However, if the insulin level is too low and the sugar level is too high, the diabetic could go into a diabetic coma. An insulin injection is the only remedy for diabetic coma.

Diabetes seems to occur more often in certain families. This means that your heredity may give you a predisposition for diabetes. Researchers believe that you may help prevent diabetes by eating properly, exercising regularly, and maintaining proper body weight. If you have relatives with diabetes, it is especially important for you to maintain good habits of diet and exercise.

Section Review

1. How is Type I diabetes different from Type II diabetes?

2. Normally the hormone _____ is released by the _____ to control the utilization of _____ and starches in the body that produce _____.

3. Sandy decided to try out for cheerleading. Although she is diabetic, she knew that if she was careful, she could do a good job. During her practices she was careful to monitor her blood sugar levels. On the day of the try-outs, she got so excited and nervous that she could not eat her lunch. Walking to class, she starts to get very dizzy and pale. You are her friend and have noticed the symptoms. What is wrong with Sandy, and how can you help her?

THE DEATH OF DISEASE

Disease is a constant threat to your health. However, you are not helpless. God has equipped you with a vast array of weapons that can protect you. He has also given you the ability to learn about disease and the opportunity to reduce your risk of disease.

Although the battle with disease must continue here on earth, God has promised a life free from disease with Him in heaven. At the resurrection He will give each of His children a body "like unto his glorious body." These glorious bodies will never know the pain and disease that the present ones must endure. This great truth has been the "blessed hope" of Christians for centuries and will help you overcome the discouragement that can come from a prolonged illness. There is no physical disease that can ever separate you from the love of God.

CHAPTER REVIEW

Terms

diagnose	immunity	fibrillation
prescribe	vaccination	thrombus
prescription drugs	exposure	embolus
nonprescription drugs	incubation	cerebral hemorrhage
symptom	outbreak	aneurysm
second opinion	convalescence	cerebral aneurysm
disease	hepatitis	blood pressure
infectious disease	jaundice	hypertension
noninfectious disease	carriers	sphygmomanometer
pathogens	STDs	systole
bacteria	sterility	dystole
viruses	cardiovascular disease	cancer
vectors	congenital heart disease	tumor
mucous membranes	atherosclerosis	benign tumor
cilia	arteriosclerosis	malignant tumor
inflammation	angina pectoris	metastasis
fever	heart failure	carcinogen
antibodies	arrhythmia	diabetes

Content Questions

1. Who are the members of your health team? Who is the captain of this team?

2. Does God still heal people today?

3. Are all pathogens spread by vectors?

4. Which two stages of an infection occur before the symptoms appear?

5. What are six major groups of pathogens? Which two are the most common pathogens?

6. What are some methods that you can practice to help keep down your exposure to pathogens? List six.

7. How can mucus and cilia help to prevent infection?

8. How can a nutritious diet, water, and rest help your body to fight infection?

9. Why are antibiotics not used to cure colds?

10. Is there a single virus which causes hepatitis?

11. What is meant by the term *cardiovascular disease?* Give a name of a cardiovascular disease.

12. What is meant by the term *congenital disease?*

13. What are the three primary risk factors of cardiovascular disease?

14. Which of the following risk factors for cardiovascular disease can be controlled?

15. Which condition is characterized by fat deposits collecting on artery walls?

16. What is the name of the blood pressure that is measured when the heart contracts?

17. What is a carcinogen?

18. What are two controllable factors that can help to reduce the risk of getting cancer?

19. How can the word *caution* help in detecting cancer?

20. Other than changing one's lifestyle to reduce the risks of cancer, what is a key factor (one of the best ways) to fight cancer?

21. What is diabetes?

22. What is insulin?

23. How does insulin shock differ from diabetic coma?

Application Questions

1. Can God use unsaved men to discover medical and scientific facts? Include in your considerations medical discoveries of the past and the beliefs of the physicians and scientists. Discuss the responsibilities of Christians in using medical discoveries of today.

2. What are the limitations of science? What is mysticism? Explain why Christians should beware of the inclusion of mysticism in the field of science.

3. Your best friend has been diagnosed as having leukemia. What words of comfort and encouragement could you give him? Also cite at least five verses of scriptural encouragement (write out the verses and references).

4. You have been asked to baby-sit a six-year-old child with chicken pox. What items can you take with you in a box or basket to help keep the child occupied until bedtime? List at least six items.

Clinical Laboratory Technologists

Job Description: In order for doctors to accurately diagnose, detect, and treat disease, they must use the abilities of clinical laboratory technologists. The tests the technologists run on specimens help doctors to determine the condition of a patient's health (as in cholesterol tests, tests for mononucleosis, diabetes, etc.). Laboratories use microscopes, specialized equipment, and computerized instruments to perform a number of tests. Medical technologists examine blood, tissue, and body substances; grow samples of bacteria, fungi, or other microorganisms from body fluid or tissue samples; and analyze samples for chemical content. They may also determine blood types and cross-match blood samples for transfusions.

Some clinical laboratory technologists specialize in certain types of testing. Many of these technologists have master's degrees. Clinical

chemistry technologists analyze chemical and hormonal contents of body fluids. Microbiology technologists identify bacteria and other microorganisms in samples. Histology technologists prepare tissue specimens for examination. Blood-bank technologists type, cross-match, and prepare blood and its components for transfusions. Immunology technologists examine responses of the immune system. Cytotechnologists prepare cells and examine them for abnormalities.

Job Location: Many hospitals and laboratories must operate every hour of every day. The personnel must work with infectious specimens and various chemicals (some of which are ill-smelling). Laboratory technologists may also spend a great deal of time on their feet. It is important for clinical laboratory technologists to be accurate, dependable, analytical in judgment, and able to work under pressure. It is also important for a clinical technologist to have good hand-eye coordination, color vision, and communication skills.

Training Required: Most laboratories require at least a bachelor's degree in medical technology or one of the life sciences (biology, anatomy) or chemistry and a one-year internship in a medical technology training program. Some people obtain an associate's degree in order to work as laboratory technicians. Laboratory technicians are used in laboratories to perform a wide range of routine tests.

PERSONAL HYGIENE

In a society that focuses on glamour and fashion, it is important to remember that God places more emphasis on having a pure heart than on having a pretty face. However, your appearance should not be offensive to those you meet. Therefore, you should be clean, your hair neat, and your teeth brushed. Proper personal cleanliness gives you the opportunity to create a good first impression for your Lord.

CHAPTER 10

"For man looketh on the outward appearance, but the Lord looketh on the heart."
I Samuel 16:7

It has been said that cleanliness is next to godliness. Certainly godliness requires much more than cleanliness, but Christians should be clean and wholesome. Since your body is the temple of the Holy Ghost, honor God with your appearance.

MAINTAIN A HEALTHY APPEARANCE— EXERCISE HEALTHFUL HABITS

Your appearance often reflects your current level of health. If you feel healthy, you usually look healthy. However, if you have a stuffy nose and sore throat, you not only feel sick, you usually look sick. When you are ill, your eyes may reflect your distress. You cannot react with vigor, and your entire demeanor lags. One of the best ways to improve your appearance is to improve your health.

You have already learned that diet, exercise, and rest are important influences on your health. Eating nutritious food, engaging in aerobic exercise, and obtaining sufficient rest affect the condition of your skin, your hair, your teeth, and your nails. Practicing good eating habits, incorporating exercise into your routine, and getting enough sleep can also help you to prevent illness. Good health habits help you to feel better and to look better.

Your health habits should also include personal cleanliness. Keeping your body clean affects not only your appearance but also your health. If you keep your teeth clean, you will have less trouble with tooth decay. Bathing and washing not only make you look and smell better, they also serve to wash away bacteria that can cause disease. *Hygiene* is a word used to describe practices that help prevent disease. It is not just a matter of appearing to be clean; it is important to be clean. Your standards for personal hygiene will affect your health, your relationships with others, and your testimony for God.

RADIATE HEALTH—PRACTICE SKIN CARE

How good are you at guessing how old people are? Have you ever been shocked to find someone was much older or younger than you thought? What do you look at when you try to guess a person's age?

Well-Wearing Skin

Careful skin care during early years promotes radiant, healthy skin later in life. At left is Frances Beisel Johnson in 1907 (age 4), 1921 (age 18), and 1947 (age 44). Proper nutrition, adequate sleep, and consistent exercise are also important.

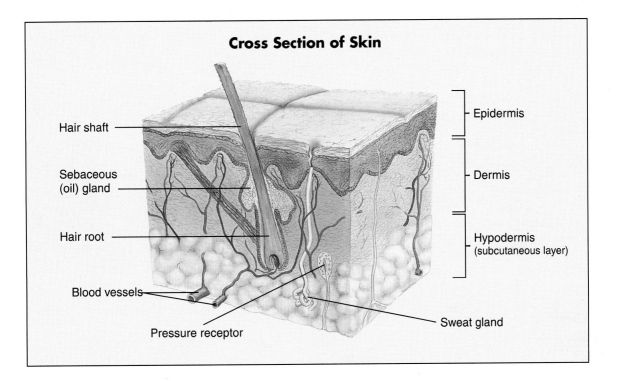

Cross Section of Skin

Hair shaft

Sebaceous (oil) gland

Hair root

Blood vessels

Pressure receptor

Epidermis

Dermis

Hypodermis (subcutaneous layer)

Sweat gland

One indicator of age is the condition of the skin. As people get older, their skin becomes drier and more wrinkled. The constant demand for make-up, skin conditioners, and face-lifts shows how much people want to keep their skin looking young. If you care for your skin properly, you may not need a face-lift to help you look young. Protective skin care can be your personal fountain of youth.

Skin Basics

Your skin is the largest organ of your body. Although you may think it is just an uncomplicated collection of cells that surrounds your body, it is much more. Skin is composed of many layers of cells and has three major divisions: the **epidermis, dermis,** and **hypodermis** (subcutaneous layer). Within these layers are a variety of structures, such as blood vessels; hair; touch, pressure, and temperature receptors; capillaries; and sweat and **sebaceous** (si BAY shus) **glands** (oil glands). The cross section of human skin shown above illustrates these structures.

Because of fluctuations in body size and the need to move, God made skin supple and flexible as well as strong. Cells in the dermis produce a substance called **collagen** (KAHL uh jun) which is an elastic fiber giving skin its strength and flexibility.

Like other organs, your skin has specific functions. You previously learned that your skin forms an almost impenetrable barrier against bacteria, viruses, and some chemicals. Another function of the skin is to help regulate your body temperature. The evaporation of sweat is your skin's method for cooling your body. Since it contains receptors for touch, pressure, temperature, and pain, skin serves to provide sensation. This special organ also assists in the excretion of wastes and the manufacture of vitamin D.

God made skin to last a lifetime. Skin cells are constantly being replaced every minute, every day. New skin cells are formed in the lower section of the epidermal layer. These new cells then travel upward toward the skin's surface, moving the older cells to the surface. During this process the layers of skin cells produce a material, **keratin** (KEHR uh tin), that helps to prevent the loss of moisture. The cells that move toward the skin's surface become keratinized (filled with keratin) and die. The cells in the outer layer of the epidermis are then dead, keratinized cells which are shed or sloughed off. It takes about twenty-eight days for cells of the epidermis to go from being formed to being shed.

Skin Problems

It is easy to get frustrated with your skin. Although others around you may not see your skin as being problem skin, you may think it is. You may have freckled or easily sunburned skin. Perhaps you naturally have dry skin or oily skin. You may also be in a constant battle to keep your skin clear from blemishes. If you are experiencing any of these skin problems, remember that God created you with

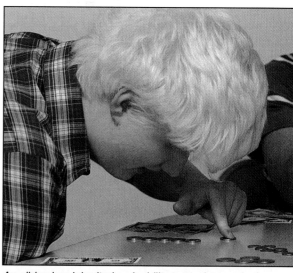

An albino has inherited an inability to produce melanine. Due to the absence of pigmentation, an albino displays light hair, pale skin, and a lack of eye coloring in the iris.

If the Barn Needs Painting

When considering the use of make-up, you may have heard people jest that "if the barn needs painting, paint it." You may have also heard others say, "A little bit of paint helps any old barn." According to the Food, Drug, and Cosmetic Act, a **cosmetic** is any article that is put on your body to cleanse, beautify, promote attractiveness, or alter your appearance without changing your body's structure or function. Toothpaste, shampoo, lipstick, make-up, and perfume are all examples of cosmetics.

In the United States all drugs have to be proven to be safe and effective before they can be sold legally. This is not true of cosmetics, however. While most cosmetic companies do test their products for safety, they are not required to do so. Some cosmetics contribute to better health. For example, toothpaste with fluoride in it may help to reduce tooth decay. Other cosmetics do not contribute to better health. They offer a quick fix which may actually lead to worse health. For example, make-up may be used to hide certain skin conditions. While the make-up may "cover up" the condition, it does nothing to cure it. Some make-up may even make the condition worse. Try to keep your use of cosmetics to a minimum. Be selective in the cosmetics you use. Take time to consider the time it takes to use it, the cost, and the final outcome. If a product is slightly more expensive because it provides necessary treatment for your skin, hair, or teeth, it may be a wise investment. However, if you decide to purchase outrageously expensive cosmetics in order to impress others, then your money is actually being wasted on pride. A good goal is to enhance your natural beauty rather than create an artificial beauty. Strive to keep your actions and appearance glorifying to your Maker.

your skin coloring and your skin type. He knows exactly how He wanted you, what you can do, and how He can use you for His own glory. Thank the Lord for His wise design and learn to control any problems the best way that you can.

Skin Coloring—Skin color is due to pigments found in the epidermis and dermis, as well as the blood in the capillaries in the dermis. Cells (melanocytes) produce the pigment (melanin) in the skin. If the cells produce a large amount of melanin, the skin appears dark. Because people who are light-skinned have very little pigment produced, the pink color of the blood in the dermis shows through their skin. In many people the pigment may tend to form patches of color called *freckles*. Raised growths of brown pigment are called *moles*. Birthmarks can be caused by either enlarged blood vessels or extra pigment. If the skin is unable to produce any pigment, **albinism** (AL buh NIHZ um) occurs. A person with this condition is an albino.

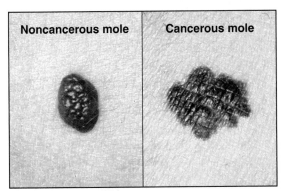

Noncancerous mole	Cancerous mole

Most moles are harmless, but some may develop into melanoma (a cancer of the cells that produce melanin). Note the ABCD rule for recognizing the warning signals of melanoma:
   Asymmetrical mole-like growth.
   Border is ragged, notched, or blurred in appearance.
   Color is not uniform.
   Diameter is greater than 6 millimeters.
Be sure to see your doctor immediately if you notice any changes in the color, size, or shape of a mole.

Skin Types—Skin has sebaceous glands which secrete an oily substance called **sebum** (SEE bum). Sebum is a mixture of fats, cholesterol, proteins, and salts. This substance helps to keep the hair from drying and becoming brittle, coats the skin to keep moisture from evaporating, keeps the skin soft and pliable, and stops the growth of certain bacteria.

The quantity of sebum produced by the skin determines a person's skin type. There are four basic skin types: normal, dry, oily, and combination. Surprisingly, *normal* skin type is not normal for most people; few people enjoy the normal skin type. Normal skin is fine-textured, smooth, and rarely breaks out with blemishes. This type skin tends to get drier as a person ages, but otherwise usually does not present problems.

Dry skin is usually characterized by a lack of sebum which reduces the amount of moisture retained by the skin. Because dry skin also tends to have smaller pores, people with this skin type may suffer from blemishes as sebum gets trapped beneath the surface of the skin. Dry skin may cause the skin to develop wrinkles early.

Oily skin is easily detected by the seemingly constant, shiny film of sebum that covers it. The skin pores are usually larger and blemishes may be a constant threat. A good characteristic about oily skin is that it ages and wrinkles slowly.

Combination skin consists of a mixture of oily skin areas and dry skin areas. The oily sections of the skin usually extend across the forehead to the nose and chin (forming a *T* shape). The remaining sections of the face, around the eyes, the cheeks, and lower jaw areas tend to be dry.

No matter which skin type you have, cleanliness is a priority. Cosmetics may cover a multitude of problems, but consistent skin care is essential for radiant, smooth, moist, healthy skin. Now is the time to prevent acne, wrinkles, and tough skin. Do not wait until you are older. Daily washing removes excess oils, dirt, dead skin, and waste products.

The type of soap you should use depends on your skin type. Many face cleansers are available (oil cleansers, cream cleansers, soap); choose the best one for your skin and use it. You may need to remove make-up and oil residue from your face first by using an oil cleanser. Then use the face cleanser that is best for you. Skin should be rinsed thoroughly with lukewarm water. Hot water can cause your skin to become dry, chapped, and irritated. Always pat your skin dry gently and do not rub it. Depending on your skin type, you may need to finish your cleansing routine by using a moisturizer or skin freshener.

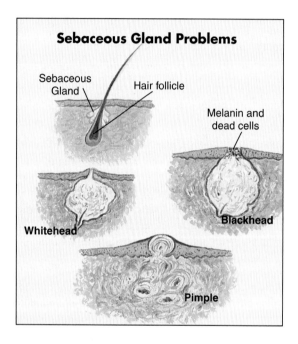

Sebaceous Gland Problems

Sebaceous Gland

Hair follicle

Melanin and dead cells

Whitehead

Blackhead

Pimple

Acne—**Acne** is a skin disorder in which the sebaceous glands of the skin become plugged with extra sebum or infection which may cause the area to be inflamed. This results in blemishes on the skin such as whiteheads, blackheads, and pimples. A whitehead occurs if sebum is trapped in a pore. If the trapped sebum is exposed to the air, the melanin and dead cells make the sebum plug appear dark and results in a blackhead. A pimple occurs if bacteria enters the blemish causing infection in the clogged pore and inflammation of the area.

Acne is one of the most common skin disorders in teen-agers and young adults. This is partially due to hormones causing the body to change. These changes often include an increased production of oil in the skin. As the body matures, oil production usually decreases. Until then, those troubled with acne must provide extra care for their skin.

Other factors that can influence acne include heredity, stress, poor hygiene, and certain cosmetics and drugs. Many people believe that certain foods such as chocolate or soft drinks cause acne. There is no evidence that any food causes acne. There is, however, evidence that a balanced diet contributes to healthy skin.

There is no single cure for acne although the effects of acne usually lessen with time. However, there are a few things that can be done to reduce the severity of it. Here are a few suggestions if you are troubled with acne.

- Cleanliness is very important. Washing thoroughly with a skin cleanser formulated for your skin type should be done daily (or more often if necessary). Use only clean washcloths and towels.
- Keep your hands, headsets, headbands, and chinstraps away from your face. These may carry oils and bacteria that can add to your problem. You should also keep your hair clean and preferably off your face.
- Avoid squeezing pimples and blackheads. Squeezing skin blemishes can make things worse by bruising and scarring your skin.
- Do *not* superscrub your face or use harsh, abrasive, highly alkaline, or deodorant soaps on your face. These damage the skin as well as promote increased oil production.
- Avoid cosmetics that are worn on the skin. If you decide to wear make-up, you should choose water-based cosmetics rather than oil-based cosmetics. If you wear make-up, be sure to thoroughly remove it daily.
- Eat a balanced diet. A balanced diet helps keep your skin healthy. Drinking plenty of water is part of a balanced diet.
- See a doctor. Severe acne needs to be treated under the supervision of a doctor. You do not want temporary skin problems to cause permanent damage.

Suntanned Skin—A tan was once considered to be a symbol of youth and health. Millions of Americans still seek the sun-bronzed look. Because having a tan was so popular, tanning salons providing a year-round service are still available all over the country. However, an increasing number of Americans now realize the potential for danger in pursuing a tanned appearance.

Sunlight is probably the most frequent source of skin damage. Any time the skin is exposed to the sun for more than a few minutes, there can be damage to the skin. Thus, some dermatologists say there is no such thing as a *healthy* tan.

The suntan that looks so good today may leave your skin dry and wrinkled in the future. Constant exposure to the sun gives skin a "weathered" look. It can make you look years older than you are. However, this is not the main danger of tanning.

The sun not only harms your appearance but is also unhealthful. Exposure to the ultraviolet rays of the sun injures the skin and causes the skin, in a protective reaction, to produce melanin (the dark pigment that is the body's natural sun block). The temporary sunburn, peeling, and blisters may mask

cellular changes that occur and may result in permanent cell damage. Skin cancer may result from regular sun exposure and tanning. In fact, tanning is the main cause of skin cancer. Teen-agers should be extremely careful since it is estimated that eighty percent of the life-threatening damage occurs in people before the age of twenty.

If you decide to spend some time in the sun or work in a situation where you are constantly exposed to the sun, here are some tips to help you to reduce damage to the skin.

- Cover up. Clothes do more than keep you modest; clothes protect you from many of the harmful rays of the sun. Tightly woven fabrics, especially cotton, can help protect you.
- Use a sunscreen. A **sunscreen** is a substance that protects the skin from the effects of the sun. Sunscreens are rated on their ability to protect the skin from sunburn by using a sun protection factor or **SPF**. The higher the SPF, the greater the protection provided. The SPF of a sunscreen is often given on the product.
- Avoid the noonday sun. The damaging rays from the sun are most intense between 10 A.M. and 3 P.M.; avoid the sun during this time period.
- Do *not* be fooled by clouds or fog. As much as eighty percent of the sun's rays can be transmitted through them and still cause sunburns.
- Remember that the harmful rays of the sun are reflected from sand and water. Use extra care when you are at the beach, on the lake shore, or in the water (swimming, surfing, boating). Use sunscreen even if you are sitting under an umbrella or a shady tree. Sixty to eighty percent of the sun's rays may be reflected to you.
- Do *not* use tanning devices (sunlamps, tanning beds). Even if the salon advertises the use of only ultraviolet A rays, they can still be dangerous.

The basic formula for maintaining youthful looking and healthy skin can be summarized in three steps. First, keep your skin clean. Second, keep your skin moisturized. Third, protect your skin from ultraviolet rays. These steps along with eating a nutritious diet, engaging in aerobic exercise, and obtaining an adequate amount of sleep should help you to radiate healthy skin.

Section Review

1. What are the four major ways to exercise healthful habits?

2. Sketch and label the following parts of skin without referring to the diagram in the book: epidermis, dermis, hypodermis, hair follicle, sebaceous gland, sweat gland.

3. Other than "keeping your insides in," list at least four functions of skin.

4. What are the four major skin types?

5. What is the difference between a whitehead, blackhead, and pimple?

6. In what way can knowing the SPF of a sunscreen be helpful in preventing cancer?

BE CONSIDERATE—BATTLE BODY ODOR

Have you ever sat next to someone who smelled like a dirty locker room? You probably did your best to put some distance between you. You can dress well and you can look your best, but if you smell bad, no one will want to be around you. Body odor can be very offensive to others.

Some teen-agers are a little sloppy about cleanliness. They may spend hundreds of dollars on the newest clothing styles, but never polish their shoes. Some pay to get their hair professionally styled, but then do not wash it regularly. Others buy expensive cologne and then go to school without taking a shower.

You may not be able to afford the best clothes. You may not be able to afford to have your hair styled, but you can be clean and smell clean.

Sweating It Out

People often think that body odor is caused by sweat. This idea is only partially true. Actually, perspiration does not smell bad. The *sweat glands* secrete odorless sweat (98% water, 2% sodium

Sweat cools the body, excretes waste, keeps skin moist and pliable, and reduces colonization of microorganisms on the skin.

chloride, with small amounts of urea, amino acids, and sugars). A person perspires about one to two pints per day. Body odor results when the bacteria on your skin react with perspiration.

The action of bacteria on perspiration does not result in body odor immediately. It takes some time for the odor to build. The odor usually gets stronger as time passes. That is why your clean gym shirt may not smell bad after a rigorous physical education class. However, if you leave your shirt at school overnight, you may be shocked at the odor when you put it on the next time.

Cleaning It Up

The best weapon in your battle against body odor is personal cleanliness. You should bathe or shower at least once a day and whenever you "work up a sweat." You do not need a lot of fancy or expensive products to get clean. All you need is soap and water.

To effectively fight body odor, both your body and your clothes should be kept clean. Clothes can be a source of unpleasant odors. Clothing such as underclothes or socks absorb perspiration. These should be changed daily and washed each time you wear them.

Because you perspire almost all the time, there are products that can help control body odor. These are deodorants and antiperspirants. A **deodorant** protects you against body odor by killing odor-causing bacteria. Deodorants do not keep you dry; that is what an antiperspirant does. An **antiperspirant** contains ingredients that reduce perspiration. Some products contain both a deodorant and an antiperspirant. Although you may not have needed to use a deodorant or antiperspirant when you were younger, as a teen-ager your body is changing. Deodorants and antiperspirants can be valuable aids in your battle against body odor.

Both deodorants and antiperspirants often contain perfumes that may help to cover any unpleasant odors that do occur. Make sure that the fragrance in your deodorant does not clash with your body chemistry or with the smell of your cologne. Perfumes that smell wonderful in a bottle may not smell good on you or when mixed with other scents. Too much perfume can be just as offensive as a bad odor; use scents with moderation. Your sense of smell may become immune to familiar odors, so do not continually increase the amount of fragrance you put on. Cologne should give just a hint of scent and should not overwhelm those around you.

Body powder may also help on hot, sticky days or after a steamy shower. Foot powders and sprays are available if your feet tend to sweat excessively. They can also help to keep your shoes (and your closet) from developing odors. Of course, nothing helps as much as cleaning. Shoes should occasionally be swabbed with alcohol or disinfectant to help remove perspiration residues.

Section Review

1. What is the basic cause of body odor?

2. What is the difference between a deodorant and an antiperspirant?

3. List at least two other causes for body odor other than unclean skin.

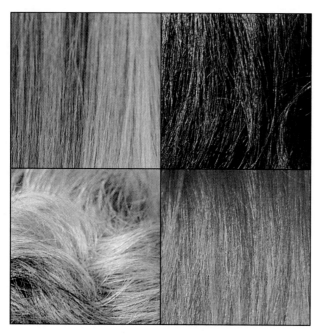

HIGHLIGHT HEALTH—GROOM YOUR HAIR

Your hair contributes little to your physical health. A person can be healthy whether he has red hair, blond hair, brown hair, black hair, white hair, long hair, short hair, or no hair. However, your hair makes a major contribution to your appearance and can be an indicator of health problems. You may not realize how much your hair contributes to your appearance until you change the style or color. Some people may not even recognize you.

The average person has between 90,000 and 150,000 hairs. About one hundred of these hairs are lost and replaced every day. It is interesting that Christ illustrated God's care for His disciples in Matthew 10 by telling them that the hairs of their head were numbered. This shows that God is concerned about every aspect of our lives, even those that may seem unimportant.

Hair Basics

Hair is composed of keratin, the same nonliving, protein fiber found in the outer layer of skin. Each hair is developed in a *hair follicle* which extends into the skin's dermal layer. (See diagram in the skin basics section.) A hair has two parts: the *root* and the *shaft*. The root is located below the skin's surface; the shaft extends beyond the follicle and the skin.

Hair does not grow at a constant rate. Most of the time a single strand grows actively (lasting two to seven years). However, the hair then begins to stop growing and becomes detached from the hair follicle (taking about two weeks). During the final phase (continuing for three to four months), the hair rests in the dermis as the follicle begins to form a new hair beneath. At any point of time, if not disturbed by disease or other factors, most of your hair (85% of it) is in the active growing stage.

What is seemingly familiar from a distance, may be a new sight close up. The familiar hair shaft actually has three distinct layers. The inner core of

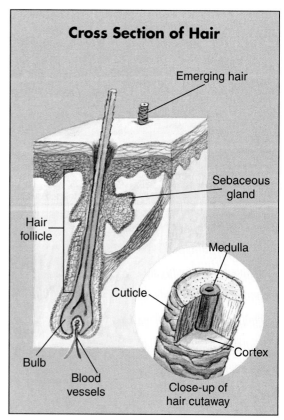

Cross Section of Hair

Emerging hair

Sebaceous gland

Hair follicle

Medulla

Cuticle

Cortex

Bulb

Blood vessels

Close-up of hair cutaway

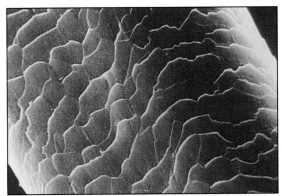

This electron microscope picture shows a hair shaft magnified over 4,000 times. The outer cuticle is composed of thousands of shinglelike scales.

a hair is called the *medulla* (muh DOOL uh). This part of the hair shaft is surrounded by the second layer, the *cortex*. The outer layer of the hair shaft is a layer that looks like shinglelike scales, the *cuticle*.

The amount of hair you have on your head (scant or thick) depends on how many hair follicles you were born with. Blond people usually have about 140,000, brunets average 108,000, and redheads average 90,000 hair follicles. The texture (thin or coarse) of your hair is determined by the density of the medulla. The color of your hair depends on the type and amount of melanin found in the cortex. The amount of shine or dullness of your hair results from the position of the cuticle. If it is lying flat against the cortex, the hair reflects light and makes the hair appear to have a sheen. If the cuticle is ruffled up, the hair will appear dull. Whether your hair is straight, wavy, or curly is determined by the way the hair is formed. If the hair shaft that is developed is round, the hair will be straight. In wavy hair, the hair shaft alternates between being round and oval in shape.

Hair Care

There are thousands of products that are sold for your hair. Some promise shiny and manageable hair. Others promise to fight dandruff or to reduce split ends. With so many choices you may feel overwhelmed with the prospect of caring for your hair properly. Actually, hair care is fairly simple.

The most important thing to do is to keep it clean. Although soap will clean hair, you should wash your hair with a shampoo. Soap can leave a filmy residue on your hair that makes it look dull.

Most shampoos contain similar ingredients. Some make extravagant claims but really can do little more than clean the hair. Despite their claims, no shampoo or conditioner can grow hair, change the chemical composition of hair (like adding protein), or cure split ends. It is true, however, that certain shampoos and conditioners can coat the hair. This provides more manageability, protection, and temporary repair of split ends by sticking them together.

How often you wash your hair depends on how oily and dirty your hair tends to get. If you have oily hair, use hair spray, engage in activities that cause you to sweat, or are in a place where dust or dirt is abundant, you may have to wash your hair daily. Do not worry about damaging your hair through frequent washings. If you use a mild shampoo followed by a conditioner, daily hair washing should not damage your hair. However, if you have dry hair, you may only need to wash your hair once or twice a week.

When you wash your hair, use warm and not hot water. Be sure to use your fingertips to work the shampoo into the scalp, behind the ears, and the nape of the neck. Thoroughly rinse the shampoo out of the hair with cool water. A cream rinse or conditioner can be applied to aid in removing residues and in restoring oils to the hair shaft. Some conditioners are formulated to help make your hair more manageable by reducing static electricity and others help to temporarily bind split ends. After rinsing the conditioners out, pat your hair dry. Do not comb or brush it when it is wet since wet hair is weak and susceptible to damage. If you must remove tangles, gently use a wide-toothed comb.

Brushing should be done to remove tangles and help to distribute oils along the hair shaft. However, it is best to avoid rigorous scalp massage and excessive combing or brushing. These place unusual stress on the hair shaft and can damage it. Combing

Natural boar bristle brushes were used in the past to distribute oil through the hair. However, excessive brushing (the proverbial 100 strokes) could damage hair rather than enhance it.

Split Ends—If the ends of the hair become dry and brittle, split ends may occur. When it comes to split ends, the word *prevention* should come to mind. It is better to prevent split ends through gentle handling of the hair than it is to get rid of split ends (since the only way to fix split ends is to cut them off). In order to avoid damaging the hair, consider the following pointers.

- Keep your natural hair moisture in by avoiding the application of harsh shampoos.
- Gently brush and comb your hair.
- Use natural bristle brushes and flexible combs with rounded tips.
- Use great care (and preferably professional application) when using permanents, hair straighteners, or hair coloring agents. Do not use them too often.
- Keep the heat on hair driers at a low or cool setting.
- Use curling irons, hot rollers, and crimpers cautiously and rarely.
- Girls should use only coated rubber bands, clips, and bobby pins in their hair. Metal edges and tight bands can damage hair.

and brushing the hair should not be so vigorous that it scratches the scalp.

In order to protect the hair from infestation of lice and other vectors and pathogens, it is wise not to share brushes, combs, and hair accessories with others and to keep them clean. Wash your grooming equipment at least once a week with a mild detergent (or your shampoo) and let them air dry (brush bristles down).

Hair Problems

Although a strand of hair that refuses to stay in place may present a temporary "hair problem," some conditions of the scalp and hair are more serious. Some of these problems can be prevented or treated. Even if you do not have trouble with your hair, basic information about hair problems should be understood.

Dandruff—**Dandruff** is a condition in which flakes of dead skin are shed from the scalp. Regular washing of the hair and scalp is the best way of controlling dandruff. Dandruff shampoos can be helpful if they are used regularly (but be careful not to overuse them). Some medicated shampoos are formulated to kill bacteria and to remove scales (those with zinc pyrithione, sulfur, or salicylic acid) or to slow down the growth rate of the epidermis (those with selenium sulfide and tars). If you have a problem with dandruff that does not respond to these treatments, you should see your doctor.

Loss of Color—Depending on the genes you inherited, you may have to deal with gray hair before others your age. When the melanocytes stop producing melanin, the hair will turn white. Why white? That is the natural color of keratin. Some diseases can cause the body to make gray hair (typhus, malaria, diabetes, hyperthyroidism, anemia, and influenza). Radiation and severe trauma can also result in the loss of hair color.

Loss of Hair—The loss of hair is termed **alopecia** (AL uh PEE shuh). There are many different reasons for the loss of hair. Most commonly, heredity causes it, resulting in male/female pattern baldness (*androgenetic alopecia*). The following list shows other reasons for hair loss.

- Age (*alopecia senilis*)
- Loss of hair due to tight pulling on it (*traction alopecia*)
- Scar-producing diseases or injuries (*cicatricial alopecia*)
- Losing hair in clumps or areas (*alopecia areata*)
- Total hair loss (*alopecia totalis*)
- Loss of all body hair (*alopecia universalis*)

Sometimes temporary hair loss can be caused by skin diseases, malnutrition, high fever, radiation, ingestion of metals (tin, arsenic, lead, mercury), fungus, and some medications. If you notice an increased loss of hair, you may need to analyze your diet, lifestyle, and genetic background. If you cannot readily identify a reason for the hair loss, see your doctor, since the loss of hair can also signal health problems.

Section Review

1. Using the diagram in the skin basics section, draw a diagram showing the following parts of the hair: hair follicle, hair root, hair shaft, sebaceous gland.

2. List the three layers that compose a hair shaft and beside each describe how it contributes to the appearance of the hair.

3. Outline basic principles to remember and the procedure to use in shampooing the hair.

TRIM THE EDGES—CARE FOR YOUR NAILS

Have you ever tried to pick up a pin or a dime when your nails had broken to the quick? Perhaps you have experienced the pain of a hangnail. You may have been introduced to a person of importance and wanted to hide your hands rather than shake hands because of broken or bitten nails. If any of these have occurred in your life, you will probably agree that hand and nail care are important.

Nail Basics

The nails on your hands and toes are made of hardened cells that have been keratinized. The nail is actually composed of three parts: the *nail root* (formed in an area under the skin), the *nail plate* (the main body of the nail), and the *free edge* (the part that extends beyond the finger or toe). The nail is formed by cells in the *nail matrix* found at the

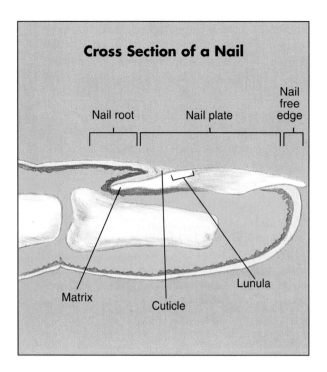

Cross Section of a Nail

Nail root

Nail plate

Nail free edge

Matrix

Cuticle

Lunula

or a nail brush. Using the end of a metal file that comes with metal nail clippers can damage the nails.

Fingernails grow faster than toenails. The average growth of fingernails is about 0.04 inch (1 mm) per week. Nails need to be trimmed; unlike skin, the old, extra cells are not sloughed off. Some people cut their nails in an oval shape. However, because they clip so close to the skin edging the nail plate, the nail can grow under the skin (causing the painful problem of ingrown nails). Toenails should be trimmed straight across. Fingernails can be rounded at the corners; however, the more pointed the cut, the weaker the nail, and the more susceptible the nail is to splitting.

Nails should be cut only if a great deal of nail is to be removed. Shaping of the nail can be accomplished by using the *fine* side of an emery board. Metal files should not be used since they can tear and split the nail. Nails should be filed from the outside toward the center. Filing back and forth may cause the nail to split.

base of the nail. When viewing the nail from above, you may notice a pale crescent shape under the nail plate. This is called the *lunula* (LOON yuh luh). This is a portion of the matrix that can be seen through the nail plate. You may also notice a thin layer of clear skin bordering the nail. This is the *cuticle,* which prevents bacteria and other pathogens from entering the matrix.

Nail Care

Nails should be kept clean and trimmed. Dirt that accumulates under the free edge can provide a growing place for bacteria as well as damage your appearance. The treatment of caring for your fingernails is called a *manicure;* caring for your toenails is termed a *pedicure.* Both men and women should take time to care for their nails. Daily care of the nails will minimize the time and effort spent on a weekly manicure and biweekly (every two weeks) pedicure. You can clean your nails immediately after a bath, when washing your hands, or after washing the dishes by using an orangewood stick

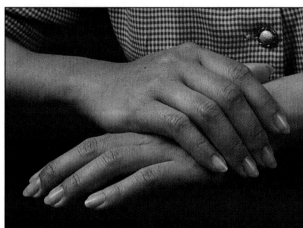

It does not take a lot of money to have well-groomed nails, but does take time and consistent care.

The following procedure outlines a manicure and pedicure.

- Cut any broken or split nails.
- File and shape nails using the fine side of an emery board and filing from the sides to the center.

- Soak nails in a solution of warm water with a drop of moisturizing shampoo.
- Push back cuticles with an orangewood stick or towel.
- Trim any hangnails immediately. Do not pull them; cut them.
- Use cuticle remover only if necessary (and then use it sparingly and according to directions). Do *not* use cuticle cutters (if you must have the cuticle trimmed, let a professional do it).
- Moisturize hands, feet, and skin around the nails with moisturizing lotion. If hands and feet are very dry, put on cotton gloves or socks after applying lotion for an easy overnight moisturizing treatment.

Nail Problems

If you have ever had a hangnail, perhaps you were surprised how one little nail problem could cause so much pain and aggravation. Amazingly, some nail problems can be extremely painful. Not that the nail itself is in pain, but the areas surrounding the nail can be injured or become infected. Ingrown nails can cause great pain. These can be avoided if you keep the cut edge of the nail above the nail bed. Trim and file only the free edge of the nail. Remember that toenails should be cut or filed straight across.

Another painful nail problem is that of hangnails. The best treatment for hangnails is prevention. Keep your hands and nails moisturized. Eat nutritious food. If you still get hangnails, be sure to cut them off immediately. Waiting may cause them to tear, damaging the skin and causing pain.

Split nails or brittle nails that constantly break can be caused by poor nutrition, sickness, or drying of the nail. Nails are often subjected to harsh and drying chemicals (detergents, polish removers, artificial nail adhesives, nail hardeners with formaldehyde). Protect nails from harsh chemicals and solvents by wearing protective gloves. Dry your hands thoroughly and apply moisturizing lotion after extended exposure to water.

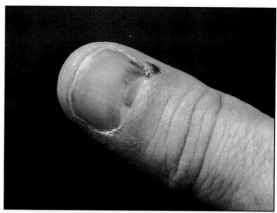

The crushing of tissue beneath a nail or skin can cause blood to accumulate in the damaged area, resulting in a black or blue discoloration.

Some nail problems look worse than they feel. Discolored nails can be caused by staining (chemicals, smoking) or hitting the nail (blue-black color from blood clotting under the nail). White spots result from air pockets of keratin which occur when the nail is damaged and a small portion of the nail separates from the nail bed. Nails with ridges or grooves in them can be caused by picking at or tearing the cuticle. Some cuticle removers can result in grooved nails. Skin diseases can also cause ridges (psoriasis, eczema, fungal infection). If you suspect a skin disease as the cause, see your doctor for help.

SAVE YOUR SMILE—CLEAN YOUR TEETH

There is power in your smile. Your smile can help eliminate fear and give hope. Your smile can show others that you are happy. It can tell those you meet that you are friendly. Your smile is worth protecting.

Some people are afraid to smile because of the condition of their teeth. They may try to smile with their mouth closed or use their hand to cover their smile. A mouth filled with stained, decayed teeth can destroy the effect of a smile. You can save your smile by protecting your teeth.

Tooth Basics

Everyone has two sets of teeth given to him by God. The first set, the **deciduous** (dih SIHJ oo us) **teeth,** are sometimes referred to as baby teeth or primary teeth. These begin to appear (usually accompanied by much drooling and crying) when a child is about six months old and continue surfacing until all twenty teeth are in. The second set, the **permanent teeth,** usually start to come in at the age of six. A total of thirty-two permanent teeth appear during growth to adulthood.

A tooth can be divided into three major sections: the *crown* is the portion found above the gums, the *root* is the portion embedded into the bone, and the *neck* is where the crown joins the root. Each tooth is composed of bonelike materials. The hard layer that covers the crown of the tooth is made of *enamel*. Enamel is the hardest substance in the body. It protects the tooth from the wear of chewing and from acids formed by bacteria in the mouth. The second layer which gives the tooth its form is made of *dentin* (DEN tin). This layer encases an area filled with blood vessels and nerves, the *pulp cavity*. The outer edge of the dentin in the root area is protected by a hard layer, the *cementum* (sih MEN tum). A tissue layer encases the root of the

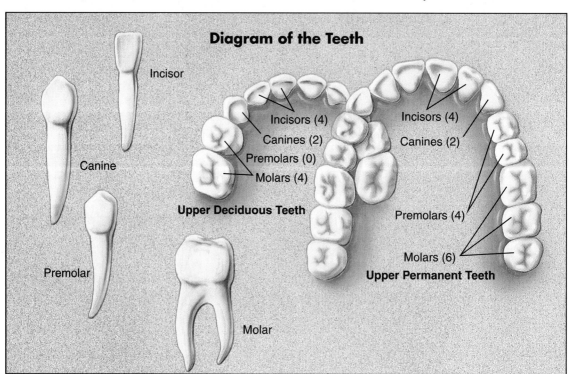

The incisors are chisel-shaped and designed for cutting into food. The canines (cuspids) have a pointed surface (called a cusp); they tear and shred food. The premolars are designed for grinding and crushing food. The molars are also designed for grinding food.

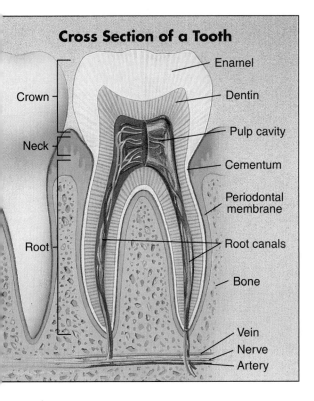

Cross Section of a Tooth

- Enamel
- Dentin
- Pulp cavity
- Cementum
- Periodontal membrane
- Root canals
- Bone
- Vein
- Nerve
- Artery

Crown

Neck

Root

They influence the shape of your entire face. Poor dental health can actually disfigure your face.

Tooth Problems

One of the most common diseases in the United States today is tooth decay. Ninety-five percent of Americans have some tooth decay. It is estimated that by age seventeen the average young adult has seven or eight decayed, filled, or missing teeth.

Tooth decay is common, but it is not inevitable. Your teeth were designed by God to last a lifetime if you care for them properly. Your teeth are such a valuable asset; they are certainly worth the time and effort it takes to care for them.

Dental Caries—Since your teeth are designed to last a lifetime, you are probably wondering what causes them to decay. **Dental caries** (tooth decay) is caused by bacteria combining with sugar to form acids. These acids are so strong that they can dissolve the protective tooth enamel. **Cavities** result when the enamel is removed to expose the dentin or pulp cavity. In order to avoid dental caries, you must reduce the length of time the enamel is exposed to the bacteria. The bacteria do not do much damage unless they are allowed to remain on the teeth. When this happens, the bacteria organize into colonies and form an almost invisible, sticky film called **plaque** (plak). Plaque can cause tooth decay and gum disease. If plaque is not removed, it can harden and form a deposit on the teeth called **calculus.** The rough surface of calculus provides a haven for plaque development and traps bacteria which causes inflammation of the gum and promotes gum disease.

Periodontal Disease—Many people are only concerned about avoiding cavities. They suppose that consistent tooth brushing will provide a sort of insurance policy against having to get dentures. They forget that dental caries is not the only problem. **Periodontal disease** (gum disease) is a major problem. Many times people can have healthy tooth enamel and diseased periodontal ligaments. It is important to keep plaque and calculus from infecting this membrane which connects the tooth and the

tooth. This membrane, the *periodontal* (PEHR ee oh DAHN tl) *ligament,* connects the tooth to the bones (maxilla or mandible) of the skull. It also acts as a shock absorber to the chewing action.

There are at least three different functions for your teeth. The primary function of teeth is to chew your food. Your teeth are a vital part of the process of eating and digesting food. Without teeth, you could probably survive, but your diet would have to be totally different.

Your teeth are also necessary for good speech. Many consonant sounds are almost impossible to say distinctly without using your teeth. You may have heard someone speak without teeth and wondered why it was difficult to understand him. Without teeth, a person cannot produce crisp, clear speech.

Finally, your teeth are a valuable contribution to your appearance. The importance of teeth in a smile has already been mentioned, but your teeth contribute more to your appearance than a pretty smile.

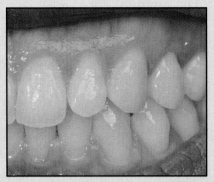
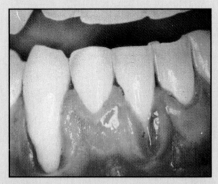

Floss To Prevent Flaws

People often grow up thinking that oral hygiene consists of brushing teeth, visiting the dentist, and avoiding candy; however, there is more to it. Daily flossing helps to prevent periodontal disease. Beautiful, polished teeth are of little good if they fall out because of diseased gums. Oral hygiene requires consistent brushing and flossing.

gum. The plaque that forms on the gums can cause inflammation as well as destroy gum tissue and bone tissue. If left untreated, periodontal disease can even cause the tooth to fall out of its socket!

Halitosis—Bad breath or **halitosis** (HAL ih TOH sis) can be an embarrassing condition. No matter how nice you look, how well you are dressed, or how healthy you may be, bad breath can cancel all the effects of good grooming. Infected tonsils, gums, or teeth can cause halitosis. However, food, tobacco, indigestion, lung infections, and a dry mouth or throat can also cause bad breath.

One of the best ways to fight halitosis is to practice good health habits. If you stay healthy, brush and floss often, and see your dentist regularly, you will probably have few problems with bad breath. Drinking plenty of water and keeping your mouth moist can also be helpful. See your dentist if bad breath persists; persistent halitosis can be a symptom of a medical problem.

Accidental Loosening—In order to prevent knocking a tooth or several teeth out, many sports require the use of a mouthpiece or teeth protectors. These help to protect against the effects of blows to the chin, top of the head, and the face. However, a thrown baseball, tennis ball, or even a frisbee can accidentally jar a tooth loose. Sometimes a fall, a car accident, or running into a wall (or another person) can cause a person to lose teeth. Accidents can and will happen. In some cases, the tooth can be successfully reimplanted into the gum. In case of an accidental loss of a tooth, place the tooth in a glass of milk or hold it inside the bottom lip and go immediately to the dentist. Do not wash the tooth or try to clean it. Also, do not disrupt the tissue around the tooth while transporting it to the dentist's office.

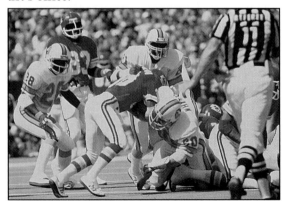

In order to prevent injury to the mouth and teeth, mouthpieces are mandatory in many contact sports.

Brace Up! Orthodontics Are Only Temporary

When a dentist refers to your **occlusion,** he is talking about the way that your upper and lower teeth fit together when you bite down. **Malocclusion** refers to the problem of having teeth that do not line up properly when biting. Some people suffer from minor malocclusions, but others must see an **orthodontist** (a dentist who practices methods of straightening teeth) in order to correct the problem.

It is not just a matter of improving appearances that may motivate a person to go to an orthodontist. A malocclusion can hinder a person from chewing and grinding food correctly (which can cause problems with digestion). Some malocclusions can keep a person from speaking distinctly. Other malocclusions can promote tooth decay if teeth are pushed against each other to impede brushing and flossing between the teeth.

Many teenagers wear braces or dental appliances in order to help them correct their tooth alignment. Fortunately, this is only a temporary inconvenience. It is important to obey the orthodontist's instructions in order to insure proper alignment. Do not give up or let up on the treatment. Because teeth tend to return to their original position, retainers are often prescribed. Many teens have had their braces removed too early or refused to consistently wear their retainers and lived to regret it later.

Some people have had to go back to the orthodontist and start all over again because they were not patient or obedient.

Those who wear dental appliances must also follow their orthodontist's instructions for cleaning and brushing their teeth. Proper methods and equipment should be used to discourage tooth decay and gum disease.

Tooth Care

It has been said that "the only thing necessary for the triumph of evil is for good men to do nothing." Tooth decay works just about the same way. All it takes for you to have a mouth full of cavities is for you to do nothing. To avoid tooth decay you must fight back. Here are five ways to fight decay.

1. *Brush your teeth*

The most important strategy for fighting tooth decay is to brush your teeth regularly. Brushing disorganizes the bacterial colonies that cause decay. It is best to brush your teeth after every meal. You should brush thoroughly at least once every day. It is particularly important to brush before you go to bed since bacteria can work overtime while you sleep.

When you brush your teeth, attempt to brush each tooth by itself. Try to brush every surface of the tooth that you can reach with your toothbrush. Plaque often builds up near the gums; therefore, special care should be given to brushing this area. Using your toothbrush, vibrate the bristles under the edge of the gum and then roll the brush on the surface toward the edge of the tooth. Because bacteria also build up on your tongue, you should brush your tongue as well as your teeth. It takes three to five minutes to brush your teeth thoroughly.

It may surprise you to know that brushing regularly is much more important than the brand of

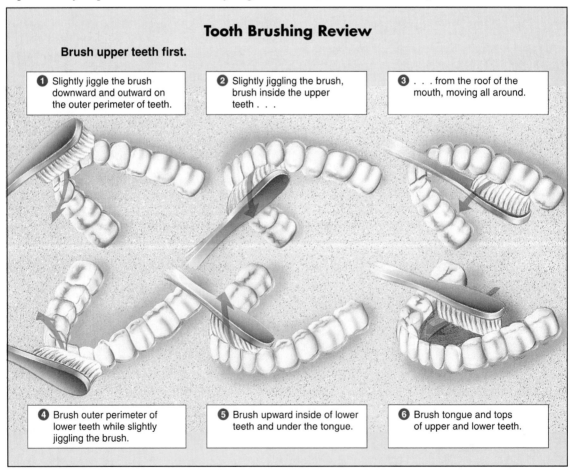

Tooth Brushing Review

Brush upper teeth first.

❶ Slightly jiggle the brush downward and outward on the outer perimeter of teeth.

❷ Slightly jiggling the brush, brush inside the upper teeth . . .

❸ . . . from the roof of the mouth, moving all around.

❹ Brush outer perimeter of lower teeth while slightly jiggling the brush.

❺ Brush upward inside of lower teeth and under the tongue.

❻ Brush tongue and tops of upper and lower teeth.

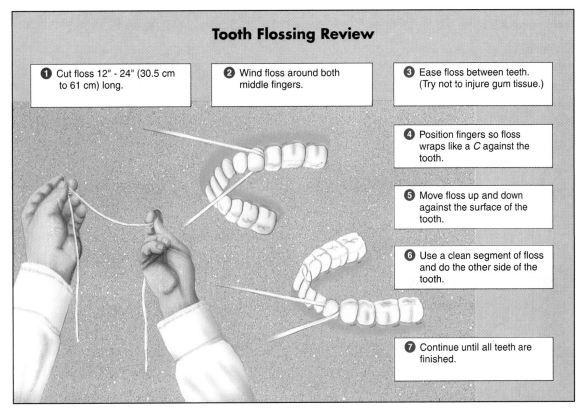

Tooth Flossing Review

1. Cut floss 12" - 24" (30.5 cm to 61 cm) long.

2. Wind floss around both middle fingers.

3. Ease floss between teeth. (Try not to injure gum tissue.)

4. Position fingers so floss wraps like a *C* against the tooth.

5. Move floss up and down against the surface of the tooth.

6. Use a clean segment of floss and do the other side of the tooth.

7. Continue until all teeth are finished.

toothpaste you use. In fact, baking soda and water can be as effective as some toothpastes. Toothpastes containing fluoride can help prevent tooth decay since fluoride strengthens the enamel and makes it more resistant to decay. Choose a toothpaste that is fluoridated.

To brush your teeth properly, you should use the proper toothbrush. Choose a toothbrush that has a head small enough that you can maneuver it in your mouth. It is also important to choose one that has soft bristles. Soft bristles are effective in cleaning the teeth and in avoiding damage to the gums. Finally, you should replace your toothbrush every three months or after you have had a streptococcal or upper respiratory infection.

2. *Floss your teeth*

Many people think that if the crown of the tooth is kept clean and polished their dental practices are complete. Although brushing is an effective way to fight tooth decay, it cannot remove the plaque that builds up between your teeth. The most effective method for removing this plaque is **flossing.** Flossing means to use a threadlike material called *dental floss* to remove plaque between your teeth. You must consistently and completely floss your teeth daily in order to prevent periodontal disease.

Floss can be waxed or unwaxed, flavored or unflavored. Although any type of floss can remove plaque, unwaxed does not leave a residue on teeth like waxed floss does. However, if your teeth are in such close contact that unwaxed floss cannot be inserted between your teeth, use waxed floss. The most important factor about flossing is to do it regularly. Floss your teeth at least once each day.

3. *Drink fluoridated water*

Drinking water that has fluoride added to it can reduce tooth decay by about 50 percent. It appears to be most beneficial, however, when it is done while teeth are forming. The fluoride in drinking water appears to harden the teeth and make them more resistant to decay.

4. *Avoid eating sweets*

Bacteria grow most rapidly when they have an abundant food supply. Sugary foods provide bacteria with an abundant food supply. You can fight decay by eating fewer sweets and by brushing your teeth any time you do eat sweets.

5. *Visit your dentist regularly*

You open the mailbox, and there on top of the stack is a reminder from your dentist that it is time for another checkup. A dentist is a doctor who specializes in the care of the mouth and teeth. It is important that you see your dentist regularly. Regular visits often allow early detection and treatment of any dental problems you might have. Another service provided by the dentist or his staff is the cleaning of your teeth. You should have your teeth cleaned every six months.

A newer technique your dentist may use is to treat your teeth with a dental sealant. Sealants are used to fill in the deep grooves of the teeth. They are used mainly on molars and permanent teeth to form a protective barrier between the acids that

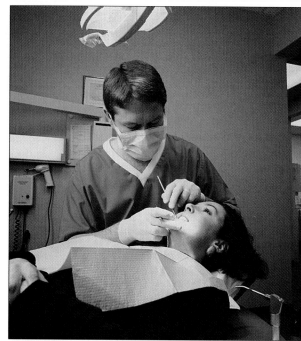

Regular visits to the dentist should begin at age four and continue at six-month intervals.

cause decay and the surface of your teeth. Sealants appear to be a valuable tool for preventing tooth decay.

Section Review

1. What are the three regions of the nail?

2. Other than giving yourself a weekly manicure, what are some other ways you can care for your nails?

3. a. What are the three major regions of the tooth?
   b. Which parts of the tooth serve as protectors?
   c. Which part of the tooth gives the tooth its form?
   d. Which part of the tooth supplies nutrients, oxygen, and feeling to the tooth area?

4. Prepare a poster or cartoon collage that teaches five ways to help prevent dental caries and periodontal disease.

LOOKING GOOD—PROTECT YOUR EYES

You have heard it before. You know, the "eat your carrots so you will have pretty eyes" line. It is not that eating carrots will change the shape, color, or vision of your eyes. However, the vitamin A found in carrots helps the membranes of the eye to function well. Healthy membranes are also better equipped to battle infection. So, healthy eyes are "pretty eyes." Other than eating nutritiously, there are other ways to care for your eyes. This section discusses ways to promote healthy eyes.

Eye Basics

God made an amazing system which enables man to see. The eye receives light and transforms the light into electrochemical signals (nerve impulses) that travel to the brain to form a mental image. In order to understand how light energy is changed into nerve impulses, you must understand the design of the eye itself.

The eyes rest in protective bony sockets of the skull called *orbits.* Each eye is surrounded by six muscles (which control eye movement) and fatty tissue (which cushions the eye and helps it move smoothly). The front of the eye is protected by the eyelids. Eyelashes on the lids help to keep debris from falling into the eye. The eyelids also protect the eyes from the direct rays of the sun and from drying. The lids sweep the fluid (tears) produced by the lachrymal glands (tear ducts) over the eye to moisten it, protect it from infection, and wash away irritants. A final layer of protective tissue called the *conjunctiva* lies under the lids and bends back to cover the exposed front of the eyeball.

There are three major layers that make up the eye. The tough outer layer, partially composed of white tissue, is called the *sclera* (SKLIHR uh). This portion gives shape to the eyeball and helps to protect the inner parts. The other part of this layer, the *cornea,* is a clear, circular area that forms a

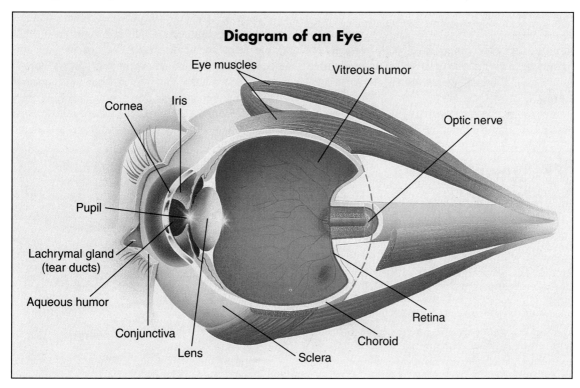

Diagram of an Eye

Eye muscles

Vitreous humor

Cornea

Iris

Optic nerve

Pupil

Lachrymal gland
(tear ducts)

Aqueous humor

Conjunctiva

Lens

Sclera

Retina

Choroid

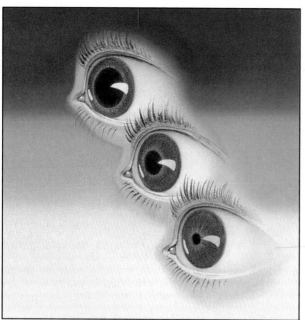

In dim light, the pupil dilates (opens up) when the muscle fibers of the iris contract, letting in as much light as possible. Intense light causes the pupil to constrict so a small amount of light will filter into the sensitive inner portion of the eye.

lining the back portion of the eye, and the *iris* with the *pupil* in the front of the eye. The iris is what you normally look at to see the color of a person's eyes. What looks like a solid disk of color is actually muscle fibers that control the amount of light allowed to enter the eye. The pupil is the dark hole in the center of the iris through which light can enter the eyeball. Directly behind the pupil is the *lens*. This flexible structure aligns the light rays as they enter the eye. The lens changes shape when surrounding fibers flatten (and fatten) or stretch (and thin) it in order to help a person focus on objects near or far.

The inner layer changes the wavelengths of light into a nerve impulse that can be "seen" by the brain. This inner layer is called the *retina*. The retina lines the back of the eyeball with special cells that are sensitive to certain colors (wavelengths) of light. These special cells, *photoreceptors,* change chemically when stimulated by light rays and send the electrochemical messages (nerve impulses) to the brain through the *optic nerve*.

There are two types of photoreceptors: rods and cones. **Rods** are cells which can distinguish light from dark. The chemical reaction of the rods enables you to see in dim light and allows you to distinguish shapes and movement. It is because they do not detect color that you cannot see colors at night. **Cones** are responsible for color vision and for sharpness of vision. These cells are stimulated

bulge in the front center of the eye. The cavity formed beneath this bulge is not empty but filled with a clear fluid called **aqueous** (AHK wee us) **humor.**

The middle layer of the eye contains the *choroid* (KOR OYD, tissue containing many blood vessels),

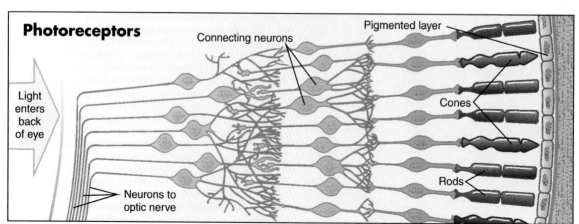

It is estimated that each eye contains about 120 million rods and 7 million cones in the retina.

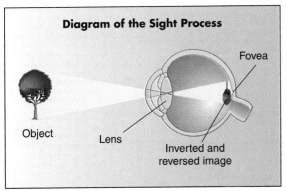

Diagram of the Sight Process

Fovea

Object

Lens

Inverted and reversed image

While it is your eyes that receive the images, it is your brain that puts the image in proper perspective and gives it meaning.

by bright light and can detect the three primary colors that provide sight with a full range of color.

In the back center of each eye is a concentrated area of cones. This area, the **fovea** (FOH vee uh), relays the sharpest images to the brain. Light rays entering the eye are bent by the lens so that they will hit the fovea. The images on the retina are upside down and reversed. The brain receives this information and automatically turns the visual image right-side-up and right-side-around.

The brain not only translates the chemical message to turn the image around but also incorporates the message sent from one eye with the message sent from the other eye. Since they are in slightly different positions, both eyes get a slightly different view of an object. The ability to focus on one object with two eyes is called **binocular vision.** The ability to use binocular vision to perceive depth (see three dimensions) is called **stereoscopic vision.** The ability to see out of the corners of your eyes to the areas to the side of your main focus is called **peripheral vision.**

The eyeball is not hollow. It is filled with a clear, jellylike substance called **vitreous** (VIHT ree us) **humor.** This substance helps to transmit light, to hold the lens and retina in place, and to give the eye its shape. Some people see shadows, dots, or squiggles when staring at a white sheet of paper or a blank wall. Because the vitreous humor is never replaced, dead cells and other *floaters* remain to cause vague

shadows. The brain usually dismisses these images to focus on other things. A sudden appearance of floaters, an increased number of floaters, or accompanying flashes of light should be investigated by your eye doctor.

Eye Problems

Need to see the eye doctor? Whom do you call for an appointment? The ophthalmologist? The optometrist? The optician? Specific differences among these three professions are regulated by the laws of each state. However, the basic differences are as follows.

- An optician is a technician who makes and sells frames and lenses.
- An optometrist is a doctor of optometry (O.D.) who is licensed to examine, measure, and treat certain defects of the healthy eye.
- An ophthalmologist is a medical doctor (M.D.) who specializes in treating diseases of the eye. Although he can also examine, measure, and treat defects of the eye, an ophthalmologist can perform surgery on the eye and treat serious eye injuries.

Needing glasses or contact lenses should not be the only reason to have an eye examination. Be sure to schedule a regular vision checkup to make sure that your eyes are healthy and your vision is accurate.

Visual Acuity—In order to determine your visual acuity (how sharp your vision is), the doctor will probably ask you to read letters from a Snellen chart that is either posted on the wall or projected on a

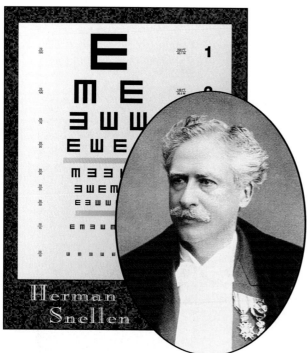

Dr. Hermann Snellen was a Dutch ophthalmologist of the nineteenth century who developed a chart that is widely used today to determine the visual capabilities of an individual. Nonreaders can be tested by using the Snellen chart, which has the letter E placed facing different directions. They need only indicate the direction of the E for the doctor to assess the limits of their vision.

converge to form an image in front of the retina rather than converging at the retina. A concave lens can be used to cause the light rays to focus on the retina and correct nearsightedness.

When the light rays converge at a point beyond the retina, **farsightedness** occurs. A farsighted person can clearly see objects in the distance but not up close. To correct this condition, a convex lens can be used to converge the light rays on the retina.

An **astigmatism** (uh STIG muh TIHZ um) is caused by a lens or cornea that is warped, not evenly curved, or not regular in shape. This causes the light rays to converge at other points in the retina and vision to be distorted and blurred. A doctor can prescribe lenses to correct this problem.

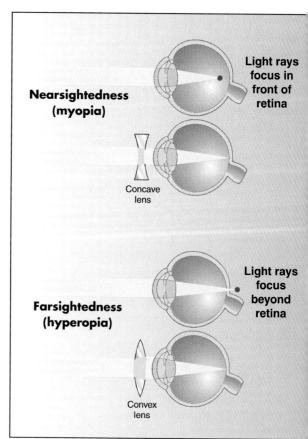

Corrective lenses do not change the shape of the eye or the lens of the eye. They focus light rays so they will hit the retina.

screen. The doctor will then determine how keen your sight is. If you have normal vision, you are said to have 20/20 vision. However, if you have 20/30 vision, it means that you can see at 20 feet what a person with normal vision can see at 30 feet. If you have 20/40 vision, you can see at 20 feet what a person with normal vision can see at 40 feet. A person with 20/15 vision has slightly better vision than most people. This number means that he can see at 20 feet what a person with normal vision could see only at 15 feet.

Some people cannot clearly focus on objects that are far away. Others cannot focus on things that are close. **Nearsightedness** occurs when near vision is clear and distance vision is blurred. When a person is nearsighted, the light rays entering the eye

Some people have a deficiency in seeing color. **Colorblind** people have some cones that do not function properly. This does not let them distinguish certain colors. Do not assume that all colorblind people live in a black and white world. Most can see some colors but cannot see all the hues. Colorblindness is a hereditary condition that affects more men than women.

Inflammations and Infections—Two eye problems which you are probably familiar with are pink eye and sties. Actually, pink eye is a form of **conjunctivitis.** Conjunctivitis is an inflammation of the layer of protective tissue (the conjunctiva) that covers the front of the eyeball. Inflammation of this thin tissue can be caused by allergies, irritations, and bacterial, viral, or fungal infections. Pink eye is a highly contagious form of bacterial infection which can be transferred by sharing towels, handkerchiefs, or make-up with an infected person. If your eyes are red and producing a sticky or crusty discharge, see your doctor.

A sty is caused when one of the small glands which line the eyelids gets infected. It looks like a pimple and can be painful. Warm compresses can help the sty to drain. If the sty does not go away within a week, see your doctor.

Glaucoma—One test given during an eye examination is for **glaucoma** (glah KO muh). This disease results in increased pressure within the eye which causes the eye to harden and restricts the flow of blood to and from the eye. This can result in damage to the optic nerve and loss of vision. Certain drugs or surgery is now available to help relieve the internal eye pressure. Glaucoma does not usually occur in young people, but it is best to have your eyes tested since most of the symptoms are very subtle and are not readily noticed.

Cataracts—Cataracts are not just an eye problem for the elderly. A **cataract** is when the lens of the eye becomes cloudy and opaque. Studies indicate that exposure to ultraviolet rays when tanning as well as exposure to infrared light or x-rays can increase chances of getting cataracts. Some diseases, injuries, or use of steroids can also cause

cataracts to form. Smoking is also suspected of contributing to cataract formation. Cataracts can be removed with surgery. New techniques are being developed to remove cataracts and to make possible better sight following cataract removal.

The bifocal lens is one of Benjamin Franklin's many inventions and accomplishments. These lens enable people with presbyopia (inability of the eye lens to change shape due to aging) to have reading and distance lenses in the same frame.

Eye Care

In order to take care of your eyes, begin by protecting them with good nutrition. What you eat will affect the health of your eyes. Your body uses vitamin A to produce the necessary chemicals to cause the nerve impulses to travel to the brain. Vitamin A and other nutrients help to keep the membranes of the eye moist and free from infection.

You can also protect your eyes with glasses. Glasses can be used in order to focus better by correcting a vision problem. This should help to reduce eye strain. However, glasses or goggles can also be used to keep debris or objects from hitting the eye. Protective eyewear should be worn when working with wood, metal, or other materials with potentially harmful splinters or dust. Beware of carelessly thrown rocks, sticks, darts, or even snowballs. Things tossed in jest may cause permanent eye injury.

Sunglasses can help to protect the eyes from harmful ultraviolet rays. Just because the lenses of sunglasses are dark does not mean that the glasses will protect from ultraviolet rays. Many protective glasses are light in color. Read the label. Do not purchase sunglasses that do not offer UV ray protection. In fact, sunglasses without UV ray protection can do more damage than good. They shade the iris causing the pupil to open more and let more harmful rays into the eye. Also keep in mind that staring directly at the sun can damage the retina and cause partial blindness.

If you wear contact lenses, be sure to keep them clean. Do not use creamy or oil-based soaps or make-up. Wash your hands before touching your eyes or lenses and carefully clean your lenses as instructed by your doctor. If your eyes are red, irritated, or infected, do not use your lenses.

It is also important to avoid straining your eyes. Using the correct lighting and distance from the television and computer will help. Watching the television in a darkened room can cause strain since the contrast between the light and the dark is so great. Glare on the television screen can also cause eye strain. The television should be placed at a distance five times the diagonal dimension of the screen. Using this rule, a person should sit eight feet away from a 19" television screen and nine feet away from a 22" television screen. Propping up at an angle and viewing the television from a twisted position can place more strain on one eye than the other.

Close concentration on a visual display terminal (VDT) can cause fatigued eyes. Computer terminals should display three to four times more contrast between the screen and the light in the room. In order to relieve the eyes, those using terminals should also take a ten to fifteen minute break at least

One should sit 18 to 26 inches away from the computer screen and 8 feet from a 19" television screen.

every two hours to look into a distant space. The computer screen should be placed eighteen to twenty-six inches from the eyes. It is also best to have any written material at the same height and distance as the display terminal. This will keep the eyes from having to change focus so often.

TUNE IN—CHECK YOUR HEARING

The assault on the ears is a daily experience. Noise is prevalent on the streets from massive trucks, blaring car stereos, and revving motorcycle engines. However, in the home and at school, people use "boom boxes" or headsets without considering the harm they may be inflicting on their ears.

Ear Basics

The ear is a finely tuned instrument for hearing and for equilibrium (balance). There are three sections of the ear: the outer ear, the middle ear, and the inner ear. Sound waves are caught by the flap of cartilage and skin of the outer ear and sent through the *auditory canal* to resonate against the *tympanic* (tim PAN ik) *membrane* (the eardrum). This thin, cone-shaped membrane transmits the sound from the outer ear to the middle ear.

Part of the middle ear, the *Eustachian* (yoo STAY shun) *tube*, helps to equalize the air pressure against the outside of the tympanic membrane and the inside located in the middle ear. This tube opens into an area of the throat located between the end of the nasal cavity and the opening of the pharynx. Yawning, chewing, or swallowing can help to force air up this tube to adjust the air pressure in the middle ear. The middle ear contains three small bones: the *malleus* (MAL ee us; hammer), the *incus* (ING kus; anvil), and the *stapes* (STAY peez; stirrup). The malleus rests against the tympanic membrane. When the sound waves cause the tympanic membrane to vibrate, the vibrations are amplified by the bones and passed on to the inner ear.

The inner ear has two regions: one transforms sound waves into electrochemical signals and one provides sensations for balance. Sound waves force the membrane covering the opening to the inner ear to vibrate. These vibrations are then carried through fluid in the snail-shaped organ, the **cochlea** (KAHK lee uh), to move hair cells which line it. These sensitive cells transform the vibrations into nerve impulses. When the brain receives these electrochemical messages, it interprets them as sound.

The *semicircular canals* of the inner ear are responsible for helping you to maintain your balance. These tubes are filled with fluid and lined with hair cells. If you tilt your head, turn, move forward quickly, or stop suddenly, the hair cells in these canals send nerve impulse messages to the brain which registers the movement.

Ear Care

In order to protect the auditory canal from dirt, foreign objects, and pathogens, the opening of the

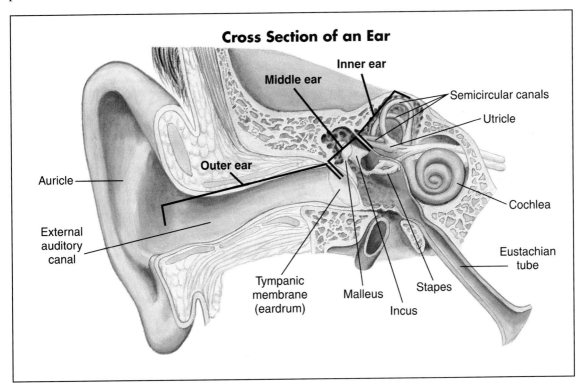

Cross Section of an Ear

Inner ear

Middle ear

Semicircular canals

Utricle

Outer ear

Auricle

Cochlea

External auditory canal

Eustachian tube

Tympanic membrane (eardrum)

Malleus

Stapes

Incus

canal is lined with special cells which secrete *cerumin* (suh ROO mun; earwax). This substance can sometimes build up in the canal and impair hearing. Using cotton swabs can sometimes pack the cerumin into the canal rather than remove it. Ear washing solutions are available to clean this canal. The outer ear should be washed with soap and water when bathing and cotton swabs used to clean the small folds.

Ears should also be protected from intense sound. People who work around high levels of noise should wear earplugs or protective earmuffs.

Be careful to control the volume of the stereo, recorder, television, or other electronic devices which can amplify the volume. Continued exposure to levels above 80 decibels can cause the destruction of the hair cells in the cochlea. This can result in permanent hearing damage. Sounds above 120 decibels can cause physical pain and above 150 decibels can cause the eardrum to rupture.

Ear Problems

Pain and frustration can be the result of ear infections or hearing impairment. Unlike the damage that

When Rover Answers

Have you ever blown a canine whistle and wondered why Rover, Fido, and all the other dogs in the neighborhood answer the seemingly silent call? In order to understand this, you must understand sound. Sound is caused by the vibration of molecules in air, water, or other substances. The frequency of the vibrations or sound waves causes sounds to be high or low; this is called **pitch**. Humans can usually hear vibrations between 20 and 20,000 vibrations per second (hertz or Hz). As a person gets older, the ability to hear higher pitches usually decreases. An extremely high pitch (with vibrations above 20,000 Hz) can often be heard by animals (such as Rover and his fellow canines) but cannot be detected by humans.

Volume is the intensity of the sound waves. Although the pitch is measured in hertz, the volume of a sound is measured in decibels (db). The softest sound level that can be heard is considered the threshold of hearing and is placed as 0 on the decibel scale. The chart below identifies common sounds at increasing levels on the decibel scale.

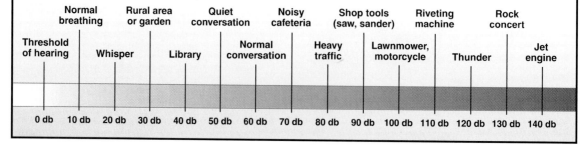

	Normal breathing		Rural area or garden		Quiet conversation		Noisy cafeteria		Shop tools (saw, sander)		Riveting machine		Rock concert	
Threshold of hearing		Whisper		Library		Normal conversation		Heavy traffic		Lawnmower, motorcycle		Thunder		Jet engine	
0 db	10 db	20 db	30 db	40 db	50 db	60 db	70 db	80 db	90 db	100 db	110 db	120 db	130 db	140 db	

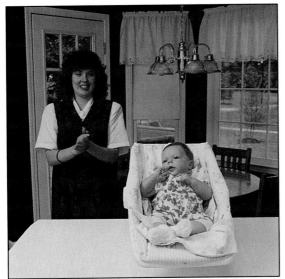

Babies are given hearing tests by someone making loud noises behind them and watching for a response.

can be caused by inflicting the ear with intense sound waves, some ear problems cannot be avoided.

Ear Infections—The most common ear problems experienced by young people are ear infections. Bacteria and infections of the throat and nose can sometimes invade the Eustachian tube. The infection then enters the middle ear, causing increased pressure in the ear and pain. Medication is usually prescribed to help cure ear infections. However, the infection may cause so much pressure that the tympanic membrane threatens to burst. In this case, the doctor may make a small cut in the ear drum to drain infection from the middle ear. This cut usually heals within a week or two.

Teen-agers are particularly susceptible to getting an outer ear infection commonly called "swimmer's ear." This type of infection occurs not only in the ears of swimmers, but in ears in which humidity, frequent showering, or recurrent exposure to water causes bacteria to lodge. A swimming pool, sauna, or hot tub in which the chlorine has become ineffective can increase the chances of obtaining this type of ear infection. The use of ear plugs or preventative ear drops may help those who frequently get infected.

Hearing Impairment and Deafness—The partial loss of hearing is called **hearing impairment.** One may suffer from hearing impairment because of ear infections, damage to the ear, obstructions, or nerve damage. Some impairments can be temporary (ear-wax build-up obstruction); but others may be permanent (noise injury; disease or accidental injury). The thickening of the tympanic membrane that occurs with age can also increase hearing impairment.

The total loss of hearing is called **deafness.** Deafness can be congenital (existing at birth), inherited, or caused by injury or disease. Atherosclerosis can contribute to deafness if the blood supply to the ears is decreased. Some diseases (encephalitis, meningitis, syphilis, multiple sclerosis, brain tumors) can impair portions of the brain needed to translate the nerve impulses into sound. Injuries to the skull or the scars caused by injuries can also keep a person from hearing.

Sometimes hearing loss is gradual. If you think that you may have a hearing problem, you need to

Persons of all ages have varying hearing abilities. Speaking directly facing others is always a good habit and helps those with hearing impairment. Over-enunciation, yelling, and gesturing are not necessary.

Modern instruments to aid the hearing-impaired have greatly improved over the unusual one pictured above.

make an appointment with an **audiologist.** An audiologist is a hearing problem specialist who can test your ability to hear clearly.

WITHOUT OFFENSE

One of the most important tasks that God has given to every Christian is the task of sharing the gospel with others. In II Corinthians 6:3, Paul admonished the Corinthians to give "no offence in any thing, that the ministry be not blamed." Christians are to avoid those things that can harm the effectiveness of the ministry of Christ.

Bad breath, uncleanliness, and body odor are offensive to people today. If you try to witness to someone and you have bad breath, you may lose any chance of reaching him. You may even give him the idea that all Christians are dirty and smelly.

When Christ sent His disciples out to the people of Israel, He told them to be as wise as serpents and as harmless as doves (Matt. 10:16). He knew they would need to have both of these characteristics to reach others with the gospel. In your witness for Christ, you too must be both wise and harmless. Part of being wise is being clean and inoffensive. Do not let your lack of personal cleanliness keep anyone from Christ. Personal hygiene can affect more than your health.

Section Review

1. List in order at least five parts of the eye through which light must pass to reach the retina.

2. Identify the following parts of the ear according to their location in the (O) outer ear, (M) middle ear, or (I) inner ear.

   a. Auditory canal

   b. Cochlea

   c. Eustachian tube

   d. Incus

   e. Malleus

   f. Semicircular canals

   g. Stapes

   h. Tympanic membrane

3. Which photoreceptors detect only light (not color) and help you to distinguish shapes and movement?

4. Which disease causes a build-up of pressure in the eye and can result in damage to the optic nerve, often causing blindness?

5. How far should a computer screen (visual display terminal) be from your eyes?

CHAPTER REVIEW

Terms

hygiene

epidermis

dermis

hypodermis

sebaceous gland

collagen

keratin

albinism

sebum

acne

cosmetic

sunscreen

SPF

deodorant

antiperspirant

dandruff

alopecia

manicure

pedicure

occlusion

malocclusion

orthodontist

deciduous teeth

permanent teeth

crown

dental caries

cavities

plaque

calculus

periodontal disease

halitosis

flossing

aqueous humor

photoreceptors

rods

cones

binocular vision

stereoscopic vision

peripheral vision

vitreous humor

nearsightedness

farsightedness

astigmatism

colorblind

conjunctivitis

glaucoma

cataract

auditory canal

tympanic membrane

Eustachian tube

cerumin

pitch

volume

hearing impairment

deafness

audiologist

Content Questions

1. What is acne?

2. What is the main cause of skin cancer?

3. How may the factors that produce body odor be controlled?

4. What is the best way to control dandruff?

5. What are the three major phases in the cyclic process of hair growth?

6. Where is the nail formed?

7. What is the difference between the lunula and the cuticle?

8. What are four tissues that make up a tooth?

9. What are the four types of permanent teeth?

10. What causes tooth decay?

11. Is flossing the teeth really necessary? Why?

12. What is it called when a person's teeth do not line up (overbite or underbite)?

13. Which parts of the eye help to protect the eye?

14. Which photoreceptors help you to see colors?

15. What are the three primary colors detected by the cones of the eye?

16. Which enables you to perceive depth: binocular vision, peripheral vision, or stereoscopic vision?

17. Which doctor should you call for cataract surgery?

18. What does it mean if a person has 20/50 vision?

19. Which lens helps to correct nearsightedness? Identify and draw this type of lens.

20. What type of infection is pink eye?

21. How can you prevent pink eye?

22. When tanning, you should protect not only your skin but also your eyes since exposure to ultraviolet rays can increase your chances of getting which eye problem?

23. How far away should you be from the television when viewing it?

24. What is the difference between pitch and volume?

25. At which volume level can hearing be impaired?

26. Physical pain can occur in the ears at which volume level?

27. Which volume level can cause the tympanic membrane to rupture?

28. Which type of doctor tests hearing ability?

Application Questions

1. How should you react to a person with a severely bad case of acne or an obvious skin problem (birthmark, albinism)?

2. Read II Kings 2:23-24. Considering the fact that the Hebrew word *naar* actually refers to young men (lads, youths, maturing and accountable boys), what lesson(s) can be obtained from this passage?

3. By using the chart of teeth on page 286, list the permanent teeth in the order of growth.

4. It is recommended that regular dental checkups begin when a child is four (and still has his deciduous teeth) and that he not wait until he is six (when permanent teeth usually begin to come in). Why is it important to take care of deciduous teeth?

5. Your best friend has halitosis and your classmates are laughing at him behind his back. What can you do? Which verses in the Bible may help you in your decision?

Dental Hygienists

Job Description: Dental hygienists are professionals who are trained to clean teeth, remove plaque and calculus from teeth, apply fluoride and sealants to teeth, expose and develop x-rays, evaluate dental health information, assist the dentist, and teach patients how to develop good dental hygiene. Although most hygienists work with individual patients, some are involved with community programs to encourage dental health.

A dental hygienist should not be confused with a dental assistant. A dental assistant may admit the patient to the office, prepare him for treatment, obtain dental records, prepare tray setups, and assist the dentist during treatment. Some assistants may be required to manage the office (schedule appointments, keep records, record payments and bills, and order dental supplies). Both dental hygienists and assistants may sterilize instruments and equipment. However, only hygienists, and not assistants, can actually use their skills to apply preventative dental care.

Job Location: Dental hygienists usually work in clean and nicely planned offices.

Because many dentists hire hygienists to work only two or three days a week, a dental hygienist can enjoy a flexible schedule. If he prefers to work part-time, he may schedule work in only one dental office. However, some hygienists work in one dental office on a full-time basis or may be employed by more than one office.

Since dental hygienists work with x-rays, they must take strict precautions to prevent exposure to radiation. Due to the nature of the work, professionals in this field must also protect themselves and follow strict guidelines to prevent contamination from diseases communicated in body fluids.

Training Required: Training for dental hygienists is available in many technical schools and universities. The minimum of an associate's degree from a dental hygiene school and successful completion of state and national examinations are usually required for a license to practice. Hygienists should have good health, exhibit personal neatness, and possess precise manual dexterity (needed to manage the instruments when working in a patient's mouth). The ability to effectively communicate with people and an interest in biology, chemistry, and health are also important in this field.

ENVIRONMENT AND HEALTH

If the world took on the traits of your bedroom, what would it be like? Would everything be orderly or chaotic, clean or dirty? Are you a good steward of your immediate surroundings (room, home, yard)? Have you taken an interest in your neighborhood or community surroundings? The things which surround you, your environment, affect your health. Filth breeds infection. Clutter can be stifling. Smoke and pollution can irritate and promote illnesses.

CHAPTER 11

"The Lord God took the man, and put him into the garden of Eden to dress it and to keep it."
Genesis 2:15

Although you may never start a garbage dump in your room (in spite of what others may suspect), the only way to keep from living in a messy, filthy place is to purposely keep it clean. This chapter investigates ways your environment affects you and ways that you can become a better manager of it.

USE, NOT ABUSE

Some people treat the environment like a god that must be protected and worshiped. They tend to resist any progress that might bring potential damage to the environment they hold sacred. For these people, protecting the environment is an emotional and religious commitment.

Others tend to disregard the effect of their actions on the environment. Some consider the environment to be at their disposal and feel free to do whatever they desire, no matter what damage may

Why are many humanists, atheists, pantheists, and unbelievers in the world so consumed with "saving the earth"? Perhaps it is because they believe that this is it; this life and earth are their only heaven. Although it is important to wisely manage earth's resources, a Christian's efforts are not to save the earth, but to see as many souls saved before Christ returns to create a new heaven and a new earth.

occur. Many people simply ignore the effects of their actions on the environment.

Neither of these attitudes is a proper one. God designed the earth to be man's home. When God created Adam, He gave him dominion over the earth. Although Adam could freely eat of the fruit in the garden, he also had the responsibility of caring for the garden.

The same type of responsibility and privilege that God gave to Adam belongs to man today. God has provided the earth's resources for the benefit of man. Man is a *consumer* of the environment. He must obtain his food by eating plants or animals. Man uses materials to meet his needs. Man can use the resources of the earth, but he should use them carefully and thankfully. God never approves of wasteful or irresponsible behavior. Although man is a consumer of nature, God expects him to be a wise *manager* of it. Failure to care for God-given resources has its consequences.

It is important to have a balanced view of the environment. A Christian should not worship nature, but he should be a good steward of it. The world's attitude is that everything must be done in order to "save the earth." Those who know Christ as their Savior realize that the earth is only a temporary home. (I Chron. 29:15—"For we are strangers before thee, and sojourners, as were all our fathers: our days on the earth are as a shadow, and there is none abiding.") However, man must be a wise manager of the earth until God chooses to destroy it. Try to use the environment God has given us without abusing it.

ENVIRONMENT AND HEALTH

In Chapter 1 you learned that your environment is one of the four major contributors to your health. Although it usually does not affect your health as much as your lifestyle, it can be a major influence. The environment is the combination of both living and nonliving factors which surround you. The hygiene of people, the absence or presence of cigarette smoke, and the amount of trash, garbage, and

The Bhopal Disaster

It happened in Bhopal, India, the capital of Madhya Pradesh state. This fairly large city located in central India with a population of about 900,000 had a Union Carbide plant on its outskirts. On a December night in 1984, five tons of a deadly chemical called MIC leaked from the plant into the air. A large cloud of poisonous gas swept across the land, leaving behind death and suffering.

MIC was normally produced at the plant to make a pesticide that could kill 180 different types of insects. But that day, the chemical's effect was experienced by humans. About 90,000 people suffered such disorders as blindness, tuberculosis, kidney and liver infections, and brain damage. In a sense, these people were the fortunate ones—they had survived the terrible tragedy; over 2,500 others did not.

As a result of this accident, many people living near such industrial plants have become concerned for their personal safety. Could it happen again? Because of the large number of dangerous chemicals manufactured, stored, and transported around the world, the potential is great. Increased safety measures have been employed in an attempt to prevent another terrible accident like the one that occurred in Bhopal.

dirt in a home, school, or work place can be risk factors for health problems.

Unfortunately, your environment area may be getting less healthful every day. Dangerous substances may contaminate your city. When potentially harmful substances, **pollutants,** are placed in the environment, **pollution** occurs. Pollution of the air, water, or soil affects living things. Pollution in the water may contaminate the fish you caught for dinner. Pollutants in the soil may seep into the water system where you obtain your drinking water.

Pollution is not a new problem. From the time of Adam, people have polluted the environment. However, most of the earlier pollution was a local problem and a temporary problem. In those times the natural processes that God ordained in nature often removed pollutants before there were any harmful health effects. Pollution today is no longer isolated or temporary. It is a much bigger and more complex problem than ever.

Your environment can change your health drastically and rapidly. For example, a nearby factory could accidentally spill dangerous gases into the air you breathe. A sudden disaster like this actually occurred in Bhopal, India. (See box on page 309.)

However, the effects of the environment on your health are usually more gradual. For example, carcinogens may be in your water, soil, or air, but it may take years before any cancer occurs. The effects of some chemicals are so gradual that it is almost impossible to determine whether they cause disease.

Some people are discovering that the water they have been drinking for years has been contaminated by pollution and threatens their health.

Section Review

1. What is the *environment?*

2. Describe two completely different but completely wrong ideas concerning man's relationship to the environment.

3. How should a Christian react and think when it comes to the environment? Why?

POLLUTION—THE AIR ATTACK

Air is vital. You need a lot of it to stay alive. In fact, you breathe about 2,000 gallons (7,600 liters) of air every day. Unfortunately, the air you breathe is far from pure. It contains all kinds of substances. Some are natural, like dust or pollen, while others are produced by man. Because the air you breathe is such a vital part of your health and life, the issue of air pollution has become a very important one.

Atmosphere Basics

The **atmosphere** is the gaseous envelope which surrounds the earth. It is divided into several temperature layers. The layer closest to the earth, the *troposphere,* contains about ninety-five percent of the earth's air.

Above the troposphere is the *stratosphere.* Thankfully, the stratosphere contains a layer of

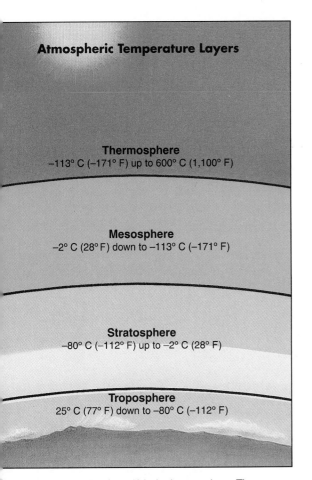

Atmospheric Temperature Layers

Thermosphere
–113° C (–171° F) up to 600° C (1,100° F)

Mesosphere
–2° C (28° F) down to –113° C (–171° F)

Stratosphere
–80° C (–112° F) up to –2° C (28° F)

Troposphere
25° C (77° F) down to –80° C (–112° F)

he area above 100 km (60 mi.) is the heterosphere. The
xosphere is the outer area above 480 km (300 mi.).

ozone. Ozone is composed of three oxygen atoms (O_3) rather than the normal two oxygen atoms (O_2). Ozone has the capacity to absorb ultraviolet light. God provided the ozone layer to shield the earth from much of the sun's ultraviolet radiation.

Above the third layer of the atmosphere, the *mesosphere,* is the final temperature layer, the *thermosphere*. It also provides some protection for the earth by reducing harmful radiation and by vaporizing meteors before they hit the earth.

The Air Polluters

Automobiles are the greatest air polluters today. Every day cars burn millions of gallons of gasoline, releasing tons of exhaust into the air. The government is trying to control the problem by requiring cars to be equipped with pollution-reducing devices. To encourage car pooling, some cities provide special traffic lanes for those who ride share. They also promote the use of subways, buses, and other forms of mass transit to alleviate the enormous amount of traffic.

Factories and power-generating plants are two other major sources of air pollution. Laws have been enacted by Congress requiring industries to control the amount of air pollutants and promoting studies in technology to reduce pollution.

Unfortunately, reducing pollution is expensive. The cost of implementing pollution control devices is usually passed on to the consumer, you. However, many companies actively engage in pollution-reducing programs, not just to comply with federal standards, but also to promote community and public relations.

In addition to these manmade causes of air pollution, nature also contributes to the problem. Dust and pollen can be irritating sources of natural air pollution, causing allergies and asthma. Dust not only is carried from your surrounding neighborhood into your home but also can be transported

The pollen of ragweed, Ambrosia psilostachya, *is a primary cause of hay fever (allergic rhinitis). Hay fever can also be triggered by allergens such as other plant pollens, fungal spores, animal dander, and dust mites.*

In old Westerns when everything seemed hopeless, the cavalry would ride in and rescue the settlers. With the abundance of pollution being generated by industries and citizens of the United States, more than just the help of the cavalry was needed. In 1970 and 1977, Congress passed the Clean Air Acts. These acts gave the federal government additional power to control air pollution. The United States government assigned the job of rescuing the environment to the **EPA** or **Environmental Protection Agency.** The EPA is responsible for setting and enforcing standards for the proper care of the environment. It also grants funds for various projects that will protect the environment, such as the construction of waste water treatment plants.

Because the EPA has such a wide range of responsibilities, it is not surprising that many people are not satisfied with the job it is doing. Some people think the EPA does not do enough to protect the environment. Others think that the EPA often does not consider all the results of the decisions they make. However, in spite of these criticisms and limitations, most people agree that the EPA has been helpful in reducing certain pollution problems in the United States.

Factories and power-generating plants are two other major sources of air pollution. Laws have been enacted by Congress to encourage industries to control the amount of air pollutants and to promote studies in technology to reduce pollution.

Unfortunately, most methods of reducing pollution are expensive. The cost of adding or implementing pollution control devices is usually passed on to the consumer—you. For instance, if your local power company converts from burning coal to nuclear energy, your electric bill would show a dramatic increase. However, many companies actively engage in pollution-reducing programs not only to comply with federal standards but also to promote community and public relations. Although the cost of change may be high, the cost of ruined health or a damaged environment may be higher.

This volcanic eruption in Augustine, Alaska, occurred in 1986. Later volcanic eruptions provided studies of climate changes caused by volcanic aerosols (particles suspended in gases) and indications of the amounts of pollution in the stratosphere following volcanic eruptions.

from thousands of miles away to your community. Dust storms also contribute to temporary states of increased air pollution. During certain seasons, many cities include an allergy or pollen report with their daily weather reports. People with respiratory problems are often encouraged to stay inside or wear masks outside during "hay fever weather."

Volcanic eruptions are sources of natural air pollution. They hurl dust and gases into the stratosphere where only gravity can pull them down. It is estimated that following some eruptions it has taken two to three years for volcanic dust to return to earth.

Naturally occurring fires in forests, prairies, and chaparrals contribute to air pollution. Although man may contribute to starting some fires, lightning is a natural cause for many fires. Drought, dry fuel (vegetative litter), and wind contribute to the spread of fires.

Nuclear Power Accidents

Imagine that it is a beautiful day in April. As you sit down for a quick breakfast before school, you turn the radio on just as the announcer reads the latest news flash.

"We have just received this news bulletin. The Russians have admitted that the nuclear power plant in Chernobyl of the Soviet Union has suffered a serious accident. An explosion occurring several days ago has produced a continuous raging fire which is spewing out large amounts of radioactivity. So far all efforts to extinguish the fire have failed."

This sudden announcement hits home a little harder for you than for the average teen-ager. Just ten miles away from your home is a nuclear plant. The news of this disaster causes you to wonder if nuclear power plants are really safe.

According to the dictionary safe means "free from danger." Nuclear power plants are not free from danger; the potential risk is always there, but in many ways they have a better track record than other energy sources. Yet nuclear power plants have not operated accident free. In the U.S.

alone there have been some serious accidents. The worst occurred on March 28, 1979, at the Three Mile Island reactor in Middleton, Pennsylvania. This accident caused a partial meltdown and released some radioactivity into the air. Although there were not any casualties, the accident at Three Mile Island stopped just one hour short of a complete meltdown.

Fortunately, many of the accidents which occurred in the U.S. did not release any

radioactivity. Of the remaining accidents where some radioactivity was released into the air, the health risk has been minimal.

But what about the accident that occurred at the Chernobyl nuclear power plant? Due to an unauthorized safety experiment in which the reactor's automatic safety and warning systems were turned off, one of the four reactors suffered two massive explosions. It is reported that the blasts blew the 1,000 ton (909 metric-ton) roof off the reactor building and set the core on fire. Although fewer than fifty people reportedly died as a result of the explosion, the health hazard was widespread. Shifting winds carried the radioactivity beyond Soviet borders and across most of Europe. No one knows for sure how many people will die prematurely of cancer caused by exposure to that radiation.

Since the Chernobyl accident there has been a lot of discussion about stopping the use of nuclear power plants. It is true that the potential danger is there; yet the benefits are also great. The choice to continue using nuclear energy or not is one some countries may have to face.

Global Warming Warning

Many people are concerned that the earth is constantly getting warmer due to increased agricultural and industrial activities. The theory of global warming is as follows.

- **Greenhouse gases** (carbon dioxide, methane, and nitrous oxides) trap heat in the earth's atmosphere.
- Human activities produce increased greenhouse gases.
- Increased greenhouse gases will result in temperature increases across the whole earth.
- Temperature increases will cause the polar ice caps to melt, coastal regions to flood, and inland areas to experience drought.

Although most of the energy on earth comes from the sun, the sun does not warm the earth's atmosphere directly. The earth's surface absorbs the sun's radiation and re-emits it as infrared radiation (heat). Greenhouse gases trap heat in the earth's atmosphere and inhibit heat from escaping. Because this process is similar to a greenhouse, which uses glass to trap heat inside, it is often referred to as the **greenhouse effect.** The greenhouse effect is a natural part of the earth's design.

How are human activities supposed to cause global warming? The burning of wood and fossil fuels (coal, natural gas, oil, and petroleum products) releases carbon dioxide. **Deforestation** (the removal of trees, forests, and jungles) is thought to reduce the ability of plants to keep up with increased carbon dioxide levels. The increase of agricultural activity as well as manmade items such as landfills contribute to the production of methane. Nitrous oxide levels are thought to increase with the use of fertilizers and livestock wastes and with the burning of organic matter. Although human activity may contribute to the production of greenhouse gases, *proof* that the earth is warming as a result of man's activities is not available.

Those who believe that the earth is getting warmer fear that the earth's average temperature will rise three to eight degrees before the year 2050. If this occurs, drought, lowered underground water supplies, and loss of crops are predicted for inland communities. Global warming would also result in the melting of the polar ice caps. If this were to happen, ocean levels would rise and cause the flooding of coastline areas and the invasion of salt water into freshwater tables. All of these are speculations.

It is not definitely known that global warming has or will occur. God is in control. However, God may allow man to reap the results of irresponsible stewardship. Unlike many environmentalists who rely on human action and human intervention for their future, Christians realize that the earth is a temporary home and that it will be destroyed in God's time and in God's way.

...n cannot control the amounts of natural pollutants of the ...rth; however, as stewards, man is responsible to God to do ...best to reduce manmade pollution.

Methane is a gas that is commonly produced by the decay of organic matter in oxygen-poor areas such as swamps, bogs, marshes, and water-logged soils. Methane also leaks out from natural gas wells and coal seams. The concentration of this hydrocarbon gas is usually so low that it does not pose a health threat. However, methane is considered a gas that contributes to global warming and the greenhouse effect.

One type of naturally occurring pollutant is **radon** (RAY dahn), a radioactive gas that results from the disintegration of radium. This colorless, odorless, and tasteless gas often rises from underground deposits of uranium, phosphate, granite, and shale. If it can disperse into the atmosphere, radon is harmless. However, many times the gas is trapped indoors as it seeps into buildings through cracks, hollow concrete blocks, drain lines, pipes,

and water pumps. If basement areas and crawl spaces are well ventilated, radon is harmlessly released into the atmosphere. In buildings (homes, schools, offices) that are well insulated and situated over radon-emitting areas, radon levels can build up to the point where they can cause health problems. Radon is linked with heightened incidences of lung cancer.

Areas of radon contamination cannot be identified without testing. People who live in a house, town house, mobile home, or on the first three floors of an apartment building should have their radon levels tested (professionally or with a reliable radon detection kit). People considering the purchase of real estate should also have their soil tested. Since radon can be released into the water of underground wells, anyone using well water should have his water tested. Drinking, cooking, and bathing in contaminated water could increase risks for premature death.

The Air Pollutants

Although there are hundreds of air pollutants, there are two major types: gases and particulates. A gas is a form of matter that is less dense than either

Because of air pollution by exhaust from automobiles, the EPA has required higher pollution control standards.

solids or liquids. Sulfur oxides, nitrogen oxides, carbon monoxide, hydrocarbons, and chlorofluorocarbons (CFCs) are a few examples of the gases that pollute the air.

Air pollutants that come from natural or human actions are considered **primary air pollutants.** Sometimes these primary air pollutants react with each other or other components in the air to form **secondary air pollutants.** An example of this would be the formation of **photochemical smog.** Photochemical smog results when primary pollutants interact to form secondary pollutants in the presence of sunlight. This smog has a brown hue and can be a problem of large cities in warm climate areas.

You learned earlier that a layer of ozone gas in the stratosphere helps absorb some of the sun's harmful radiations. However, when pollutants cause the formation of ozone in the troposphere, ozone becomes a hazard rather than a help. Ozone can result in the troposphere when two primary air pollutants (hydrocarbons and nitrogen oxides) react with each other in the presence of sunlight. Ozone can irritate or damage mucous membranes of the

respiratory tract and cause headaches, fatigue, coughing, and eye problems.

Particulates are small pieces of liquids or solids that are suspended in air. Dust, pollen, soot, asbestos fibers, smoke, lead, and pesticides are examples of particulates that can contribute to air pollution. Particulates often drop out of air to form a film on the objects they contact. You may have seen a film like this on your car when there was a lot of pollen in the air. **Industrial smog** forms when particulates mix with sulfur dioxide and droplets of sulfuric acid in the air. Gray coloring is a characteristic of industrial smog.

A variety of health problems are associated with particulates. Asbestos fibers have been shown to cause cancer. Soot, smoke, and dust can contribute to lung problems. Lead and pesticide exposure can be toxic, and some particulates can impair vision.

The Effects of Air Pollution

Do a few gases and particulates in the air you breathe really make that much difference? After all, you are probably not suffocating, and plenty of people are living many years breathing the same air you breathe. Why all the fuss?

Health Problems—Air pollution does make a difference. It can damage clothes and cars, mar buildings

Paper fibers such as these might be found in the air of a paper recycling plant.

and statues, and kill plants and animals. It also affects the health and life of a large number of people. For example, during a smoggy day you might experience headaches, coughing, stinging or watery eyes, and an inability to think clearly. It can be particularly damaging to your respiratory system. That is why people who already suffer from other respiratory disorders must be very cautious. When air pollution is bad, there are often "extra" deaths. Most of these deaths occur because the pollution aggravates a medical problem that already exists.

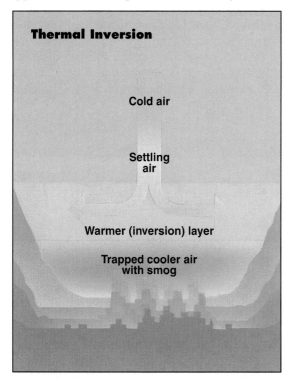

Thermal Inversion

Cold air

Settling air

Warmer (inversion) layer

Trapped cooler air with smog

Thermal inversion occurs when cool air is temporarily below warm air. Instead of moving pollutants and warm air up to cooler atmospheric levels, the cool air and its pollutants are held by the warm air "lid" close to the earth's surface.

Thermal Inversion—Gases and particulates often dissipate before they become a major problem. Occasionally the conditions of the atmosphere can make the problem worse. A **thermal inversion** is an example of how atmospheric conditions can aggravate normal air pollution problems. In ordinary conditions, warm air is found near the earth's surface and cooler air is above. Most air pollution is carried away by the warm air as it rises into the cool air above it. However, in a thermal inversion, cool air and pollutants are trapped beneath a warm air layer. Because pollution cannot escape in upward-flowing air currents, it continues to build up. Thermal inversion has caused some of the worst cases of air pollution and even resulted in deaths.

Ozone Reduction—As mentioned earlier in this chapter, the ozone layer in the stratosphere helps to absorb ultraviolet radiation. Some chemicals can deplete or reduce ozone amounts. In communications about the threatened ozone layer, you have probably heard of chlorofluorocarbons (CFCs) or the name Freon (which is the Du Pont trademark for chlorofluorocarbon).

Chlorofluorocarbons are odorless, nonflammable, nontoxic, noncorrosive chemicals which have been used in air conditioners, refrigerators, and aerosol cans. CFCs have also been used as industrial solvents, computer chip cleaners, hospital sterilants, and in the manufacturing of polystyrene or Styrofoam. CFCs were thought to be too good to be true since they were so efficient, harmless, simple to manufacture, and inexpensive. However, the chlorine atoms in the chlorofluorocarbon molecule have proven to be catalysts for ozone decomposition. Other chemicals used in some fire extinguishers, metal cleaning solvents, dry cleaning sprays, spray adhesives, correction fluids, and bug killers and foggers can also cause ozone to decompose.

The use of propellants in aerosol cans, evaporation of industrial solvents, and leakage from refrigerators and air conditioners release chlorofluorocarbons into the atmosphere. Regulations are being implemented by the government in order to control the release and use of ozone-depleting chemicals. It is feared that the depletion of the ozone layer in the stratosphere could increase the amounts of skin cancer, eye cataracts, and problems associated with photochemical smog. Research is underway to find alternative chemicals.

the pollution of air will be decreased. Walking, biking, car pooling, and using mass transit systems reduce air pollution by reducing the use of fuel-burning cars. Consider your errands of the week and consolidate your traveling as much as possible. Try not to make unnecessary trips.

You can also help to reduce air pollution by using energy as efficiently as possible. A well-tuned car and correctly inflated tires should help to increase the number of miles traveled per gallon. If you drive, drive at a steady pace.

Use less energy at home—Insulating your home will allow you to use fuel more efficiently. Thermostats should be set at 65° F in the day and 55° F at night when heating your home. When cooling, the thermostat should be set at 80° F. Turn off lights, appliances, and equipment as soon as you are finished using them.

Preventing Air Pollution

Like most health problems, it is better to prevent pollution than it is to try to reduce its effects. Because air pollution is a national problem, you may think that there is little you can do to prevent it. Although you cannot stop air pollution by yourself, you can do your part to reduce the problem. You can also encourage others to prevent pollution. Below are a few things that can be done to fight air pollution.

Use less energy in travel—Most air pollution comes from the burning of fuel. If this amount is reduced,

Energy can be saved in the kitchen too. Thaw frozen foods in the refrigerator before cooking them. If possible, use a microwave oven or small appliance rather than the oven or range when cooking. Avoid preheating ovens. You could also allow dishes in the dishwasher to air dry following the final rinse.

Instead of using hot water, use cold or warm water when washing clothes. Setting the water heater temperature at 120° F (49° C) is suggested not only to conserve energy, but also for safety.

Make use of a clothesline rather than the dryer when possible. Be a wise consumer and look for energy-saving features in all your purchases. Look for ways to conserve energy.

Use cleaner sources of energy—There are some forms of energy that cause much less pollution than other forms. For instance, coal is a very dirty source of energy while solar energy is a very clean source of energy. Using more clean sources of energy can reduce air pollution.

Use filtering devices that reduce pollution—Even when dirty fuels are used, there are often ways to trap the pollutants and keep them from entering the air. For example, filters can be placed in smokestacks to reduce industrial air pollution, and most new cars are built with pollution-reducing devices on their exhaust systems. These filters are effective only if they are used and maintained properly.

Support efforts by others to reduce pollution—There are many people who are working to clean the air. Reasonable and legal efforts to curb pollution deserve your support. These efforts cannot be successful without your support and the support of others like you. Do your best to help. Some extremist organizations intentionally violate laws, obstruct the legal rights of others, and make unrealistic and unreasonable demands. These organizations should not be supported. A balanced position is essential.

Section Review

1. Why is the ozone layer important?

2. What are the three major manmade sources of air pollution?

3. List five natural sources of air pollution.

4. Select one of the following topics and explain how it contributes to air pollution and affects health: radon, greenhouse gases, chlorofluorocarbons.

5. How does photochemical smog differ from industrial smog?

6. Make a poster that would encourage your schoolmates to conserve energy and that lists ways to save energy.

POLLUTION—THE WATER ATTACK

You have already learned that water is an essential nutrient. If you did not have water to drink, you would die in just a few days. You drink about two gallons of it every day, and you use water for much more than drinking. You cook with it, bathe in it, swim in it, and clean with it. A lot of clean water is necessary to keep you healthy. In fact, the average American uses 100 to 150 gallons of water every day in his home.

It is easy to take water for granted. Just turn the knob, and you usually have all the clean water you need. However, in many areas of the country, it is getting more difficult to find clean sources of water. Pollution is making many water sources unfit for human use.

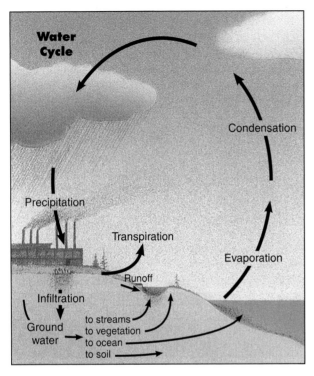

Water Cycle

Condensation

Precipitation

Transpiration

Evaporation

Runoff

Infiltration

Ground water

to streams
to vegetation
to ocean
to soil

The Bible alludes to the water cycle in Ecclesiastes 1:7: "All the rivers run into the sea; yet the sea is not full; unto the place from whence the rivers come, thither they return again."

Hydrosphere Basics

"Water, water, everywhere,
Nor any drop to drink."

When Samuel Taylor Coleridge wrote this phrase in *The Rime of the Ancient Mariner,* he hit on an interesting observation concerning the amount of usable water on earth. Although there are approximately 1,460,000 cubic kilometers (350,000 cubic miles) of water on the earth, only a fraction of the water is available for man's use. The oceans contain over ninety-seven percent of the earth's water. The remaining three percent is found in glaciers and permanent snowfields, in ground water, in soil, in the atmosphere, and in streams, rivers, and lakes.

Water is constantly in a cycle of evaporation, transpiration, precipitation, infiltration, and accumulation. Because water is not confined to lakes and streams, water pollution does not only consist of dumping toxins in bodies of water. Air pollution and land pollution also promote water pollution.

The Water Polluters

The biggest user and polluter of water in the United States is industry. In the past, many industries poured harmful substances into water and returned it to the environment without any attempt to remove pollutants. Laws were passed in an effort to curtail water pollution. Insufficient or improper water treatment has made many rivers and lakes near industrial centers unfit for human use. Some companies have also contributed to water pollution indirectly by releasing chemicals that pollute the air and soil. These chemicals can then combine with water to pollute the environment and bodies of water where it collects.

Globally, the largest user of water is agriculture. Using water for irrigation increases the amount of sediment in water. Mineral salts may build up excessively in irrigated soil. Additional problems arise if the plants (and therefore the water) are tainted with chemical fertilizers and pesticides. Another problem occurs in moving water from one area to another or removing water from ground water reserves. Using water that is replaced or restored at a slower rate than it is being used can result in sinkholes and water shortages.

Water is also polluted with waste products from bathrooms and kitchens. This waste water is often called **sewage.** Although sewage is 99.9 percent water and only 0.1 percent solid matter, it is not fit for human use. Sewage is an ideal medium for the growth and spread of bacteria. Sewage treatment plants clean the water before it is released into the environment. Unfortunately, many countries release raw sewage and dump garbage directly into their water supplies.

Landfills and deteriorating underground gasoline tanks leak contaminates into the ground that then pollute ground water. Many times industrial and hazardous waste dumps that are located near water sources slowly seep their toxins into water supplies.

Another dangerous source of water pollution is the dumping of radioactive wastes and the disposing of nuclear submarine reactors into the oceans. The potential for nuclear garbage to be distributed by ocean currents poses a threat. As these radioactive waste containers deteriorate, the risk of radioactive contamination rises.

Thermal pollution occurs when heated water is released into the environment. This type of pollution is usually caused by factories and nuclear power plants immediately draining warmed water back into water sources. This type of pollution can destroy plant and animal life or make them susceptible to certain parasites and toxins. Thermal pollution can also contribute to oxygen depletion of water.

The Water Pollutants

There are three major classes of water pollutants: sediment, organic, and chemical. **Sediments** or earthy materials are usually added to water by erosion. Soil is eroded through agriculture, forestry,

any tropical and Middle Eastern areas, oil or pesticides are inely sprayed into water sources to control mosquito ulations.

construction, and mining. Sediment can cause water to become cloudy and may disrupt natural food chains (reduction of photosynthesis in aquatic plants, destruction of feeding grounds for fish).

Organic pollutants include bacteria, viruses, protozoa, and parasitic worms. These pathogens enter the water cycle through human and animal wastes. Organic pollutants have also been added by canneries and paper pulp plants. You probably have been warned since childhood not to drink water from streams and brooks, even if it looks clear. It is often what you cannot see that can harm you.

Imbalances in biological cycles can also be caused by water pollution. Sometimes large amounts of oxygen-consuming bacteria accumulate in order to break down organic matter in water. If the levels of organic pollutants are great, this bacteria can deplete the water of dissolved oxygen gas to a point that fish and other aquatic life die.

Another problem of organic pollution occurs with the addition of phosphate and nitrate compounds. These chemicals promote plant growth, which is fine on your lawn and in your garden. However, it is harmful to aquatic life when algae and aquatic plants begin to grow in such an abundance that they deplete water of dissolved oxygen.

The final group of water pollutants is a large one. Chemicals of various sorts constantly threaten the water supply. Acids, salts, lead, mercury, oil, gasoline, plastics, pesticides, cleaning solvents, and many other chemicals have been dumped directly into some water sources. Many of these chemicals have **leached** or seeped from upper layers of soil and have been carried down into ground water supplies. Contact with some of these chemicals has harmed fish, disrupted aquatic life, and even threatened human life and development.

One group of water pollutants causing concern is polychlorinated biphenyls (PCBs). This group has over two hundred different toxic and oily compounds. Because these are stable, heat-resistant compounds, they have been used in transformers and electrical capacitors. As discarded and broken transformers leak PCBs into water supplies, this

Monumental Changes by Acid Rain

In order for acids to form from air pollution, specific conditions of temperature, moisture, light, and chemicals must be combined. When acid rain does occur, it causes statues and public buildings to deteriorate. Note the destruction caused on this stone figure on a castle in West Germany. The first picture was taken in 1908. The figure was almost completely ruined by the time the second picture was taken in 1968.

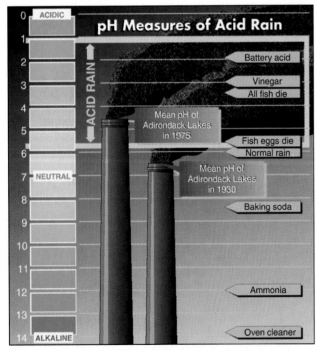

pH Measures of Acid Rain

- 0 — ACIDIC
- 2 — Battery acid
- 3 — Vinegar / All fish die
- 4 — Mean pH of Adirondack Lakes in 1975
- 5 — Fish eggs die
- 6 — Normal rain / Mean pH of Adirondack Lakes in 1930
- 7 — NEUTRAL
- 8 — Baking soda
- 12 — Ammonia
- 14 — ALKALINE / Oven cleaner

ACID RAIN

The pH of a substance is a measure of the concentration of H^+ ions. The lower the pH, the more acidic; pH 7 is neutral, above 7 is alkaline (basic), and below 7 is acidic. Acid rain has pH below 5.6.

toxic substance causes liver, kidney, gastric, and reproductive disorders; skin lesions; and tumors.

Industrial air pollutants and vehicle emissions have contributed to water pollution. Gases such as sulfur oxides and nitric oxides can mix with moisture in the air to form sulfuric and nitric acid. When these acids mix with water vapor, they produce **acid rain.** Acid rain is more acidic than normal rain. *Acid rain is a term that also includes acid snow, sleet, and fog.*

Acid rain affects water sources by raising the level of acid in the water and soil. The acidity levels of water can be lowered by the acid rain itself. However, much damage is also caused by the reaction of acids on solids. Corrosion (the release of toxic metals such as lead, zinc, and aluminum from soil into water) and the removal of nutrients from the soil both contribute to the pollution of ground water, the death of plants and fish, and the potential for increased health problems. It should be noted, however, that there are natural buffers against acid rain in areas where the land has a high alkali content (such as limestone). In these areas, the acid rain may react to produce compounds which are not harmful.

Chemical pollutants combined with trash have ruined many water sources and aquatic areas. Because studies indicate that phosphate promotes organic water pollution, lawmakers have created laws to reduce or eliminate its use.

Because acid rain may affect areas many miles from the source of the pollution, it is often difficult to trace the exact source of the problem. For instance, air pollution produced in the United States may cause acid rain to fall in Canada. Toxins in the air released from industries in Mexico contaminate rain and water in the United States.

The Effects of Water Pollution

Probably the most serious danger from water pollution is the spread of disease. Even water that looks and smells clean can contain harmful organisms. Dysentery, diphtheria, typhoid fever, and hepatitis are a few of the diseases that can be spread in polluted water.

Polluted water often contains dangerous chemicals. Some of these can cause death or illness in just a short period of time. Others cause damage that may not be detected for many years. Some of these chemicals are very difficult to remove once they have contaminated water.

Water pollution also kills fish and other wildlife. In some polluted streams even the fish that are not killed are dangerous to eat because of the harmful chemicals that are stored in their body tissues. Pollution has turned many clear streams that thrived with wildlife into surface sewers where most fish cannot live. Pollution has also turned some lakes into clear bodies of chemical water that will not support life at all.

Water pollution affects not only the quality of water but also the quantity of usable water. If usable water is polluted or removed and wasted, then water shortage could become a real threat.

Preventing Water Pollution

Everyone wants clean water. The problem is that many people who want clean water are unwilling to do their part to keep it unpolluted. There are at least three things that can be done to reduce water pollution.

Conserve water—To **conserve** means to use less of a resource. Conserving water will reduce the amount of water that is polluted. Most Americans do not conserve water. They are used to having all the water that they need and seldom even think about the amount they use. It is easy to waste a lot of water by using it carelessly.

There are many ways to use less water. Shutting the water off while you are brushing your teeth,

How Many Gallons of Water Are Used?	
Average residence annually	107,000
Average person daily	168
Flushing a toilet	5-7
Taking an average shower	25-50
Brushing teeth (with water running)	2
Shaving (with water running)	10-15
Washing dishes by hand	20
Using an automatic dishwasher	10

SOURCE: The World Almanac and Book of Facts (New Jersey: Funk & Wagnalls Co., 1993), p. 176.

washing full loads of clothes in your washer instead of several small loads, placing a brick in the commode tank to reduce the amount of water stored and used, installing water-saver showerheads, and taking quick showers instead of baths are just a few suggestions. How many more could you employ?

Reduce pollutants in water—It is important to reduce the pollutants that are put in water. Rivers, lakes, and oceans must not be thought of as dumping grounds for waste. Many pollutants are almost impossible to remove once they are released into a river or stream. Read the labels of products that you purchase (detergents, cosmetics, shaving cream, lawn care products) and make use of those which are environmentally safe. If you change your oil at home, take the oil to a recycling center rather than dumping it into the soil. If you see trash and empty cans in or near a lake, stream, or brook, take the initiative to remove them. It may not be your mess, but it is good citizenship to help if you can.

Treat waste water—Finally, waste water should be treated so that it can be used again. Sewage treatment plants in many areas of the country can take waste water and treat it so that the water is reusable. Encourage industries and factories that have implemented pollution controls by writing or calling in a message of commendation. Unfortunately, treatment plants and pollution controls are expensive to build and maintain. However, it is worth the cost to insure a future supply of clean water.

Section Review

1. Diagram the water cycle using the following terms: evaporation, transpiration, precipitation, infiltration, and accumulation.

2. Why is understanding the water cycle important for understanding water pollution?

3. What are the two major sources of water pollution?

4. Match the following terms with the type of water pollution they represent.

_____ 1) acid rain	A. sediment
_____ 2) algae	B. organic
_____ 3) bacteria	C. chemical
_____ 4) mercury	
_____ 5) PCBs	
_____ 6) phosphates	
_____ 7) protozoans	
_____ 8) sewage	
_____ 9) soil	
_____ 10) viruses	

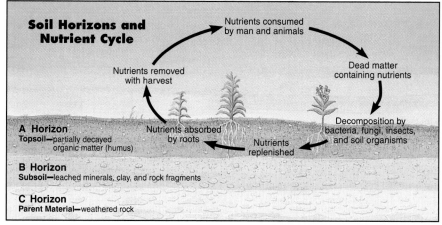

Soil Horizons and Nutrient Cycle

Nutrients consumed by man and animals

Nutrients removed with harvest

Dead matter containing nutrients

A Horizon
Topsoil—partially decayed organic matter (humus)

Nutrients absorbed by roots

Decomposition by bacteria, fungi, insects, and soil organisms

Nutrients replenished

B Horizon
Subsoil—leached minerals, clay, and rock fragments

C Horizon
Parent Material—weathered rock

The depths of the soil horizons vary by the climate and vegetation of a region or areas within a region. Rainfall, evaporation, and temperature influence the development of soil. The type and amount of plant and animal life also make a difference as to the texture and nutrient levels of soil.

POLLUTION—THE LAND ATTACK

Air and water are not the only pollution problems. Even the land is becoming polluted. If every American produces an average of three pounds of solid waste per day, you can imagine how massive the problem of solid waste can be. It is important to consider the effect of your lifestyle on the lithosphere (solid earth) as well as on the atmosphere and the hydrosphere.

Lithosphere Basics

There are approximately 58,000,000 square miles (150,000,000 square kilometers) of land on all the continents, including Antarctica. Not all of this land is accessible or inhabitable. However, man cannot use all of this land for the disposal of waste products. Much of the land must be used for man to live on and to produce needed food.

Soil is a constantly changing part of the earth's crust. It is a necessary part of the cycle to produce food, wood, paper, clothing, and many other materials needed and used in life. Soil also helps to filter and purify water. The composition of soil depends largely on materials which are broken down by climate, water, and living organisms. The upper part of soil, the topsoil, is usually the most fertile and holds most of the nutrients needed by plants and trees for growth. However, if the soil nutrients are tainted or the parent materials cannot be decomposed or broken down, then the soil quality and quantity are endangered. The entire nutrient cycle

can also be disrupted if there is too much material to be decomposed.

The Land Polluters and Pollutants

So who is responsible for accumulating waste? All living things, plant or animal, take in nutrients and give off waste products. The solid portion of

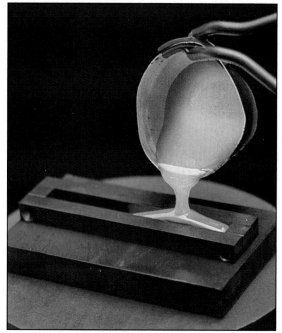

Liquid nuclear wastes are often reduced by precipitation into a solid form. This process reduces it to one-tenth its original volume.

these organic waste products are classified as **solid waste.** Normally, solid waste is decomposed by natural means (bacteria, fungi, insects) to release minerals and make humus, which forms most of the topsoil. Materials that can be decomposed by living organisms into harmless waste products are considered **biodegradable.** Biodegradable materials do not cause pollution unless they are accumulated in such amounts that they can no longer be decomposed by natural means or unless it takes so long for them to be broken down that they disrupt the natural cycle.

Any time that men discard manmade materials that are not biodegradable, they contribute to the pollution of the land. The solid pollution added by plastics, rubber, metal, Styrofoam, and glass is alarming. Although many metals will eventually rust and cardboard will decompose, the time it takes to return these to the soil makes it necessary to classify many of these products as pollutants.

Many times biodegradable materials such as leaves and branches are bagged in nonbiodegradable materials so that they cannot decompose quickly. If organic materials are mixed with oils or

According to 1992 EPA facts, New Jersey tops the list of total hazardous waste sites (with 108 sites). Pennsylvania follows with 100 sites, and California has 95.

other petroleum products found in landfills, the time it takes for them to break down is increased.

Although all waste products are a problem, there are some that are more dangerous than most. These are called **hazardous wastes.** Hazardous wastes can be solid, liquid, or gas. They also have one or more of the following characteristics:

- Ignitable—can easily catch fire.
- Corrosive—are highly acidic or alkaline.
- Reactive—can cause explosions or toxic fumes.
- Toxic—can be poisonous or promote cancer, mutations, or birth defects.
- Radioactive—can emit ionizing radiation.

Because of their potential danger, hazardous wastes cannot be routinely dumped at the local landfill. They must be packaged, handled, transported, and disposed of with extreme caution. Their dumping sites must also be carefully chosen. Since hazardous wastes can remain dangerous for many years, disposing of them is one of the most difficult and perilous environmental problems today.

Although factories are the main source of hazardous waste, ordinary citizens are also contributors. Toxic wastes include household wastes that are chemically tainted and agricultural pesticides. It is common for people to use corrosive cleaners and solvents and then to throw the dust cloths or polishing rags away. People changing oil in their cars, mowers, and chain saws often pour the old oil in the ground or put it in a container in the trash can. Every spring and summer, pesticides are used by home gardeners to protect their lawns and gardens from insect pests. As you can see, hazardous wastes are commonly released into the soil. Many of these toxins enter food chains or disrupt natural nutrient cycles. Sometimes leaching occurs when chemicals in the upper layers of soil are dissolved and carried into the lower layers and ground water.

The Effects of Land Pollution

The quality of the soil has an effect on the quality of your health. If the soil is drained of nutrients, plants are less productive. Polluted soil

The Nightmare of Love Canal

Nightmares rarely come true. However, the once unthinkable nightmare of living on a hazardous waste site actually came true for the residents of Love Canal (a suburb of Niagara Falls, New York). When the Hooker Chemical and Plastics Corporation placed their carcinogenic and toxic wastes into steel drums, buried them in William Love's canal excavations, and covered the site with clay and soil, people did not dream of the future problems.

The corporation later sold the property to the school board for a dollar and specified in the deed that they would not be held liable for any injury or damage caused by the presence of the dump.

An elementary school, playgrounds, and homes were placed on the land. In 1976, residents began to complain about smelling chemicals and of children getting chemical burns when playing in the canal. Chemicals were leaking out of the now corroded drums. The air, water, soil, and basements of homes near the canal were contaminated. After health surveys revealed high occurrences of birth defects, miscarriages, cancer, and respiratory, nerve, and kidney problems, the state of New York closed the school and relocated 238 families. In 1980, President Jimmy Carter declared the land a federal disaster area, and 711 more families were moved. Only 45 families remained in the deserted city as the dump site was capped with clay and provided with a drain system to remove and treat toxic wastes. In 1990, the EPA approved the sale of some of the boarded-up homes at bargain prices. The new name of the neighborhood? It is now Sunrise City.

may also lead to polluted water which may ruin drinking water as well as disrupt aquatic life. Soil that is tainted with hazardous substances can also lead to a variety of diseases and health problems (depending on the type of substance and the amount of it in the soil). As noted earlier, some toxic substances can cause cancer, birth defects, or mutations. Contact with radioactive, corrosive, or ignitable soils can cause burns and long-term health problems.

Preventing Land Pollution

What happens to all the trash? Have you ever wondered what happens to your garbage when it leaves your house? It does not magically disappear.

Most open dumps currently appear in secluded countryside areas or on privately owned land.

In 1898 New York began dumping municipal waste in the Atlantic Ocean. The dumping ended due to a 1934 U.S. Supreme Court ruling.

It must be disposed of. Currently there are five basic ways for the disposal of solid wastes.

For many years a common method for disposing of solid waste was to deposit it in an **open dump.** In an open dump, waste material is piled in a large vacant field. Since the dump was open, it often became a breeding ground for various pests such as rats and mice. The dumps also looked and smelled bad. In addition to these problems, the dumps contributed to other types of pollution and required large amounts of land. Open dumps are not a good solution to the problem of solid waste, and they are seldom used in the United States today.

Sanitary landfills are a better method for disposing solid waste. In a sanitary landfill, solid waste is deposited and covered with fresh soil every day. This reduces unpleasant odors and problems with pests. Although landfills require a large area, the land can be reclaimed later for such things as golf courses and community centers.

Another method is to burn solid wastes at high temperatures. This is called **incineration.** Incineration reduces the amount of land needed for the disposal of waste and eliminates many of the problems

Ways to Reduce Solid Waste

- Recycle all plastic, glass, metal, and paper items that you can.
- Compost food and yard wastes.
- Use reusable items rather than disposable ones (mugs, not paper or Styrofoam cups; plastic, string, or cloth nets rather than plastic or paper grocery bags; plastic lunch boxes rather than paper sacks, etc.).
- Reuse paper grocery bags to collect paper, leaf cuttings, or other organic disposables.
- Donate or sell used clothing and appliances.
- Repair and maintain products rather than replace them.
- Make use of old paper by using it for scrap notepaper. Dispose of it in a compost pile or recycling center.
- If possible, purchase food items in recyclable or reusable containers.
- Buy recycled products.
- Purchase items in the economy size to reduce the number of containers.

Solid waste is a big problem; there are no "perfect" solutions. You can help reduce the problem by reducing the amount of waste you produce, using materials more completely, and recycling materials when possible. Solid waste is not a problem you can simply "throw away."

with pests. However, incineration can contribute to air pollution.

Ocean dumping has also been used by many seacoast cities. Trash is loaded onto barges and then taken to offshore dump sites. This practice often can change the natural habitats for marine plants and fish in the area. Sometimes nonbiodegradable items have been carried to the beaches by ocean currents.

Probably the best method for handling solid wastes is to **recycle** them whenever possible. Recycling means to process waste materials so they can be reused. Recycling reduces most of the problems with solid waste and also helps conserve natural resources. Although all solid wastes cannot be recycled, it certainly makes sense to recycle what can be recycled. Aluminum, paper, glass, plastic, and clothing are a few materials that can be recycled.

Some municipalities are also composting organic material (food scraps, leaves, paper) in order to better manage waste disposal. Compost from municipal compost facilities has provided benefits for agricultural facilities which use it. Although there is the problem of sorting out nonbiodegradable items that are mixed with the biodegradable items (coated papers, disposable diapers) and potentially harmful items, solutions are being researched.

Recycle America! These recycling symbols have become familiar in the city, at schools, and in the business place as municipalities have found recycling to be a help to overflowing landfills. Many products that can be recycled also display this symbol.

Other ways of recycling solid wastes are being studied. It is possible to use wood and yard wastes to produce ethanol, a cleaner burning fuel than gasoline. Unfortunately, the current process is also an expensive one. However, new methods are being studied in order to get the most value from waste products.

Section Review

1. How can adding toxic substances to the soil pollute it and perhaps even affect the water?

2. What are five different types of hazardous waste?

3. Describe five ways that have been used to dispose of solid waste.

POLLUTION IN PERSPECTIVE

Psalm 119:90-91 states that "Thy faithfulness is unto all generations: thou hast established the earth, and it abideth. They continue this day according to thine ordinances: for all are thy servants." It is amazing how God in His wisdom created the earth with the capacity to renew and recycle itself naturally. Of course, due to sin, man has managed to disrupt the natural order of things. Although the

problems of pollution seem to make headlines in the news and overwhelm those who place undue emphasis on the planet, Christians must remember that God is not only the creator but also the maintainer of all.

Christians are answerable to God for their management of the resources provided by God. Understanding the hazards that can occur by misuse and carelessness is a step in wise management. You can better understand ways that the air, water, and land can be polluted and how it can affect your health.

A wise steward uses all his resources carefully. A wise *Christian* steward tries to use all his resources carefully in order to bring glory to God. Recycling and using resources to their fullest potential may not seem like it would make a bit of difference. However, many people doing a little bit individually can make a big difference. Picking up trash on the side of the road or beside a garbage container may not be a distinguished task, but it is a helpful one.

It is one thing to dislike pollution. It is another thing to decide to do your best not to pollute the environment. It is quite a different thing to put action to your decision and to be a wise manager. You may not have much influence on the actions of others, but you can control your own actions. You can refuse to litter. You can seek ways to use less water. You can contribute to your community's recycling efforts. You can change your habits to include practices that help to conserve energy. You cannot "save the earth," but God expects you to be a good manager of it.

CHAPTER REVIEW

Terms

pollutants	secondary air pollutants	conserve
pollution	photochemical smog	solid waste
atmosphere	particulates	biodegradable
ozone	industrial smog	hazardous waste
EPA	thermal inversion	open dump
greenhouse gases	sewage	sanitary landfill
greenhouse effect	thermal pollution	incineration
deforestation	sediment	recycle
radon	leaching	
primary air pollutants	acid rain	

Content Questions

1. What is the difference between how a Christian views "saving the earth" and how an atheist may see it?

2. Which part of the global warming theory do Christians agree with?

3. What does EPA stand for, and what does it do?

4. In which part of the atmosphere is ozone helpful and how?

5. In which part of the atmosphere is ozone harmful and how?

6. Smog is a major problem for Los Angeles. Because it is at its worst when the sun is out during the afternoon, which type of smog is Los Angeles known for?

7. How can air pollution contribute to water pollution?

8. What is thermal pollution?

9. How can dumping oil in your back yard affect the quality of water?

10. What are three major ways to prevent water pollution?

11. What is the difference between solid waste and hazardous waste?

12. What are six ways to reduce land pollution?

Application Questions

1. Quarantine! Suppose you were totally confined to your home and yard (your home is on a quarter-acre lot) for one year. You are not allowed to dispose of anything outside the perimeters of your yard. However, a kind friend has offered to come once a month to bring a carload of provisions and to take a carload of recyclable items away. At the end of the year, you will be penalized for each pound of unusable waste. What items would you need before you were placed in isolation? What restrictions would you place on items your friend brought in to you? How would you dispose of refuse and waste products?

2. In 1906 Upton Sinclair wrote *The Jungle,* which alerted the public to the unhealthy practices of food processing manufacturers. As a result, food inspection laws were passed. In 1962, Rachel Carson wrote *Silent Spring,* which alerted the public of the dangers of environmental pollution. If you had the opportunity to write a book alerting the public of one environmental health hazard, what would you research and write about? Compose a title and write a three- to six-point outline with informative chapter titles of a book with a Christian philosophy which warns people of one environmental health problem.

3. The first law of thermodynamics (the principle of conservation) says that energy and matter are not now being created or destroyed but only changed from one form to another. The second law of thermodynamics (the principle of entropy) says that things tend toward a state of disorder, not a state of order. What do the first and second laws of thermodynamics have to do with pollution?

Health Inspectors

Job Description: It seems to be part of human nature to require inspection before thorough compliance with rules and regulations is given. There are many different types of health inspectors to insure sound practices that affect the health of American citizens. Consumer safety inspectors inspect cosmetics, drugs, feeds and pesticides, food, medical equipment, and weights and measures. They check for accurate labeling, contamination of the product, and collect samples for analysis. Food inspectors inspect meat and poultry for proper and sanitary handling, processing, packaging, and labeling. Agricultural quarantine inspectors, common at borders and shipping, railroad, and air terminals, attempt to prevent the spread of plant pests and animal diseases. Agricultural commodity graders determine the quality and grade of certain commodities (eggs, meat, poultry, fruits, and vegetables). Environmental health inspectors check for the cleanliness and safety of food, water, and air. They test for pollutants; collect samples for analysis; examine handling, processing, and packaging of food and beverages; and inspect restaurants, hospitals, and other institutions.

Job Location: The job of a health inspector may require traveling to a variety of places and meeting many people. A food inspector may be in the slaughterhouse on one day and in an office another day. An environmental health inspector may be in a school cafeteria in the morning and in a restaurant at noon. The work place and the amount of time walking or standing depends on the type of inspection being done. There are hazards to be met in any job situation. However, an agricultural quarantine inspector working in customs may meet drug smugglers or other criminals. Some inspectors must work long hours or come in contact with unpleasant odors.

Training Required: Health inspector jobs may be offered by state or federal departments. The U.S. Food and Drug Administration and the U.S. Department of Agriculture are the main employers on the federal level. These jobs are often filled by professionals who have passed civil service examinations, examinations in the specialized field, and have experience in a related field. State or local positions usually require related job experience, a passing grade on an examination, and college training in related fields.

DRUGS, ALCOHOL, AND TOBACCO

"When I grow up" is a childhood phrase that often haunts teenagers. What will they be doing as adults? Where are their present decisions leading them? One thing is certain—most teens do not plan to become drug addicts, alcoholics, or chain smokers. These are not usually included in a person's "I want to be" list. However, these dangerous habits often become a deadly reality in many lives.

CHAPTER 12

"That ye put on the new man, which after God is created in righteousness and true holiness."
Ephesians 4:24

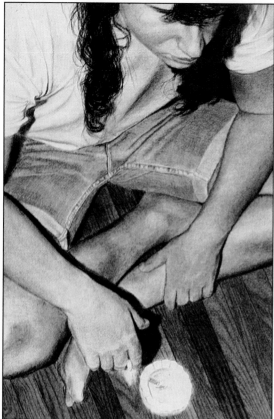

A psychoactive drug primarily targets the brain, producing changes in the activity of the central nervous system and in a person's moods, perceptions, and consciousness. Art—John M. Nolan, *Addiction.*

Samuel Johnson's saying "The chains of habit are generally too small to be felt till they are too strong to be broken" is an accurate description of the effects of drugs, alcohol, and tobacco. These substances quietly affect the body and the mind until a person thinks that he cannot live without them. Although this chapter discusses drugs, alcohol, and tobacco separately, alcohol and tobacco are correctly classified as drugs.

Drugs are found throughout society today. They are in schools, businesses, and even in churches. In some circles, drugs are used as a part of a religious ceremony to enable worshipers to get closer to God, supposedly. Some of these "worshipers" claim that using drugs is a door to great spiritual awareness.

This idea is completely foreign to the teaching of the Bible. You do not need drugs to "experience" God. He has clearly revealed Himself in His Word, and many drugs only work to destroy man's ability to see God through His Word. In fact, God's Word has the power to renew a believer's mind and can deliver one from the power of drug abuse. As you learn more about drugs in this chapter, determine that by God's grace you will never be trapped in the destructive grip of drug abuse.

DRUG USE, MISUSE, AND ABUSE

A **drug** is any chemical substance (except for food) that changes bodily functions when it is taken into the body. Some drugs are powerful, while others are weak. Some are harmful, while others are helpful. Drugs can cripple and kill as well as cure and heal.

Drugs can drastically affect both the body and the mind. Some drugs are **psychoactive** (SY koh AK tiv), meaning they can affect a person's behavior, perceptions, and moods. As you may already know, marijuana and cocaine are psychoactive drugs; but you may not have realized that alcohol and tobacco are also psychoactive drugs. You do not need to be a drug expert, but it is important for you to know some basic information about drugs.

Drugs or Medicines?

When Carol went to bed early, her parents were slightly concerned about the mild fever she had. They thought she might be getting the flu that was going around. Two hours later, Carol's temperature was 106°F, and she could not talk. Carol's parents rushed her to the emergency room.

At the emergency room, medical personnel went to work immediately. First, they began procedures to reduce Carol's temperature and took some blood tests to determine what was causing her fever. The tests revealed that she had a serious type of bacterial infection. The doctor told Carol's parents that without immediate treatment Carol could die, but with proper medication complete recovery was possible. The medicine Carol needed was an antibiotic.

Once treatment began Carol improved rapidly. In fact, after twenty-four hours, the only remaining symptom of Carol's severe illness was a slight fever. Carol's parents felt that they had seen a miracle. They thanked God that He had allowed man to discover medicines like the one that saved Carol's life.

Some of the greatest discoveries of modern science have been discoveries of drugs that can prevent disease, cure disease, relieve pain, and control chronic conditions. Drugs that are used to fight disease or to relieve pain are distinguished from other drugs; they are called **medicines.**

Although medicines are drugs, this chapter does not focus on the proper use and different types of medicines. If you have questions about a medication, your doctor or your pharmacist can help you. It is important to read all warnings on prescription and nonprescription drugs and information given by the pharmacist. It is also important to guard against drug misuse. If a drug is taken for the medically intended purpose, but not used in the amount, frequency, or manner that is prescribed, this is drug misuse. A common practice of drug misuse is illustrated by people who habitually take aspirin for a headache without noting how many they take or how often they take them. Always follow the directions of your doctor and the instructions on prescription and nonprescription drugs.

Sharing prescription drugs with others who have similar symptoms is also a form of drug misuse. Do not take prescribed medication without consulting your doctor. Drug misuse includes not only taking another person's prescription drug but also using one that is past the prescription date.

When different drugs are taken together, their combined effect can be much greater than would be expected. Sometimes two mild drugs can produce

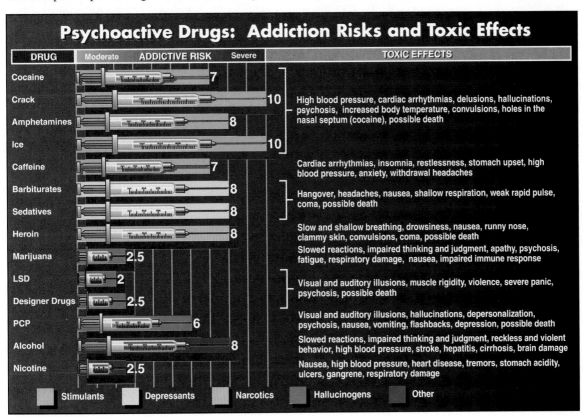

Psychoactive Drugs: Addiction Risks and Toxic Effects

DRUG	ADDICTIVE RISK (Moderate — Severe)	TOXIC EFFECTS
Cocaine	7	High blood pressure, cardiac arrhythmias, delusions, hallucinations, psychosis, increased body temperature, convulsions, holes in the nasal septum (cocaine), possible death
Crack	10	
Amphetamines	8	
Ice	10	
Caffeine	7	Cardiac arrhythmias, insomnia, restlessness, stomach upset, high blood pressure, anxiety, withdrawal headaches
Barbiturates	8	Hangover, headaches, nausea, shallow respiration, weak rapid pulse, coma, possible death
Sedatives	8	
Heroin	8	Slow and shallow breathing, drowsiness, nausea, runny nose, clammy skin, convulsions, coma, possible death
Marijuana	2.5	Slowed reactions, impaired thinking and judgment, apathy, psychosis, fatigue, respiratory damage, nausea, impaired immune response
LSD	2	Visual and auditory illusions, muscle rigidity, violence, severe panic, psychosis, possible death
Designer Drugs	2.5	
PCP	6	Visual and auditory illusions, hallucinations, depersonalization, psychosis, nausea, vomiting, flashbacks, depression, possible death
Alcohol	8	Slowed reactions, impaired thinking and judgment, reckless and violent behavior, high blood pressure, stroke, hepatitis, cirrhosis, brain damage
Nicotine	2.5	Nausea, high blood pressure, heart disease, tremors, stomach acidity, ulcers, gangrene, respiratory damage

Stimulants   Depressants   Narcotics   Hallucinogens   Other

Medication Remediation

Taking medicine, both prescription and nonprescription, has become so commonplace that many good habits have been forgotten. Here is a quick primer of correct medicine usage.

- Never take any medicine until you or your parents:
—understand the diagnosis of your condition.
—inform the doctor of any other drugs you are taking.
—know the name of the medicine prescribed.
—know when, how much, and for how long you must take the medicine.
—understand when to take it in relation to meals.
—understand any **side effects** (a different, unknown, or undesirable reaction).
—know if you can substitute a **generic drug** (a drug with the same active ingredients as name brands but which may have different inactive ingredients).
- Read and follow the directions on labels and inserts.
- Do not use two or more drugs at a time without checking first with your doctor or pharmacist.
- Do not consume medications or products containing alcohol with other medications.
- Since not all side effects can be predicted, call your doctor if the medicine produces an unexpected reaction.
- If your prescription medicine is not working, call your doctor.
- Take prescription medicine for the prescribed number of days, even if you start to feel better.
- Do not drive or work in areas which can potentially place you or others in danger (baby-sitting, cooking, construction, mechanics) when taking medicine that causes drowsiness.
- Never take medicine at night without turning on the light and reading the label.
- Do not take medicine that has passed its expiration date.
- Never share your prescription medicine with others.

drastic, even fatal, effects. This is why doctors must always consider the effects of one medication on another when they prescribe medicine and why it is important to let your doctor know about any other medicine you are taking when he gives you a new prescription. You should not combine medicines without your doctor's or pharmacist's advice.

Although drug misuse is usually unintentional, it can be just as dangerous as drug abuse. In many cases the distinction between drug misuse and drug abuse may be hard to determine. Repeated drug misuse is, in fact, considered drug abuse. It is your responsibility to follow the instructions given for prescription and nonprescription medicines. The effort you take in communicating with your doctor and understanding the directions of your prescription may keep you from grave health risks.

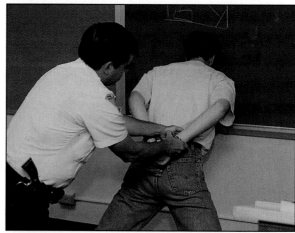

It is illegal to give or sell prescription medicine to anyone other than the person for whom it is prescribed. Knowingly storing, distributing, or accepting prescription drugs as well as illegal drugs can result in arrest.

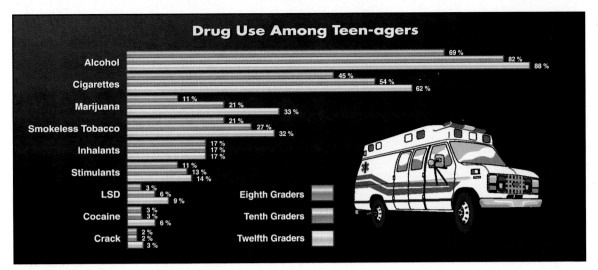

Drug Use Among Teen-agers

Drug	Eighth Graders	Tenth Graders	Twelfth Graders
Alcohol	69 %	82 %	88 %
Cigarettes	45 %	54 %	62 %
Marijuana	11 %	21 %	33 %
Smokeless Tobacco	21 %	27 %	32 %
Inhalants	17 %	17 %	17 %
Stimulants	11 %	13 %	14 %
LSD	3 %	6 %	9 %
Cocaine	3 %	3 %	6 %
Crack	2 %	2 %	3 %

SOURCE: Avram Goldstein and Harold Kalant, "Drug Policy: Striking the Right Balance," Science, September 1990, pp. 1513-21, Table 2.

Drugs Can Harm

Although drugs have saved many lives, when they are used incorrectly they can destroy lives. Crime, suicide, depression, and many physical and mental illnesses can result from using drugs incorrectly. **Drug abuse** occurs when drugs are repeatedly misused or used in a manner, for a purpose, or in an amount which can damage a person's health or ability to function. Using drugs for the pleasant side effects that they may cause or relying on drugs to cope with daily routine are common forms of drug abuse. Drug abuse is a serious problem. Adults, teen-agers, and even young children can be drug abusers.

Unfortunately, the Christian community has not escaped the influence of drug abuse. Drugs are showing up in Christian schools, and a number of Christian young people have become drug abusers. For the Christian, drug abuse is additionally harmful because it causes a break in the relationship between a holy God and His child. Do not let anything come between you and your Savior or cause you to defile the temple which God has entrusted to your care. Drugs can harm your health spiritually, physically, mentally, emotionally, and socially.

Drug abuse is harmful and dangerous. Certain drugs, such as heroin and marijuana, are illegal to have in your possession. Other drugs may be used legally when they are prescribed by a doctor, but are illegal to give, trade, or sell to another person. Using drugs is not only dangerous to your health, it is also a crime. Illegal drug use has often proved to be a deadly practice. Unfortunately, illegal drugs have been deadly to many innocent people who have been caught in the crossfire of drug deals and drug trafficking.

Drugs can also lead to exposure to deadly diseases. For instance, sharing needles to inject drugs can potentially spread diseases such as AIDS and hepatitis. Drugs can also cause a person not to think clearly and to engage in dangerous practices (playing Russian roulette, walking on railroad tracks, driving down the wrong side of the street).

Another dangerous aspect of drug abuse is that it can be difficult for a person to stop using a drug once he starts. The desire for drugs can become so strong that he cannot think of anything else. Some drug users will go without food, commit crimes, abuse their friends and family, and even risk their lives to get more of the drug they crave. They are no longer in control; drugs have taken control of them.

Physical dependence—Drug dependence can be physical, psychological, or both. In **physical dependence** the desire for the drug results from a physical need of the body for the drug. **Addiction** is a physical dependence on drugs. When a drug user repeatedly takes a drug, his body adapts to the presence of the drug and cannot function normally without it. If the drug user suddenly stops taking the drug, he can become very ill. This illness is called **withdrawal.** A runny nose, nausea, vomiting, convulsions, hallucinations, sweating, fever, increased blood pressure, tremors, depression, digestive difficulties, abdominal pain, and joint and muscle pains are common symptoms of withdrawal. Because the symptoms of withdrawal can be fatal, a person who is trying to overcome his physical dependence on a drug should be under a doctor's care.

Another aspect of physical dependence is that the body often develops a tolerance for a drug. **Tolerance** means that it takes more and more of a drug to get the same effect. Drug users who develop a tolerance for a drug often keep increasing the amount that they take. This can be a fatal mistake.

Psychological dependence—Drug dependence that does not result from a physical need for a drug is called **psychological dependence.** As opposed to drug addiction (a physical dependence), a psychological dependence is often described as a drug habit. Some people turn to drugs to help them cope with problems, unpleasant memories, anxiety, or nervousness. The drugs offer only temporary support but do not help people solve their problems. In fact, drugs often increase a person's problems and can reduce his ability to face them. Drugs, alcohol, and tobacco offer short-lived **euphoria** (a feeling of well-being) and not real solutions to life's problems.

Because psychological dependence does not cause the severe symptoms that are common in withdrawal, many people do not take it seriously. These people reason that they can quit whenever they want because it is "all in their mind." This attitude is dangerously wrong. Psychological dependence can be just as difficult to overcome as physical addiction.

Section Review

1. Why are alcohol and tobacco included in this chapter?

2. What are four helpful uses of medicine?

3. Give three examples of drug misuse.

4. How can drug abuse be harmful?

Why People Abuse Drugs

If drugs can be so dangerous, you may be wondering why anyone would ever start abusing them. There are no good reasons for abusing drugs, but there are plenty of bad ones. One of the worst reasons for taking drugs is that your friends are doing it. If you really think about that reasoning, you will soon see how ridiculous it is. You do not usually try to get sick just because "all your friends are doing it." You probably do not ask to be put on restriction just

because all your friends are on restriction. Yet thousands of young people start taking drugs just because they think everyone else is doing it.

In Chapter 4 you learned that the influence your friends exert on you is called peer pressure. Peer pressure can be very strong. Have you ever done something that you really did not want to do just because your friends wanted you to do it? If you have, you have given in to peer pressure.

Peer pressure to abuse drugs can be difficult to resist. For example, if you are in a car with your friends and they begin passing a bottle of beer around, what will you do? If you refuse to drink it, they may make fun of you and call you names. They may even get angry with you and decide to exclude you from their circle of friendship.

Losing friends is not easy for anyone. However, people who encourage you to engage in "recreational drug use" or "social drinking" are not true friends. Do you think a true friend would give you poison to eat? Yet that is exactly what many "friends" do when they encourage you to misuse drugs. Recreational drug use is drug abuse, and social drinking can lead to alcoholism. The sweetened terminology does not gloss over the fact that using drugs, alcohol, or tobacco is harmful.

Another bad reason for abusing drugs is to find out what they are like. God made you with a natural curiosity about the things around you. When you use this curiosity properly, it can help you to become wiser. However, curiosity must be controlled. You do not need to find out for yourself what drugs are like any more than you need to find out firsthand what being in a head-on collision is like. If you must satisfy your curiosity about drugs, visit a drug treatment center or a rescue mission, and you will see the effects of drugs.

Other young people choose to use drugs to escape from their problems. Unfortunately, their problems do not go away; they multiply. Drugs can offer only a temporary escape from bad problems and usually result in worse problems. Christians should turn to Christ and not to drugs when they need help.

Some people think that using drugs is a good way to show that they are in charge of their life. They are tired of parents, teachers, and pastors telling them what to do. Many young people fall prey to the false idea that using drugs, drinking alcoholic beverages, or smoking proves that no one else runs their life. However, the truth is that drugs, alcohol, and tobacco take control. Rebellion and

The world views substance abuse as a disease. Most treatment centers use humanistic methods that fail to address the root problem, which is sin. Believers should look to Christ and biblical counseling for help.

pride can result in a teen-ager ruining his own life and the lives of those who love him too.

There are many other bad reasons for using drugs. Some people use them "just for fun," or to feel more grown up, or even just because they want to. A bad reason is a bad step toward a bad habit. It is more than just bad to abuse drugs; it is wrong. Sin and sinful habits always have their consequences. The payment for doing wrong may be slow in coming, but it will come. Instead of letting self, drugs, or friends control your life, determine to let God control your life.

The Christian and Drugs

Although there are no good reasons for abusing drugs, there are plenty of good reasons for avoiding them. Drugs can have a powerful influence on your mind. Some can wake you up; others can put you to sleep. Some can make you hallucinate, or have dreamlike experiences, even when you are awake. Others can affect your mind so that you are willing to do things you would not ordinarily do. In Ephesians 4, the key to putting off the old sinful man and putting on the new righteous man is a renewed mind. In Romans 12, an important step for knowing God's will is the renewing of your mind. You need a sound mind to serve God. You should avoid drugs that can dull, damage, and destroy your mind.

Another reason to avoid drugs is the power they can exert over your life. The Christian should be dependent on Christ alone. In I Corinthians 6:12 Paul says, "All things are lawful unto me, but all things are not expedient: all things are lawful for me, but I will not be brought under the power of any." The drug dependence that comes from using certain drugs can dominate the way you think and the things you do. A Christian has no business experimenting with anything that can dominate his life as drugs do.

Not only can drugs damage your mind and dominate your life, but they can also damage your body. Drugs can damage or destroy just about any organ in your body including your lungs, heart, liver, and kidneys. Those who abuse drugs usually have much shorter lives than normal. Drugs can be an expensive ticket to an early grave.

Finally, using drugs can ruin your testimony. It takes many years to build a good reputation, but you can ruin it in just a few minutes. Using drugs could destroy any chance you have of reaching your unsaved friends for Christ and could cause your Christian friends to desert you.

How Are Drugs Taken?

There are three primary ways of taking drugs. Probably the most common way of taking drugs is to *ingest* or swallow them. Ingested drugs are absorbed into the bloodstream from the stomach and the intestines. Pills, powders, syrups, and seltzers are some of the forms of drugs that can be ingested.

Other drugs are *inhaled* or breathed. Drugs that are inhaled pass into the bloodstream through the lungs. Some drugs such as cocaine, glues, aerosols, and butane are inhaled through the nose. Another common method of inhaling drugs is by smoking the drug. Tobacco and marijuana are examples of drugs that are usually smoked.

Finally, some drugs are *injected*. These may be injected directly into the bloodstream or injected into the skin or muscles and then absorbed into the bloodstream. Although a needle and syringe may be used to inject such drugs as heroin or cocaine into

the body, a few drugs may be absorbed directly through the skin.

TYPES OF DRUGS

Of the thousands of drugs available today, only a small number are routinely abused. Most of these drugs can be divided into five categories: stimulants, depressants, narcotics, hallucinogens, and inhalants. Learning about these categories and a few of the drugs that are in them will acquaint you with some of the specific problems of drug abuse.

Stimulants Incite Body Processes

One major category of drugs includes those that speed up the work of the central nervous system. These drugs are called **stimulants.** God has designed your body with the ability to speed up or slow down when necessary. This allows you to respond forcefully to an emergency and to go to sleep at night. Stimulants speed up your body artificially. However, your body cannot tolerate this stimulation indefinitely; eventually it will break down. Cocaine, amphetamines, and caffeine are stimulants.

Cocaine—One of the most popular drugs abused is **cocaine.** Cocaine is a stimulant that is made from the leaves of the coca plant. In the 1800s, cocaine was an ingredient in many popular remedies. In fact, minute quantities of it were used as stimulants in historic "Kola" formulas (which were marketed as healthful soft drinks and brain tonics). However, once the addicting effects of cocaine became better known, its legal use was greatly restricted. In 1910, President Taft declared cocaine to be Public Enemy Number One. Remedies which used cocaine were either taken off the market or the cocaine was replaced by caffeine.

Today cocaine is seldom used legally for any medical purposes, but it is often used illegally. Cocaine users report that the drug makes them feel confident, energetic, and happy. Because these effects last only for a short period of time, the drug is often used repeatedly. Psychological dependence on cocaine can become so strong that the cocaine

Police officers are often invited to speak to students about the dangers of drug abuse.

user may feel almost helpless without the drug. Anxiety, depression, fearful delusions, and psychotic reactions are common results of cocaine use. Because the number of people addicted to cocaine is estimated to be four times greater than those addicted to heroin, cocaine is considered to be one of the greatest health threats in the United States.

Although drug dealers try to sell cocaine as a drug with no harmful effects, it is a dangerous drug. When it is sniffed, it can destroy tissues in the nose, causing the mucous membranes of the nose to atrophy and holes to form in the membrane dividing the nostrils. Using cocaine also suppresses the appetite to the point that many users are malnourished and suffer illnesses caused by poor nutrition. Cocaine can push the body past its normal limits and eventually cause it to break down. Cardiovascular problems, heart attacks, strokes, abnormal heart rhythms, and pulmonary problems are associated with cocaine use. Cocaine can be deadly.

When it is sold on the streets, cocaine is usually sold as a white powder or in a hardened form called crack. Cocaine in powder form can be sniffed into the nose, injected, or processed to form crack. Crack cocaine is taken into the body by smoking. Injecting cocaine, like injecting any drug, increases the risk of contracting AIDS, hepatitis, and other diseases transmitted by body fluids. Using crack can cause convulsions, respiratory failure, or a heart attack. Crack is known for its power to cause addiction rapidly.

Using cocaine is expensive and illegal. Cocaine was once so expensive that its use was a status symbol among the rich. Today, however, cocaine is used by poor and rich alike. Many users turn to illegal activities to support their drug habits. These may range from becoming a drug dealer to prostitution and even murder.

Amphetamines—**Amphetamines** (am FET uh MEENZ) are strong stimulants that are sometimes called pep pills. Amphetamines can cause an increase of activity, suppress fatigue and hunger, and create feelings of euphoria. Because they are strong

Whether driving long distances for work or vacation, never use drugs to keep alert. Sufficient sleep, frequent stops, and mental stimulation (tapes, sing-along songs, or conversation) provide healthful alternatives.

stimulants, amphetamines are sometimes abused by those who feel they must stay awake or work longer than usual. For example, a truck driver who must drive all night to reach his destination might use amphetamines to keep himself awake. A student who wants to study all night for a test is another type of person who might abuse them. Amphetamines are much too dangerous to be used for these purposes. Too many amphetamines may result in agitation, increased body temperature, hallucinations, convulsions, and possibly death.

Ice is a new and extremely hazardous drug. It has become very popular to use since it is more potent than crack cocaine and is easily synthesized from chemicals available over the counter. Because ice is usually smoked, it can damage the lungs and pulmonary arteries. Repeated intake of ice causes an accumulation of its chemicals in the body. Typical symptoms include restlessness, tremors, rapid respiration, confusion, hallucinations, violent behavior, and panic. Episodes are usually followed by a craving for prolonged sleep. The need for another intake usually follows.

Those who use amphetamines can develop a strong psychological dependence on them. Users may find that they need to take larger and more frequent doses of the drug because tolerance often develops quickly. The body cannot tolerate this stimulation indefinitely, and physical damage can occur if use continues. Never think that taking drugs just once will not hurt you. Harmful habits cannot be formed if you never start.

Caffeine—**Caffeine** (ka FEEN) is a mild stimulant that is common in many of the beverages Americans drink today. Coffee, tea, and many soft drinks contain caffeine. It is also found in cocoa products, such as chocolate, and in certain medications. Unlike other stimulants, caffeine is legal, and its effects are usually mild.

Despite its normally mild effects, many people are becoming concerned about caffeine. It is a drug that affects your body like other stimulants, and many Americans ingest large amounts of it each day. These large amounts of caffeine may affect

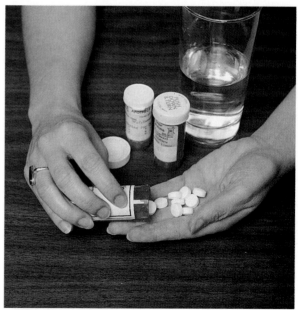

Barbiturates—**Barbiturates** (BAR bi TOOR its) are strong depressant drugs that are sometimes called downers. These drugs can lead to both physical and psychological dependence. The withdrawal sickness a person experiences when he stops taking barbiturates is severe and can be fatal.

Although barbiturates induce sleep, there are problems with using them for this purpose. Barbiturates do not work as well if a person continues taking them. They may also reduce the quality of sleep. The person who uses them may not feel rested even after sleeping for a long time. Side effects from using barbiturates include hangovers, nausea, headaches, dizziness, and drowsiness. The risk of driving or work-related accidents increases. Barbiturates depress the activity of the brain and can result in drunkenlike behavior. Combining barbiturates with other depressant drugs like alcohol can cause death.

Sedatives—**Sedatives** are another type of depressant drug. They slow the body's systems down (heart, brain, nervous system). These drugs are often prescribed by medical professionals to help

Sedatives are sometimes referred to as hypnotics because they can have sleep-inducing effects.

moods, increase anxiety, disturb sleep, and contribute to other disorders. Some people even seem to become dependent on caffeine. If a person suddenly stops consuming caffeine, he may suffer withdrawal symptoms such as headaches, feeling ill, anxiety, and muscle tension.

Today, many people are reducing the amount of caffeine they ingest. Manufacturers are selling these people their favorite beverages with the caffeine removed. When caffeine is removed from a product, it is said to be **decaffeinated.** Today you can buy decaffeinated coffee, tea, and soft drinks. Although the effects of caffeine are not nearly as dangerous as other drugs, it is probably wise to reduce the amount of caffeine you use each day.

Depressants Retard Body Processes

Depressants are drugs that slow down the action of the central nervous system. They have the opposite effect of stimulants. In fact, many people who take stimulants to speed up also take depressants to slow down. The following discussion will acquaint you with a few of the depressant drugs.

Opiates come from the opium poppy and are used to make the narcotics opium, morphine, and heroin. Opioids are synthetic drugs that are chemically similar to opiates.

relieve some of the symptoms of stress. These are effective only for a short period of time and do not make problems go away. They can become addictive and overdoses can kill. Some sedatives are especially lethal if taken with alcohol.

Narcotics Produce Dependency

Depressant drugs that come from the sap of the opium poppy or that have similar effects to drugs that come from the opium poppy are called **narcotics** or *opiates*. Narcotics are used medically to relieve pain, suppress coughing, and to treat diarrhea.

Paregoric (PAR uh GOR ik) and laudanum (LAHD n um) are medicines derived from crude opium. Because they were frequently prescribed in the late 1800s, it has been estimated that one out of 400 Americans was addicted. Now that the great danger of physical and psychological dependence for those who use narcotics is known, the use of narcotics is strictly controlled. Opium, morphine, heroin, codeine, and Demerol (synthetic morphine) are examples of narcotics.

Morphine—Morphine is the active ingredient in opium. Because it is a powerful painkiller, morphine is often prescribed by physicians to relieve

severe pain. Great care is given in administering and regulating the amount of morphine given to a patient since there is a potential for drug dependence to develop before the injury is healed. An overdose of morphine can result in shallow breathing, clammy skin, convulsions, coma, and death.

Heroin—Heroin is a drug made from morphine. It is also one of the most frequently abused narcotics. Because it is not used for any medical purposes in the United States, it is illegal to have it in this country.

Heroin is a dangerous as well as illegal drug. An overdose can have the same effects as an overdose of morphine. However, since heroin is usually injected either directly into the bloodstream or beneath the skin surface, heroin users face the added dangers of contaminated needles (AIDS, hepatitis, abscesses, blood poisoning, vein infections). Heroin is often mixed with substances such as strychnine (a poison), cornstarch, flour, or talc before it is sold. These substances can cause death by poisoning or clotting of the blood.

Codeine—Codeine is another chemical found in opium. It usually makes up about five percent of crude opium. Although it is not as effective as

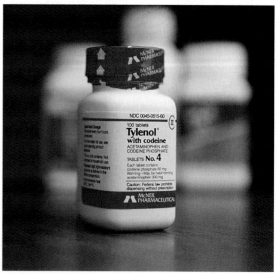

Medicine containing codeine is not an over-the-counter drug.

morphine in pain reduction, it does help suppress coughing. Medicines containing codeine may require a doctor's prescription.

Hallucinogens Distort Reality

Drugs that alter the senses so that the users see, hear, feel, or smell things that do not exist are called **hallucinogens.** Hallucinogens distort reality. People who take hallucinogens may think they can fly or report that they can see sounds or taste colors. Bizarre behavior is often seen in those who use hallucinogens. Hallucinogens can result in a strong psychological dependence.

Marijuana—**Marijuana** is a drug made from the Indian hemp plant (*Cannabis sativa*). **Hashish** is a product of marijuana. Hashish is produced from resins collected by scraping the flowering tops of the plant and is usually placed in a pipe and smoked. Unfortunately, millions of Americans have tried marijuana, and many use it regularly. In fact, marijuana follows only alcohol and nicotine in the list of the most used recreational drugs in America. However, unlike alcohol or tobacco, it is illegal to have or sell marijuana or hashish.

Because marijuana is milder than most hallucinogens, many people mistakenly believe that it is not harmful. Users say smoking a "joint" helps them relax and gives them a feeling of well-being. It tends to make sights, sounds, smells, and tastes seem more vivid. Like other drugs, marijuana is used to escape reality. However, the picture is not as nice as some would like to think. Although a person who has used marijuana may believe that he is being witty or speaking more fluently, he may actually be speaking nonsense. Although he may think that he is driving safely, his perception and response time may actually be impaired.

Evidence of the danger from using marijuana is mounting as studies are completed. Many scientists believe that marijuana smoke is more damaging to the lungs than tobacco smoke. Some of the over 400 chemicals found in marijuana are now linked to the development of lung cancer. Toxic pesticides and

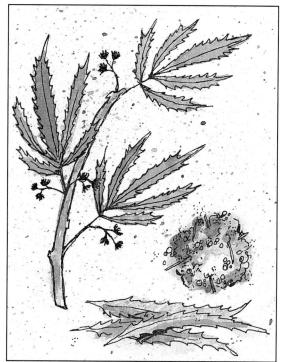

The Indian hemp plant (Cannabis sativa), *which is the source of marijuana and hashish, may also be an avenue to anhedonia (inability to feel pleasure) and memory problems.*

poisonous molds have also been known to contaminate some marijuana crops.

The effects of marijuana extend beyond the lungs to the entire body. Those who are constant users of it may also damage their immune systems, cause damage to their reproductive systems, and increase the risk of birth defects or low birth weight in their offspring. There is also evidence that marijuana can alter one's heartbeat, causing irregular rhythms. Although there is no evidence that marijuana *causes* users to use other drugs, there is evidence that many people who use harder drugs started with marijuana.

Some of the greatest dangers from marijuana result from the way it affects the brain. In the short term, marijuana distorts reality. This can lead to bad judgment and accidents. Some experts believe that many unexplained automobile accidents are caused by drivers who were using marijuana. There is also evidence that extended use may change the physical structure of brain cells. This may explain why long-time marijuana users may suffer from impaired memory and from a lack of motivation.

LSD (lysergic acid diethylamide)—There are many hallucinogens. Some come from natural sources such as psilocybin and psilocin (which are found in certain types of mushrooms) and mescaline (a chemical found in the peyote cactus). Others are manufactured in chemical laboratories. Some of these substances are so powerful that minute amounts can cause hallucinations for hours. LSD is probably the best known example.

The effects of chemically manufactured hallucinogens are unpredictable. One time a user may report seeing lovely colors and the next time experience a terrible nightmare. LSD is noted for its ability to cause **flashbacks** (when the effects recur even though the user has not used the drug for a long time). Choosing to use LSD can lead to frightening and dangerous experiences.

Although LSD may not be physically addicting, the effects of it (even a one-time try) may result in a reaction one will always regret. LSD has been known to cause some people to have severe reactions, continuous visual hallucinations, panic attacks, nightmares, short-term memory loss, depression, paranoia, and psychoses. Because LSD is so unpredictable, one doctor described taking it as the "equivalent to playing Russian roulette with chemicals."

PCP (phencyclidine)—Phencyclidine or PCP was developed to be used as an animal tranquilizer. However, it is now known to be an extremely unpredictable drug that can cause users to become aggressive and even commit brutal, violent crimes. Some drug experts believe that the effects of PCP are more dangerous than those of any other commonly abused drug. Many deaths have resulted from this dangerous drug. Because those who have taken PCP are often so disoriented that they cannot discern direction, pain, or danger, some have died from drowning in inches of water (they could not determine which way was up), burned to death (they could not feel pain), or walked off of rooftops (they could not understand the danger). PCP can accumulate in the body's cells and episodes of bizarre behavior have been known to recur months later.

PCP can be produced in liquid, tablet, or powdered forms. It is often taken in a variety of ways (injected, swallowed, or sprinkled on tobacco, marijuana, or herbs and smoked). No matter how it is taken into the body, it has the potential of being deadly.

Designer Drugs—Designer drugs are drugs made by chemists that are chemical versions of certain other drugs. For example, the molecular structure for fentanyl (china white) is almost the same as heroin. Amphetamine variants include ecstasy, MMDA, STP (DOM), MDA, TMA, PMA, DOP, and 2.5-DMA.

Illegal drug manufacturers who produce designer drugs usually work in home laboratories mixing varying amounts of various impure chemicals to produce a substance that may or may not turn out to be the intended drug. In one instance, a chemist produced a batch of designer heroin that caused the users to become immediately and permanently paralyzed. His concoction destroyed the portions of their brains that control motor activity.

Inhalants Promote Respiratory Damage and Death

Inhalants are substances that are breathed into the body in order to obtain a euphoric feeling. Products such as gasoline, paint thinner, aerosols, insecticides, model airplane glue, chloroform, ether, nitrous oxide, and butyl nitrite have been used. If you have ever used one of these products around the house, the fumes from it may have assaulted your senses temporarily. However, some of these substances can cause permanent damage, disability, or death, even if they are abused only once. Many teen-agers have died just experimenting with inhalants. Users may become aggressive and eventually experience cardiac or respiratory failure and shock. Using inhalants can damage vital organs such as the lungs, heart, liver, kidneys, and brain.

Forfeiting the Future

A wise man once said, "Never sacrifice the permanent on the altar of the immediate." This maxim means that you should never make a decision that will damage your future just to satisfy a present desire. Esau learned this lesson when he sold his birthright to Jacob. Because he was hungry, Esau was willing to sacrifice his rights as firstborn just to satisfy his hunger. He filled his belly, but he lost the blessing. Esau lived to bitterly regret the decision he had made.

Using drugs is a way to sacrifice your future. Many drug addicts that sleep in the streets and stay at rescue missions are people who once had great abilities. Some were leaders in their schools, and some were even leaders in their churches. One day, however, they decided that what they had was not enough. They wanted the excitement or the acceptance that trying drugs seemed to offer. They never dreamed that a little fun would cost them so much.

If you face the temptation to use drugs, do not look at the smiling faces of those who are promising you an experience you will never forget. Instead, remember the painful agony of a drug addict suffering from withdrawal. Or think of the drug users who live and eventually die on the streets. Many are so alone that no one even claims their bodies when they die. Is this the future you want?

Section Review

1. Why do some teen-agers take drugs? List at least four reasons and refute each.

2. What are the three major ways people take drugs?

3. Match the following with the correct category:

_____ aerosols	_____ hashish	A. stimulants
_____ amphetamines	_____ heroin	B. depressants
_____ barbiturates	_____ ice	C. narcotics
_____ caffeine	_____ insecticides	D. hallucinogens
_____ china white	_____ LSD	E. inhalants
_____ cocaine	_____ marijuana	
_____ codeine	_____ morphine	
_____ crack	_____ opium	
_____ ecstasy	_____ PCP	
_____ ether	_____ sedatives	
_____ gasoline		

ALCOHOL: LEGAL BUT LETHAL

Ethyl alcohol (ethanol) is the type of alcohol used in alcoholic beverages. It is a chemical compound of carbon, oxygen, and hydrogen that acts as a depressant when it is taken into the body. Beer, wine, liqueurs, wine coolers, and whiskey are some of the beverages that contain alcohol.

Alcohol is often considered to be the most abused drug in the United States today. The main difference between alcohol abuse and other types of drug abuse is the attitude of society toward it. Drugs that have harmful effects and that serve no medical purpose, like PCP and heroin, are illegal and socially unacceptable. However, alcoholic products can be legally sold without a prescription and are freely used for purposes other than medical reasons. Although many people regard the use of alcohol as a matter of personal choice and as socially acceptable, their approval does not make it good or right.

Because the use of alcohol is widely accepted, you may not fully realize the risks involved in using

it. The use of alcohol is responsible for the deaths of thousands of Americans every year. It is also responsible for much physical and emotional pain.

Alcohol is even a problem for many teen-agers. Studies show that most high-school teen-agers have tried alcohol. Millions of these teen-agers develop a serious drinking problem. Although the problem is probably not as great in most Christian schools, some Christian teen-agers have also used alcohol.

Because many of the drugs that people abuse today were not used in Bible times, they are not specifically mentioned in Scripture. In contrast, alcohol has been used for thousands of years, and the Bible has much to say about it. Proverbs 20:1 warns about the deceptiveness of alcohol, "Wine is a mocker, strong drink is raging: and whosoever is deceived thereby is not wise." It may look like fun, and it may be popular; but it is a mocker. Alcohol has deceived people for ages, and it is still deceiving many today. As you learn more about alcohol in this chapter, you should not be so easily deceived.

The Effects of Alcohol

Proverbs 23:29-35 says that alcohol can destroy social, physical, and spiritual health. The result of too much alcohol and the addiction that can come from using alcohol are also given in this passage. These problems may be even greater today than they were when Proverbs was written. The following sections will acquaint you with current dangers.

It May Destroy Social Health—Proverbs 23:29-30 says, "Who hath woe? Who hath sorrow? Who hath contentions? Who hath babbling?...They that tarry long at the wine; they that go to seek mixed wine."

Alcohol is often sold as an opportunity for social health. Advertisers promote the idea that fellowship, friendship, and fun are ingredients packed into every can of beer. Wine is sold as a drink of romance and family tradition. Advertisements encourage you to think that if you are lonely, just open an alcoholic container, take a drink, and you will be surrounded by fun-loving friends.

Such advertisements may make alcohol consumption sound great, but they are lies. Alcohol

The ABC symbol or a red dot is used in some regions of the country to identify an establishment that sells liquor (a package store).

physical problems. Unfortunately, those who use alcohol also hurt other people. This section will first examine the physical effects alcohol can have on you and then will look at the effects it can have on other people.

Harm to self—All alcohols are toxic. Ethanol is the least toxic but is poisonous when taken in sufficient quantities. Chugging beer or gulping quantities of other alcoholic beverages at one sitting can result in alcohol poisoning which may lead to shock, coma, and even death. Some of the other types of alcohols can cause death when swallowed or blindness if inhaled. Poisoning can occur if even small amounts of common household products containing alcohol are ingested (after-shave lotion, antiseptics, rubbing alcohol, paint products, cologne).

The effect of alcohol on the mind and body depends on how much ethanol is in the bloodstream. This is called the **blood-alcohol concentration** or **BAC.** A person under the influence of alcohol will often do things he might not ordinarily do. If the BAC continues to rise, other more obvious effects appear. Judgment, hearing, speech, vision, and balance become impaired, and one loses the ability to function normally. When a person loses his ability to function, he is considered to be drunk or intoxicated.

contributes to separation and divorce. It can also destroy your family and come between you and your friends. Some of the loneliest people in the world are those who wander the streets at night searching for another drink. No one seems to care whether they live or die. Alcohol abuse can lead to a lonely life.

Alcohol also contributes to poverty. Proverbs 23:21 says, "the drunkard and the glutton shall come to poverty." Alcohol leads to poverty in two ways. First, it is expensive to buy alcoholic beverages. Regular drinkers can easily spend hundreds or even thousands of dollars on alcohol in their lifetimes.

Second, it can damage your ability to earn money. People who abuse alcohol may not be good employees. As they drink more and more, the quality of their work usually deteriorates. They miss work frequently and may have more than their share of accidents. It is estimated that these problems cost the country over twenty-five billion dollars each year.

It May Destroy Physical Health—Proverbs 23:29 says, "Who hath wounds without cause? Who hath redness of eyes?"

The physical effects of alcohol are often more obvious than the effects on your social health. People who abuse alcohol suffer from a variety of

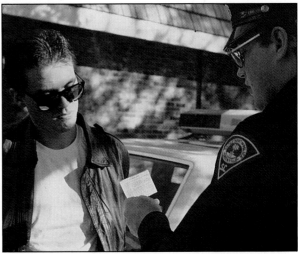

In most states a BAC of .10% is the level of legal intoxication for offenses such as drunk driving. As the BAC levels continue to rise, so does the risk of coma and death.

If you choose to drink, you are not making a wise decision. Alcohol abuse can destroy your body. It is estimated that a heavy drinker shortens his life span by ten to twelve years. Alcohol abuse harms many body organs. Health Journal on page 351 indicates some of the damaging effects of alcohol on the body.

The amount of physical harm done depends not only on the amount, type, and frequency of alcohol consumed but also on the size and age of the imbiber. Studies indicate that drugs and alcohol are especially damaging to the central nervous systems of teen-agers. The amount of damage that may take an adult ten years to accrue could occur in a teenager in only six months of use.

Alcohol abuse often leads to malnutrition. Unlike other drugs, alcohol supplies the body with calories. However, it does not supply the body with needed nutrients; in fact, it tends to starve the body of needed nutrients. Because alcohol may replace healthy foods in a person's diet, people who drink large amounts of alcohol may suffer from diseases that are caused by poor nutrition. Malnutrition is also a threat because the alcohol hinders the absorption of and increases the excretion of any nutrients that are consumed.

Drinking alcohol may also result in injuries from accidents, falls, or violent behavior. Alcohol can reduce a person's coordination, reaction time, ability to see or to judge distances, and decision-making faculties. People who are typically quiet may become loud and rowdy under the influence of alcohol.

Drownings and boating accidents increase when alcohol is involved. Most states view drinking alcohol while driving a water vehicle to be a criminal offense. Many teen-agers have drowned while swimming or boating under the influence

Damaging Effects of Alcohol on the Body

1. Alcohol adversely affects the mouth, throat, and esophagus. It may cause—
   a. thirst as it numbs the membranes.
   b. irritation and inflammation of the esophagus.

2. Alcohol adversely affects the stomach and intestines. It may cause—
   a. nausea.
   b. vomiting.
   c. ulcers.
   d. organ corrosion.
   e. bleeding.

3. Alcohol adversely affects the liver. It may cause—
   a. the accumulation of fat in the liver cells (fatty liver).
   b. **fibrosis** of the liver (scarring of liver tissue).
   c. **cirrhosis** of the liver (liver cells harden, turn orange, and die).
   d. alcoholic hepatitis (a chronic inflammation of the liver that may be fatal or lead to cirrhosis).

4. Alcohol adversely affects the brain. It may cause —
   a. hangovers.
   b. memory lapses.
   c. blackouts.
   d. brain cells to die.
   e. irreversible deterioration.

5. Alcohol adversely affects the heart. It may cause—
   a. high blood pressure.
   b. heart failure.
   c. atherosclerosis (fat deposits).

6. Alcohol adversely affects the lungs. It may cause—
   a. respiratory distress.
   b. respiratory failure.

7. Alcohol adversely affects other body functions. It may cause—
   a. dehydration.
   b. malnutrition.
   c. loss of muscle coordination.
   d. increased risk for cancer. (The development of cancer of the mouth, throat, breast, esophagus, stomach, liver, lung, pancreas, colon, and rectum is being studied.)
   e. the immune system to be weakened.
   f. bladder damage.
   g. kidney damage.

of alcohol. In fact, alcohol is involved in sixty-nine percent of all drowning incidents.

Suicide is another major danger for those who use alcohol. While there are many suicides that do not involve alcohol, there is evidence that alcohol abusers are thirty to fifty-five times as likely to commit suicide as other persons.

Those who drink may increase the risk of death by poisoning if they take drugs while consuming alcohol. Barbiturates and alcohol produce a potentially fatal combination. However, other drugs (antihistamines, acetaminophen, aspirin, sedatives) can also result in dangerous chemical interactions.

Harm to others—Often those who choose to use alcohol will defend their actions. They may support their choice with the idea that "it is no one's business but my own. I have a right to do what I want to with my own body. After all, I am only hurting myself." This line of thinking is not necessarily accurate. Alcohol users may hurt themselves, but they also hurt others. In fact, they not only *hurt* others, they often *kill* others.

A common way that alcohol abusers hurt others is through the automobile accidents they cause. Traffic accidents kill over twenty thousand Americans each year. Thousands of others are seriously injured. At least half of those killed in traffic accidents are killed because of drunk drivers. Some studies suggest that alcohol may be involved in as many as 90 percent of traffic accidents. Many states have increased their penalties for drivers who are arrested for driving under the influence (DUI) or driving while intoxicated (DWI).

The use of alcohol is also linked with increased crime. Incidents of child abuse, wife beating, rape, assault, random violence, and even homicide are increased by alcohol use. Alcohol numbs normal sensitivities and breaks down the barriers a person may set up to discourage his natural tendency to sin.

Finally, alcohol can harm the unborn. Expectant mothers who drink may damage their unborn babies. An expectant mother who abuses alcohol may deliver a child with **fetal alcohol syndrome.** These

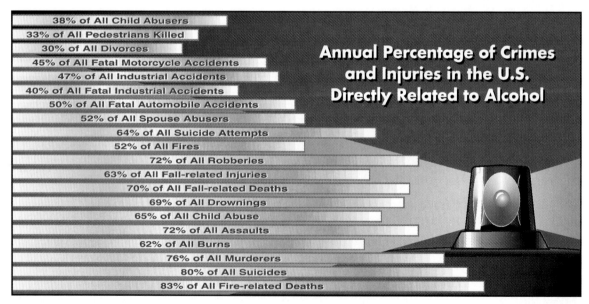

38% of All Child Abusers
33% of All Pedestrians Killed
30% of All Divorces
45% of All Fatal Motorcycle Accidents
47% of All Industrial Accidents
40% of All Fatal Industrial Accidents
50% of All Fatal Automobile Accidents
52% of All Spouse Abusers
64% of All Suicide Attempts
52% of All Fires
72% of All Robberies
63% of All Fall-related Injuries
70% of All Fall-related Deaths
69% of All Drownings
65% of All Child Abuse
72% of All Assaults
62% of All Burns
76% of All Murderers
80% of All Suicides
83% of All Fire-related Deaths

Annual Percentage of Crimes and Injuries in the U.S. Directly Related to Alcohol

SOURCE: George Pratsinak and Robert Alexander, Understanding Substance Abuse and Treatment *(Laurel, Md.: American Correctional Association, 1992), p. 50.*

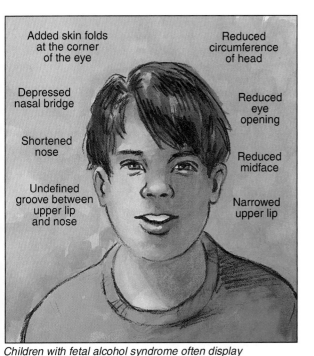

Children with fetal alcohol syndrome often display characteristic facial features. Mental disabilities can range from mental retardation to impaired memory, short attention span, and poor judgment.

Added skin folds at the corner of the eye
Depressed nasal bridge
Shortened nose
Undefined groove between upper lip and nose
Reduced circumference of head
Reduced eye opening
Reduced midface
Narrowed upper lip

babies may be mentally retarded, suffer from physical deformities, and fail to grow normally. Taking just one drink of alcohol during a critical time of fetal development can result in permanent impairment of the child.

It May Destroy Spiritual Health—Proverbs 23:33 says, "Thine eyes shall behold strange women, and thine heart shall utter perverse things."

Some people think alcohol is a stimulant. They serve it at parties to "loosen things up" and to stimulate conversation. They claim people act more like themselves when they have had a couple of drinks.

As stated earlier, alcohol is a depressant and not a stimulant. The reason it seems to add life to parties is that one of the first areas of the brain it affects is the part that controls judgment or inhibitions. An inhibition is an inward caution that keeps a person from doing foolish things. After a few drinks, a man who is usually mild-mannered may start to sing loudly in a restaurant or try tap dancing on the dining room table.

Inhibitions not only keep people from doing foolish things, but they also help keep people from doing evil things. They are a defense that God has built into man to help keep him from sin. Vile language, wicked stories, and immoral conduct may seem to be more acceptable to someone under the influence of alcohol. A Christian should not take drugs, and a Christian should especially not take drugs that encourage him to do wrong.

It May Have Aftereffects—Proverbs 23:34-35 says, "Yea, thou shalt be as he that lieth down in the midst of the sea, or as he that lieth upon the top of a mast. They have stricken me, shalt thou say, and I was not sick; they have beaten me, and I felt it not: when shall I awake?"

Another reason for avoiding alcohol is to avoid the effects of alcohol following a drinking binge. The combination of these effects is usually called a **hangover.** A hangover can have many different symptoms, but they are all unpleasant. A person with a hangover looks and feels miserable. He may have a severe headache, an upset stomach, feel exhausted, and ache all over.

It is a myth that drinking coffee, taking a cold shower, or taking more alcohol or other drugs can remove a hangover. There is no known cure for a hangover except time. It takes time for the body to recover from the effects of drinking too much. Although few people die from a hangover, many feel as if they might.

It May Lead To Dependence—Proverbs 23:35 says, "I will seek it yet again." You may wonder why people continue to drink even though it can destroy their health, ruin their testimony, and make them feel awful. One reason people continue to drink is that alcohol can cause both physical and psychological dependence. A person who abuses alcohol may suffer severe withdrawal symptoms if he stops drinking. Sometimes these withdrawal symptoms can be fatal.

Often people become so dependent on alcohol that they cannot carry on their normal duties without alcohol. These people are called **alcoholics** or alcohol addicts. The life of an alcoholic is dominated by alcohol. Work, church, school, and even family may fade in importance compared to the "need" for another drink. Alcoholism can transform a successful surgeon or a brilliant lawyer into a homeless bum. However, not all alcoholics are bums. Some are able to cover up and cope with their drinking problem for years before they even realize that they are alcoholics. There are millions of alcoholics in the United States today.

Alcoholism is difficult to treat. There is no medicine or surgery that can correct the problem. There is no drug today that will cure an alcoholic. The alcoholic must change his life, and that can be

Mel Trotter, a famous evangelist who lived from 1870 to 1940, was more than an alcoholic saved and transformed by faith in Jesus Christ. He was a servant of Christ who used his life to preach the gospel, establish rescue missions, and introduce thousands of drunkards and nondrinking sinners to God.

very difficult. Fortunately, even when things are impossible for man, nothing is impossible for God. The power of God is great enough to transform anyone, even an alcoholic.

Is Alcoholism a Disease?

The answer really depends on how you define disease. If you think that anything that makes you sick is a disease, then alcoholism is a disease. However, a disease is usually thought to be something that is beyond one's control. Things that can be controlled, such as overeating, staying up too late, or lying in bed all day, are usually not considered diseases. These are things you choose to do. You will have to face the consequences of your choices, but that does not make them diseases.

Alcoholism can make you sick. The urge to drink can be so strong that it may seem impossible to stop, but it is a matter of choice. A person chooses to drink or not to drink. In this sense alcoholism is not a disease.

The Bible always depicts drunkenness (alcoholism) as a sin. It does not treat alcoholism as a disease, and it holds the drunkard responsible for his behavior. Does this mean that Christians should look down upon and condemn those who face this terrible problem? No! Christians are commanded to be compassionate and not condemning. It is God's grace that keeps any Christian from any sin. Furthermore, no one is free from sin. A person's sins may not be as obvious to others, but they are obvious to God. If you know someone who is fighting this problem, pray for him and "consider . . . thyself, lest thou also be tempted" (Gal. 6:1).

Is Alcohol a Medicine?

I Timothy 5:23 says, "Drink no longer water, but use a little wine for thy stomach's sake and thine often infirmities."

Because alcohol can be so harmful, some people think it should never be used, not even for medical purposes. These people point out that there is no disease that is cured by alcohol, but there are many that may be caused by alcohol.

Read the label before you buy. Some medications contain alcohol and should not be combined with other medicines.

There are many other people who never drink alcoholic beverages but who take medicines that contain alcohol. You may have taken these medicines without even realizing it. For example, many cold medications contain alcohol. Some cough syrups contain 7 to 8 percent alcohol, and some elixirs may contain as much as 25 percent alcohol. There is little harm in the occasional use of medicine that contains alcohol (unless taken during pregnancy). Although alcohol cannot cure a cold, the medication may help relieve some of the symptoms and promote rest.

Whether you choose to use alcohol as a medicine or not, you need to be aware of the medicines that contain alcohol. The next time you choose a cold medication, check the list of ingredients and find out if alcohol is listed. If you choose to take a medicine that contains alcohol, make sure that you follow the directions for using it. Even when it is taken as a medicine, alcohol affects your ability to do certain tasks and can cause serious problems if it is taken with other medications. If you are taking another medicine, you should check with your doctor before combining it with any medicine containing alcohol.

Abstinence—the Answer to Alcoholism

Choosing not to use alcoholic beverages is called **abstinence.** About one out of every ten persons who choose to drink will become an alcoholic, and no one knows who these people are. Abstinence is the only totally effective way of avoiding alcoholism. No one has become an alcoholic who refused to take the first drink.

Abstinence may keep you from becoming an alcoholic, but there are many things that you will miss if you choose to abstain. You may miss the opportunity of fellowshiping with some of the world's most evil people in some of the world's most evil places. You will miss many opportunities to destroy your Christian testimony. You may miss the opportunity of killing an entire family because of drunk driving. You will miss the experience of having a tremendous hangover. In other words, abstainers will miss such miseries.

Section Review

1. True or False? Alcohol is a stimulant drug.

2. If, on the average, a person is killed by a drunk driver every 23 minutes, how many people are killed each day by drunk driving?

3. What are some of the long-term effects of alcohol on the body?

4. What are at least two verses that significantly direct your view concerning the use of alcohol? (Write out the complete passages and references.)

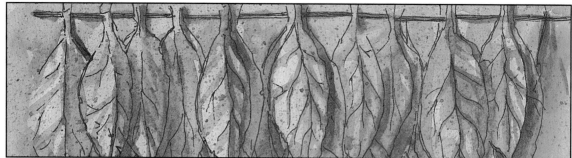

Tobacco has been a cash crop for many regions of America. Politicians often face the difficult choice between the cost of the economy and the cost of health and lives.

TOBACCO: A HAZARD TO HEALTH

Tobacco is a multibillion dollar industry in the United States. Tobacco companies spend billions to promote their products. Although cigarette advertising is banned on television and radio, the industry uses magazines, newspapers, billboards, and sporting events to sell the idea that smoking is a habit enjoyed by beautiful women and handsome men. These advertisements provide the illusion that smoking is pleasurable, sophisticated, mature, popular, and glamorous. They do not show the whole truth.

The advertisements do not show lung cancer or heart disease. The hospital bills and the pain and suffering of the patient or his family are not mentioned. The graveyards filled with those who have died because of tobacco use are not pictured. They do not show people avoiding the choking smoke of a smoker. They do not show the yellowed teeth and bad breath caused by nicotine. They do not picture a home blazing in fire or people burning to death because of a forgotten cigarette. They do not show the money and potential savings that have gone up in smoke.

Smoking is one of the most unhealthful habits people engage in. In fact, health authorities view smoking as the number one preventable cause of death and disease in the United States today. It is estimated that smoking contributes to over 390,000 deaths each year, about one-fifth of all American deaths. Because tobacco-related deaths exceed all other drug and alcohol deaths combined, many health-related groups such as the American Cancer Society and the American Heart Association are actively combating the problem of tobacco use.

There are many reasons for a person to choose not to smoke, but it is especially important for a Christian to take a stand against using tobacco. Tobacco does more than harm the body; it defiles God's temple. Defiling God's temple has always been viewed by God as a serious matter with serious consequences. I Corinthians 3:17 states, "If any man defile the temple of God, him shall God destroy; for the temple of God is holy, which temple ye are."

Why Decide Now?

There are about fifty million smokers in the United States today. Most of these smokers are adults who began smoking when they were teen-agers. Studies show that many smokers begin experimenting with tobacco in elementary or junior high school and become regular smokers during their teen-age years. The decision not to smoke or use any form of tobacco is a decision that you need to make now.

Even though the health effects of smoking are well known today and although the numbers of those who smoke and the popularity of smoking is in decline, there are still many teen-agers who start smoking. At one time, smoking was more of a problem with teen-age boys than teen-age girls. Unfortunately, teen-age girls are now smoking as much as teen-age boys. For some reason, girls become addicted to nicotine faster and find it harder than boys to break the habit. These teens have

Enticing the Public

Advertising is the business of making a product or client known, appreciated, and desired. For years the tobacco industry has tantalized the public with sultry, idealistic, and sometimes humorous advertisements. Approximately $3 billion are spent each year promoting tobacco products. In 1984 Dr. C. Everett Koop, the U.S. Surgeon General, set a goal for a smoke-free society by the year 2000. Later that year, President Reagan signed the Comprehensive Smoking Education Act to promote awareness of the hazards of smoking. The four Surgeon General's warnings are required on cigarette packages and advertisements on a three-month rotating cycle.

chosen to start a habit that may haunt them for the rest of their lives and could eventually kill them. The following information will help you understand why choosing to smoke is a foolish decision.

What Is in Cigarette Smoke?

SURGEON GENERAL'S WARNING: Cigarette Smoke Contains Carbon Monoxide.

The labels state that cigarette smoke contains carbon monoxide. However, cigarette smoke also contains about 4,000 other substances of which at least eighty are major toxins, forty are carcinogens (cancer-producing substances), and one is the addictive psychoactive drug nicotine.

Carbon Monoxide—**Carbon monoxide** is a colorless, odorless, hazardous gas. It is highly dangerous because it impairs the body's capacity to carry oxygen. If oxygen and carbon monoxide are both present, your blood cells will carry the carbon monoxide first. Since your body must have a constant supply of oxygen, carbon monoxide poisoning can be fatal.

Smokers do not die from carbon monoxide poisoning in this way since the amount of carbon monoxide in the bloodstream usually does not get high enough to kill the smoker directly. It can, however, cause some of the symptoms of carbon monoxide poisoning, such as headache, nausea, or dizziness. The most serious effects of carbon monoxide are its ability to reduce the efficient functioning of the heart, brain, and other organs and to increase the risk of cardiovascular diseases. It is suspected that the increased risk of heart attack and strokes is caused by the reduction of the oxygen supply to the heart. Carbon monoxide is also linked with a smoker's lowered endurance and shortness of breath.

Nicotine—**Nicotine** is a colorless, oily poison that is found in tobacco leaves. Nicotine can be extremely toxic if a sufficient amount comes into contact with the skin or if it is swallowed. Nicotine poisoning can cause dizziness, faintness, increased pulse, cold clammy skin, nausea, vomiting, diarrhea, convulsions, and death. When people smoke for the first time, they usually experience some form of nicotine poisoning. Although it takes only a small amount of nicotine in the body to be fatal, smokers do not inhale enough nicotine to kill them immediately. A smoker's body can build a tolerance to nicotine, allowing the symptoms to decrease.

Besides being a toxin, nicotine is also addictive. It is a psychoactive drug that first acts as a stimulant and later as a mild depressant. In reality then, nicotine is the addictive drug and tobacco is the means of administering it to the body. This drug begins to affect the body whether it is smoked (cigarettes, cigars, pipes), chewed (snuff, chewing tobacco), or inhaled (snuff). A smoker can become physically and psychologically dependent on nicotine.

When cigarette smoke is inhaled, the nicotine rapidly enters the bloodstream and begins to adversely affect the nervous system, the endocrine

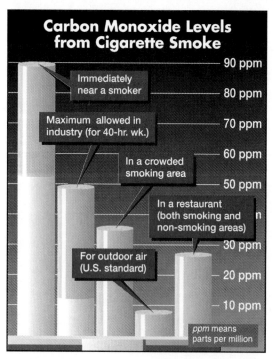

Carbon Monoxide Levels from Cigarette Smoke

90 ppm

Immediately near a smoker — 80 ppm

Maximum allowed in industry (for 40-hr. wk.) — 70 ppm

60 ppm

In a crowded smoking area — 50 ppm

In a restaurant (both smoking and non-smoking areas) — 30 ppm

For outdoor air (U.S. standard) — 20 ppm

10 ppm

ppm means parts per million

SOURCE: Lori W. Turner, et al., Life Choices: Health Concepts and Strategies *(New York: West Publishing Co., 1992), Figure 11-4.*

system, the circulatory system, and the digestive system. The nicotine remains in the body until it is metabolized by the liver.

ch person's tolerance to nicotine varies. However, 60 *ligrams of nicotine is usually fatal to most adults. One arette may contain from 50 to 2,500 micrograms of nicotine. cause the filter on the cigarette absorbs some nicotine and smoke burns up even more of it, a smoker does not inhale full amount.

Tar—Particles other than nicotine and moisture that are present in cigarette smoke are classified as **tar.** Hundreds of different residues found in tobacco form a dark, thick, sticky substance. When a smoker inhales smoke, particles enter the lungs. As time passes, tar begins to build up and to damage the mucous lining of the lungs. In fact, studies indicate that a person who smokes twenty to sixty cigarettes a day may accumulate as much as one-fourth to one and a half pounds of black tar in his lungs in a year. Because of the hazardous composition of many of the tar particles, it is possible for them to be carcinogenic (able to produce cancer).

Tars are not only dangerous to cigarette smokers but are also especially dangerous to pipe smokers, cigar smokers, and those who use smokeless tobacco. Because these forms of tobacco do not usually have any filtering system, more tar is taken into the body. The tar accumulation in the mouth, throat, and larynx makes oral cancer and throat cancer a very real risk.

Smoking Is Hazardous to Your Health

SURGEON GENERAL'S WARNING: Smoking Causes Lung Cancer, Heart Diseases, Emphysema, and May Complicate Pregnancy.

Lung Cancer—Cancer is a dangerous and greatly feared disease. Lung cancer is one of the most dangerous forms of cancer. In fact, it kills more Americans than any other type of cancer. It is sometimes difficult to detect and usually difficult to treat. Only about ten percent of those with lung cancer are alive five years after diagnosis.

If you remember the anatomy of the respiratory system (Chapter 2), you should recall that God made the tissue lining the passages to the lungs with the ability to capture and expel foreign particles. The tar in smoke hinders the action of the cells lining the lung passageways so that they can no longer do their cleansing work. The tissues of the lungs begin to come into direct contact with the tar. Mucous begins to build in the passageways. The smoker then begins to cough to get the airway clear. As irritation continues and carcinogenic compounds build in the lungs, the cells may begin to undergo cancerous changes.

Incidences of cancer of the mouth, throat, and pancreas are also higher in smokers. Other organs in the body may be subject to raised risks of cancer because they filter carcinogenic substances brought into the body by tobacco. The liver, kidneys, and bladder are examples of organs that have high incidence of cancer in smokers. One of the best decisions you can make to lower your risk of getting cancer is deciding not to smoke.

Heart Disease—Do you remember what disease kills more Americans than any other disease? It is heart disease. The ten factors your text mentioned included stress, diabetes, obesity, lack of exercise, family history, gender, age, high blood pressure, high blood cholesterol, and *smoking*. In fact, you may remember that smoking was one of the primary risk factors. Smokers are about twice as likely to die from a heart attack than nonsmokers.

There are several ways smoking promotes heart disease. For instance, the nicotine in tobacco causes the blood vessels to constrict, making the blood pressure rise. This constriction makes the heart work harder to pump blood through the body. Nicotine also causes the body to release a stimulant that increases the rate at which the heart beats. This increase of activity causes an increased need for oxygen. However, the carbon monoxide in the smoke serves to weaken the body's ability to transport oxygen, so the heart and lungs must again struggle to respond to the body's need. Tars further reduce the ability of the lungs to supply necessary oxygen.

The incidence of heart disease is also increased because nicotine causes blood platelets to tend to clump together (platelet adhesiveness) and form clots. Because the clots can lodge in arteries to the heart, the risk of having a heart attack is increased.

New research also indicates that nicotine serves to increase the levels of LDLs (low-density lipoproteins) and decrease the levels of HDLs (high-density lipoproteins) in the body. The presence of more LDLs and fewer HDLs increases the risk of developing atherosclerosis.

Chronic Lung Diseases—Have you ever seen a smoker struggling for every breath? Smoking damages the lungs. Not every smoker gets lung cancer, but every smoker damages his lungs. At first this damage is minor and reversible, but after many years this damage can mount up until the lungs cannot function properly. This health problem is called chronic obstructive lung disease (COLD).

Chronic **bronchitis** (brahn KIE tis) is a lung disease that is often caused by smoking. In bronchitis, the tubes in the lungs (bronchi, bronchioles) become irritated and diseased. Mucous begins to build in the passageways. The smoker then begins to cough to clear the airway. There is often congestion in the lungs and a constant cough (sometimes called a "smoker's cough").

Emphysema (EM feh SEE mah) is a chronic lung disease that is mainly caused by smoking. In emphysema the tiny air sacs in the lungs (alveoli) become damaged. A person who has emphysema

Lungs—Effects of Smoking

Lungs that are healthy process the intake of oxygen and the exchange of carbon dioxide without trouble. However, tar in cigarette smoke hinders the action of the cells lining the lungs so that they can no longer do their proper work. Mucous begins to build in the passageways. As irritation continues and carcinogenic compounds build in the lungs, the cells may begin to undergo cancerous changes.

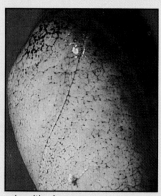
a healthy lung

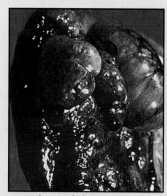
a carcinogenic lung

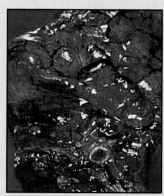
a smoker's lung

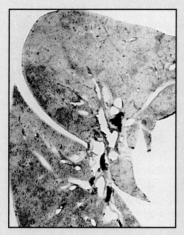

Emphysema—One Result of Smoking

In a normal healthy lung (left picture), the alveoli are too small to be seen individually. However, the lung tissue of a heavy smoker shows damaged, enlarged air sacs (right picture). A person with emphysema may constantly feel short of breath or as if he is suffocating. Once a person's lungs have reached this point, the tissue damage is permanent.

cannot exhale forcefully and may constantly feel short of breath or as if he is suffocating. If a person has reached this point of lung disease, the tissue damage is permanent.

Chronic lung diseases are frightening. If you have ever felt like you could not breathe, you have experienced a little of the panic that people with these diseases experience every day. Chronic lung diseases can become so severe that victims can do little more than sit quietly and struggle for every breath. One of the most frightening aspects of these diseases is that once this damage has occurred, there is little that can be done to reverse it.

Complications During Pregnancy—Doctors are now encouraging expectant mothers to quit smoking. They have found that each time the mother takes a puff on a cigarette, she depletes the oxygen supply to the **fetus** (the unborn child). In fact, exposure to the carbon monoxide from the smoke and the chemicals in cigarettes increases chances of **miscarriage** (the premature fetus dying before birth) or **stillbirth** (the baby dead at birth).

Tobacco not only hinders a healthy pregnancy but also increases the health risks of the expectant mother. The nicotine released in her body can increase her blood pressure, promote gastric distress, and lower her immune system's ability to battle disease.

Smoking Is Hazardous to the Health of Others

SURGEON GENERAL'S WARNING: Smoking by Pregnant Women May Result in Fetal Injury, Premature Birth, and Low Birth Weight.

Harm To Unborn Babies—One of the most serious examples of ways in which smoking hurts others is that of the possible damage caused to an unborn baby by an expectant mother who smokes. These babies are more likely to be born early, to suffer from a variety of defects, and to have a lower weight at birth than the babies of nonsmoking mothers.

But what does this have to do with you? You are only a teen-ager, and you are not planning on having a baby for ten years or so. Why should you worry about what smoking can do to an unborn baby?

Although it may be several years before you become a parent, remember that most smokers choose to smoke during their teen-age years. Few mothers begin smoking right before they start a family. Many start smoking when they are young and later find it difficult to stop smoking, even though they want to quit. If you begin smoking now, you may not be able to stop when you decide to have a family. Because women seem to have more trouble quitting than men do, it is particularly important for young women to avoid smoking.

Harm To Nonsmokers—Have you ever gone to a restaurant and been bothered by the cigarette smoke of others? Or have you gone to a bowling alley and come home smelling like cigarette smoke? Do you think smokers should be allowed to pollute the air you breathe?

Breathing the cigarette smoke of others is called **passive smoking.** Smoke is categorized into three groups. Smoke that is inhaled and then exhaled by a smoker is called **mainstream smoke.** The smoke that comes directly from the end of a lighted cigarette is called **sidestream smoke.** And then there is **environmental tobacco smoke** (ETS), which is the smoke that remains in an area of air.

The conflict between smokers and nonsmokers has been going on for years. Nonsmokers have complained about burning eyes, hurting throats, and aching heads caused by the cigarette smoke of others. However, even though they disliked the effects of cigarette smoke, many of them regarded this discomfort as an unavoidable hazard of living in a smoking society.

Today attitudes are changing. There is increasing evidence that passive smoking is more than just a minor irritation. Studies show that inhaling the smoke of others can harm health. For instance, the children of smokers have been found to have more respiratory disorders (asthma, bronchitis, pneumonia, middle ear infections) than the children of nonsmokers. Smoke has proven to be especially dangerous to infants. In fact, infants who are subjected to sidestream or environmental tobacco smoke face almost the same risks as the fetus of a smoking mother does. Impaired physical and mental development for a lifetime and death in the first six weeks of life are threats.

Nonsmoking spouses married to smokers have a greater risk of lung cancer than normal. Recently an EPA report has concluded that the risk from passive smoking is greater than the risk from industrial air pollution.

Sidestream smoke contains many more harmful pollutants than mainstream smoke. In fact, studies have shown sidestream smoke to be two times higher in tar and nicotine, three times higher in benzopyrine, five times higher in carbon monoxide, and fifty to seventy times higher in ammonia than mainstream smoke.

Even mainstream smoke that is exhaled adds toxins to the air. Quantities of carbon monoxide, ammonia, nicotine, cyanide, and carcinogens are released into the air. If you consider the pollutants and dangers found in sidestream smoke and add to it the pollutants of exhaled mainstream smoke, you can understand why environmental tobacco smoke has contributed to about 3,000 lung cancer deaths in America each year.

Because of this evidence many nonsmokers are insisting on their right to breathe air unpolluted by the cigarette smoke of others. As a result, many public places are restricting the areas where smokers can smoke or making it illegal to smoke in certain buildings. Smokers are a minority, and the

All government buildings now restrict smoking. In order to provide clean air for their clientele and workers, many other businesses also have nonsmoking requirements.

current nonsmoking movement is moving to restrict the ability of this minority to harm the health of others.

As a Christian who chooses not to smoke, what should your attitude be about passive smoking? First, you should avoid smoke whenever possible by sitting in nonsmoking sections. If someone's smoke is bothering you, you can politely ask them not to smoke. In restaurants, stores, or other public places you may want to express your concern to the management. You may also encourage your city and county government to pass legislation that restricts smoking in public areas.

The most important thing to remember is that you should always be friendly and polite. Remember that spreading the gospel of Jesus Christ is even more important than your health. If you are rude and offensive, you may succeed in keeping someone from smoking but hopelessly damage his openness to the gospel. Stubbornly insisting on personal rights is not a proper attitude for a Christian.

Harm To Residents—Smoking has also caused many fires. Although people have been warned not to smoke in bed, many do. People have dozed off in their living rooms with lit cigarettes in their hands. In fact, there are about 2,000 deaths and 4,000 injuries each year because of fires started by cigarettes that have been dropped or carelessly discarded.

Quitting Smoking Reduces Risks

SURGEON GENERAL'S WARNING: Quitting Smoking Now Greatly Reduces Serious Risks to Your Health.

Quitting Is Hard—Before you learn the benefits of quitting, you need to understand that smoking is a very difficult habit to break. Some alcoholics have claimed that it was easier to give up alcohol than cigarettes, and about nine out of ten smokers say they want to quit yet continue to smoke year after year. Why?

First, current evidence shows that many smokers become addicted to the nicotine in cigarettes. When a smoker puffs a cigarette, nicotine has an almost immediate effect on his body. He might experience an increase in his heart rate, higher

blood pressure, and constriction of certain blood vessels. He may not be as hungry as he was before, and his taste for food might be dulled. Every time a smoker takes a puff on a cigarette, he gets another dose of the drug. Soon the body develops a dependence on nicotine and experiences withdrawal symptoms if the smoker decides to quit. Irritability, tension, depression, difficulty sleeping, and restlessness are some of the withdrawal symptoms that a smoker may experience. The smoker may become so miserable that he decides that quitting is just not worth it.

Another reason smoking is hard to stop is that it becomes a well-learned habit. After smoking hundreds or thousands of cigarettes, a smoker lights his cigarette without even thinking about it. Some smokers light more than one cigarette at a time because they do not even realize that they are smoking. Smoking becomes an automatic behavior, and well-learned habits are often difficult to break. You may have found this out if you have tried to change your eating or exercise habits recently.

Quitting Is Possible—Have you ever heard someone say, "I would love to quit smoking, but I just

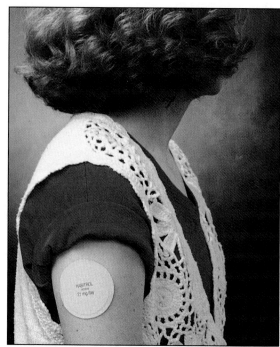

Smoking leads to an addiction to nicotine. Some people have used nicotine patches (as pictured) or nicotine gum to help them gradually withdraw and taper off their habit. Many people have found it best to just quit all at once ("cold turkey").

Quitting smoking is one of the hardest things to do. Mark Twain summed up the attempt in saying, "It isn't so hard to quit smoking. I've done it hundreds of times."

can't do it. It's impossible for me to quit." Although many smokers feel this way, it is possible to quit smoking. About thirty-five million smokers have quit. Many of them tried to quit several times before they finally succeeded. Few, if any, of these ex-smokers found it easy, but they still quit. The only smoker who cannot quit is a smoker who has stopped trying to quit.

A Christian who decides to quit smoking has a source of strength that the unsaved do not have. The Apostle Paul said in Philippians 4:13, "I can do all things through Christ which strengtheneth me." The power of God is greater than any habit. A Christian does not have to be a slave to tobacco.

You are fortunate to grow up in a time when the dangers of smoking are well known. Many adult smokers started smoking before these dangers were known. Now they may feel trapped by a habit that they dislike and would like to quit. If you know someone who is trying to quit smoking, remember that they are facing a tough battle. You should encourage them and pray for them.

Make certain that you treat adults with respect even if you do not like their habits. This is especially important if your parents smoke. An attitude of respect and concern may help your parents decide to quit, but a disrespectful attitude is unhelpful and ungodly.

Quitting Is Worth It—Although many smokers would like to quit, some are not convinced that quitting is really worth it. They may not realize that smoking reduces a person's life by at least 18 years. Some think that they have already done so much damage to their body that quitting would not really help. This attitude is wrong. As the following reasons show, quitting is worth it.

Quitting improves health—Quitting smoking improves a smoker's health. This is especially true if a smoker quits before he has the symptoms of a serious disease. Quitting cannot make lung cancer go away or restore your lungs once you get emphysema. However, much of the damage caused by cigarettes will reverse itself when a smoker quits. This improvement becomes greater the longer a smoker goes without smoking. After ten years of not smoking, the death rates for ex-smokers who quit smoking before getting diseases associated with tobacco use are almost the same as for those who have never smoked.

Quitting enhances appearance—Cigarette ads try to sell the idea that smoking makes people more attractive. Actually the opposite is true. Smokers often have yellow teeth and fingers. Their breath smells bad, and they usually look older than they are. The smell of smoke often clings to everything they wear, and they leave a trail of dirty cigarette butts and ashes behind them. Quitting smoking is an inexpensive and effective way to look better as well as feel better.

Quitting improves influence—Most young people begin smoking because of the influence of a smoker on their life. Older brothers and sisters,

parents, and friends who smoke actually influence others to smoke, even though they may not want to. It is bad enough to smoke, but it is worse to influence others to smoke. On the other hand, a smoker who quits can be a great inspiration to others. Nonsmokers and ex-smokers can have a positive influence on smokers. A person who has quit smoking is a living testimony of how God can help break the chains of nicotine.

A person who stops smoking can reap benefits for herself and for those around her (positive influence on her family; clean air with nicotine-free environment; and reduced possibilities for asthma, bronchitis, and lung cancer).

Quitting saves money—Smoking can be an expensive habit. Most people do not realize how much money they spend on cigarettes because they usually just spend a few dollars at a time. Many people spend hundreds of dollars each year on a product that is destroying their health. Surely this money could be better spent. Some people who have quit smoking have used the money they saved to take a vacation across the country, to Europe, and even to Hawaii.

Quitting brings freedom—Cigarettes have a powerful influence on an addicted smoker. For many smokers it is much easier to miss a meal than it is to miss a cigarette. They begin to panic if they sense that their supply of cigarettes is running low.

Cigarettes control a part of their life. The only way they can regain this freedom is to quit smoking.

Many who have quit smoking also enjoy the freedom from guilt and the freedom from worry. It is a heavy burden to continually do something that you know to be wrong and dangerous. When a person quits smoking, these burdens are removed.

Not Starting Is Better Than Quitting—The only thing better than quitting is never starting. Every advantage that comes from quitting smoking is even better if you never start. It is much easier to stop before you start.

Smokeless Tobacco—Another Bad Choice

Because the health effects of smoking have become obvious, many people are choosing another tobacco product that they do not have to smoke. This is called **smokeless tobacco.** Snuff and chewing tobacco are the two most popular smokeless tobacco products.

Smokeless tobacco is not a safe substitute for cigarettes. It contains nicotine just like cigarettes and may be even more addictive. In fact, smokeless tobacco products are now required to have warnings placed on them. The following warnings are placed on a rotation basis.

- WARNING: This product may cause gum disease and tooth loss.
- WARNING: This product may cause mouth cancer.
- WARNING: This product is not a safe alternative to cigarette smoking.

Using smokeless tobacco is a dirty habit that many people find offensive. Smokeless tobacco can cause more than discolored teeth, bad breath, and increased dental caries. A person who uses smokeless tobacco is two to three times more likely to lose his teeth because of the increased chances of developing periodontal disease.

Smokeless tobacco may not contain tar or carbon monoxide, but it does have nicotine and a host of carcinogens. The heart diseases which threaten a

smoker also threaten the user of smokeless tobacco. The addictiveness of nicotine is also a danger.

Although a person who uses smokeless tobacco may not worry about getting lung cancer, chances of getting oral cancer and throat cancer are real risks. For instance, a person who is a long-term user of snuff increases his chances of getting cancers of the lower lip or gums fifty times that of a nonuser.

Users of smokeless tobacco are also at risk for **leukoplakia** (LOO koh PLAY kee ah). Leukoplakia is a white, thickened area of irritation in the mouth caused by the mouth tissues being in direct contact with tobacco juice. Seven percent of the patients with leukoplakia develop oral cancer. As you can see, tobacco, in any form, is not a good choice.

Smoking Is "Out"

Smoking was once a much more popular habit than it is today. Today there are many more non-smokers than smokers. Many of those who have smoked for years are choosing to quit. Smoking is a habit that is "out of style."

In spite of this trend, each year thousands of teen-agers chose to smoke. Although surveys show that less than 20 percent of those who graduate from high school are smokers today, this is still far too many. Some think that they look more grown up because they smoke. Others are pressured by their friends to smoke. Still others feel they can show everyone how "cool" they are by smoking. Smoking does not make you a better person or make you grown up, but it does make you and other people sick. Choosing to smoke is a bad decision; do not let anyone talk you into it.

Your future depends on the choices you make. In other chapters you have learned how to feel fit and stay well. You have learned how to choose friends and how to keep your body safe. Drug abuse (which includes alcohol use and smoking) is a road that goes in the opposite direction. It is an expressway to physical, emotional, and social death. The best way to stay off this highway is never to get on any of its entrance ramps.

Section Review

1. Which main substances make tobacco so harmful to health?

2. How much nicotine is usually fatal to adults?

3. What are at least ten health risks and diseases associated with tobacco use?

Chapter Review

Terms

drug	caffeine	hangover
psychoactive	depressants	alcoholic
medicines	barbiturates	abstinence
side effects	sedatives	nicotine
generic drug	narcotics	tar
drug misuse	hallucinogens	bronchitis
drug abuse	marijuana	emphysema
physical dependence	hashish	fetus
addiction	flashbacks	miscarriage
withdrawal	inhalants	stillbirth
tolerance	blood-alcohol concentration (BAC)	passive smoke
psychological dependence	intoxicated	mainstream smoke
euphoria	fibrosis	sidestream smoke
stimulants	cirrhosis	environmental tobacco smoke (ETS)
cocaine	fetal alcohol syndrome	smokeless tobacco
amphetamines	inhibition	leukoplakia

Content Questions

1. What is the difference between drug misuse and drug abuse?

2. In considering drug usage, what is the difference between a habit and an addiction?

3. Which drug was commonly used in soft drinks and health tonics before its addicting effects were realized?

4. How do stimulants and depressants differ?

5. What are three examples of stimulants and three examples of depressants?

6. What is a designer drug?

7. Which drug is especially noted for its ability to cause flashbacks?

8. Which drug is known for its unpredictable effects and often causes users to act violently and brutally?

9. Which seemingly mild drug is linked to lung cancer, heartbeat fluctuations, birth defects, low offspring birth weight, driving accidents, and low motivational attitudes?

10. Which of the following are true statements?

    a. Morphine is a form of opium.

    b. Ice is a form of cocaine.

    c. Hashish is derived from marijuana.

    d. Crack is derived from LSD.

11. Which hallucinogenic drug is derived from the peyote cactus?

12. Why is the sale of cough syrup with codeine usually regulated?

13. Concerning alcohol, is there a hazard with drinking too much too fast?

14. Is there any danger in drinking rubbing alcohol?

15. In what ways can drinking alcohol present a danger to others?

16. Is a person who is drunk an alcoholic?

17. True or False? A teen-ager can become addicted to alcohol and suffer greater physical damage faster than an adult.

18. True or False? Alcohol kills brain cells.

19. Besides damaging the physical body of the abuser, what are three other ways alcohol can harm the drinker?

20. What BAC is considered to be the legal level of intoxication in most states?

21. Why would damaged alveoli make a person feel tired?

22. How can tobacco be a danger to others?

23. What two diseases are smokers more likely to get than nonsmokers?

24. Is smokeless tobacco a good substitute for cigarettes? Why or why not?

25. What are at least five good reasons for a person to quit smoking?

Application Questions

1. Choose a verse or text that inspires you to avoid the temptations of drugs, alcohol, and tobacco. Make a sign for your room with this verse or text written out.

2. Your younger sister confides to you that some of her friends are enticing her to experiment with drugs. What would you say? What should you do?

3. Although recreational drugs, social drinking, and smoking may be acceptable in your community, why should a Christian not participate in these activities?

4. You have been witnessing to your neighbor. Because his (your friend is the same gender as you are) parents have gone out of town, he is going to spend the weekend with you. To your dismay, your friend has raided his parents' bar and comes to your house drunk. He passes out on your living room couch. At intervals his body tries to rid itself of the toxin by vomiting. Other than making sure that he does not ruin your furniture and carpet, why should you and your parents keep a careful watch over him while he sleeps it off?

5. Your sister-in-law has decided to try to quit smoking. Make a plan of action of things that you can do to help her meet her goal.

IN SERVICE

Pharmacists

Job Description: New drugs are being developed in laboratories each year. Research is being done to discover the effects of drugs on certain diseases, how drugs interact with other drugs, and the possible uses of drugs. A pharmacist does much more than just fill prescriptions. He tells the patient how to take the medicine properly and what side effects to look for. He knows the latest news in drug research findings, works with the doctor to monitor a patient's drug therapy, and helps to enforce federal drug laws. You are probably familiar with pharmacists as professionals who can answer questions about both prescription and nonprescription drugs. However, you may not know that they can also specialize in radioactive pharmaceuticals (radiopharmacists or nuclear pharmacists) or make rounds with a doctor in a hospital to help determine proper drug therapy for patients.

Job Location: Many pharmacists work in retail stores to provide convenient access to medicines needed by the community. However, pharmacists are also needed around the clock in hospitals. Hospital pharmacists not only dispense medicines (tablets, capsules, etc.) but also prepare injections in a sterile environment. The hours worked and the requirements of work depend on the place of employment. For instance, a pharmacist in a small town drug store may own the store and also sell nonhealth-related items (lawn care, holiday items, stationery, etc.). One thing that all pharmacists do have in common is that they are usually required to be on their feet much of the time. Pharmacists today are often proficient in using computers to monitor a patient's medication profile, possible drug interactions, amounts and frequency of medicine purchases, as well as supplies on hand.

Training Required: A pharmacist must be more than an honest, conscientious person; he must be licensed by the state to practice. Most states require a degree from an approved college of pharmacy and a passing score on a state board examination. Many states also require time worked as an intern or practical experience. Of course, a person interested in this field should have an interest in mathematics, chemistry, biology, and physics.

GROWTH AND DEVELOPMENT

Infancy is a period of life filled with firsts. First sights, first sounds, first words, first relationships, and first steps. You probably do not re-member most of your first years; however, as a teen-ager, your body is once again going through profound growth and develop-ment. This time you may be aware and sometimes bewildered by the way you are maturing. Your health for the rest of your life may be affected by decisions and actions made today.

CHAPTER 13

"And Jesus increased in wisdom and stature, and in favour with God and man."
Luke 2:52

Joy! Despair! Excitement! Depression! Welcome to the ever-changing world of adolescence. **Adolescence** is the name given to the period of time between childhood and adulthood. It is a time of transition. You know you are not a child anymore, but you are not an adult either. Frequently you are treated like a child; yet you are expected to act like an adult. How can you not merely just survive this stage of life but live it joyously?

A LIFE TO FOLLOW

One of the most mysterious and amazing events in human history occurred when God became man. The One who created the universe came to earth as a helpless child. The One who rules over all submitted to the authority of His parents. The One who fills the universe grew and developed just like you.

Luke 2:52 tells how Christ fared during this turbulent time. It says that He "grew in wisdom and stature, and in favor with God and man." Christ grew mentally, physically, spiritually, and socially. Even in adolescence, Christ was the supreme example.

You probably think that there is no way that Christ could have experienced the feelings and frustrations that you experience. He may have become man, but He was different. He was God. How could God face the type of temptation that you face?

Well, He is God, but He is also a man. As a man He experienced many of the things that you experience. Hebrews 4:15 states that Christ "was in all points tempted like as we are." The difference is that He was without sin. Christ went through the changes of life and did all that His Father had for Him to do. He did more than just survive life—He lived His life for the glory of God. What an example for Christians to follow! God wants His children to live a full and abundant life through Him. A Christian should strive to be like his Master, the Lord Jesus Christ, by living his life for God and in a way that glorifies God.

A LIFE OF CHANGE

You are constantly changing. Because these changes usually occur gradually, you probably do not even notice them. But if you get out a family album and look at old pictures of yourself, you will clearly see that you have changed. As you look at those pictures, you may think you are looking at an entirely different person who has little in common with the person you are today.

Life is filled with change. You are neither the same as you were yesterday, nor the same as you will be tomorrow. Take time to consider the changes that you have experienced, the changes you are experiencing, and the changes you will experience. It is an amazing journey to look at where you have been, where you are, and where you are going.

Where You Have Been

Conception to Birth—If your teacher asked you to calculate exactly how old you are, how would you do it? You would probably start with the day you were born and calculate how many days have passed since that time. If your teacher then asked

The Virgin Birth

Conception takes both a mother and a father. Every child who has ever been born, except one, has been conceived this way. This is the normal method of reproduction.

The conception of Christ was entirely different. The first chapter of the Gospel of Luke gives an account of how this occurred. It says, "And in the sixth month the angel Gabriel was sent from God unto a city of Galilee, named Nazareth, To a virgin espoused to a man whose name was Joseph, of the house of David; and the virgin's name was Mary. . . . And the angel said unto her, Fear not, Mary: for thou hast found favour with God. And, behold, thou shalt conceive in thy womb, and bring forth a son, and shalt call his name Jesus. . . . Then said Mary unto the angel, How shall this be, seeing I know not a man? And the angel answered and said unto her, The Holy Ghost shall come upon thee, and the power of the Highest shall overshadow thee: therefore also that holy thing which shall be born of thee shall be called the Son of God."

It is clear from this account that Jesus was born without an earthly father. This is what is meant when Christ is referred to as being virgin

Carlo Dolci, Madonna and Child, *Bob Jones University Collection of Religious Art.*

born. Because he was virgin born, Christ was not born with the taint of sin passed down from Adam.

Many people today refuse to believe the Bible account of the virgin birth. They say that

it is impossible for anyone to be born without a human father. To some extent they are right. With man it is impossible, "but with God all things are possible" (Matt. 19:26). The virgin birth was a miracle, but it is also an essential tenet of the Christian faith. If Jesus were not virgin born, then He would have been a mere mortal and sinful man. However, Jesus was born of a virgin, He is God the Son, and He was made man to die for the sins of all mankind, so all men can have eternal life. "Who, being in the form of God, thought it not robbery to be equal with God: But made himself of no reputation, and took upon him the form of a servant, and was made in the likeness of men: And being found in fashion as a man, he humbled himself, and became obedient unto death, even the death of the cross" (Phil. 2:6-8).

you to calculate the length of time you have been in existence, would your answer be the same?

It should not be. Although age is usually calculated from the day you were born, you actually existed months before that time. You lived for these months inside of your mother. You were just as real then as you are today. In fact, this was the most amazing period of growth and development that you have ever experienced.

Your real beginning started with an event called **conception.** At conception, a special cell from your father (called a sperm cell) *fertilized* a special cell from your mother (called an egg or ovum). Fertilization is the beginning of biological reproduction. The union of these two cells resulted in one new cell or a **zygote** (ZIE GOHT). Although this cell was so small that it could be seen only with a microscope, it contained all the genetic instructions for

Although these identical twins have similar physical characteristics, they are individuals with individual tastes.

your appearance, for your personality, for your mental capacity—for you.

A zygote, the fertilized ovum, is part of the mother and part of the father, but it is different from both parents. In fact, unless the cell develops into identical twins, this cell is different from any other cell that has ever existed. Identical twins occur when a zygote completely divides early in its development. Because identical twins share the same genes of the mother and father, they are the same gender and look alike.

Fraternal twins begin as two different egg cells fertilized by two different sperm cells. This results in twins that may be different in gender and that look like brothers and sisters, which is exactly what they are.

Shortly after fertilization, the zygote began to divide—first into two cells, then four cells, then eight cells, and so forth. While these divisions were occurring, you were traveling within your mother's body to the place that would be your home for the next nine months. This place is a specialized organ called the **uterus** (YOO tur us) or womb. Your mother's uterus was designed by God to nourish and protect you until you were born. Once you

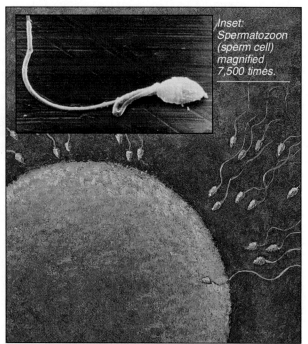

Inset: Spermatozoon (sperm cell) magnified 7,500 times.

Pregnancy begins when an egg (ovum) is fertilized in a fallopian tube. A fertilized ovum is a zygote. As the zygote develops and implants in the uterus's lining, it is termed an embryo (EM bree OH). After three months of development, it is referred to as a fetus (FEE tus).

Fetal Development

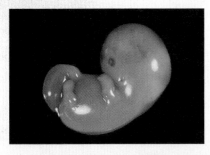

This developing embryo (about two months old) will go through many important and rapid stages of development. It is extremely vulnerable to viruses, chemicals, and radiation at a time when its mother may not even know she is pregnant. Psalm 139:16 states, "Thine eyes did see my substance, yet being unperfect; and in thy book all my members were written, which in continuance were fashioned, when as yet there was none of them."

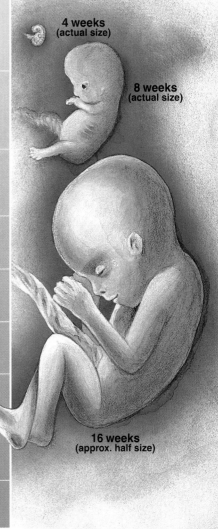

4 weeks
(actual size)

8 weeks
(actual size)

16 weeks
(approx. half size)

End of Month	Approximate Size	Developmental Changes
1	³⁄₁₆ in. (0.6 cm)	Termed an embryo; formation of backbone and vertebral canal; formation of body systems; budding arms and legs; formation of embryonic heart; development of special sense organs (eye, ear, and nose)
2	1¼ in. (3 cm) ¹⁄₃₀ oz. (1 g)	Formation of face and features; distinct divisions in limbs (arm, elbow, forearm, hand, fingers); formation of major blood vessels; continued development of internal organs; development of bones
3	3 in. (7.5 cm) 1 oz. (28 g)	Termed a fetus; all organ systems formed but not functional; formation of tooth buds in gums; developed eyes are fused; detectable heartbeat; development of nails
4	6½ in. (18 cm) 4 oz. (113 g)	Appearance of hair on head; head large in proportion to body; formation of joints; continued development of body systems
5	10 in. (25 cm) 1 lb. (454 g)	Formation of fine hair on body; head more proportioned to the body; audible heartbeat; distinct movements felt by mother
6	14 in. (35 cm) 1½ lb. (781 g)	Eyelids separate; formation of eyelashes; definite movements and position changes
7	17 in. (42 cm) 3 lb. (1,362 g)	Capable of survival outside the womb; head and body more proportioned; refinement of respiratory system
8	18 in. (45 cm) 5 lb. (2,270 g)	Accumulation of fat; soft bones formed in the head; refinement of respiratory system
9	20 in. (50 cm) 7½ lb. (3,405 g)	Additional accumulation of fat; ready for birth

reached the uterus, the **placenta** (pluh SEN tuh) developed to serve as the passageway for nutrients and oxygen from your mother's body to your developing body.

At this point you had no fingers, no legs, no heart, not even a head. But soon these seemingly identical cells began to specialize and to develop into different organs. Within about a month you had grown 10,000 times as big as you were at conception.

You continued to grow rapidly, and by the time you were two months old, you had reached the enormous size of three centimeters and weighed about as much as a paper clip. Although you were small, you had changed drastically. Your head, legs, arms, and internal organs were already formed. Your heart had been beating for weeks. By the time you were three months old, your nails and even your fingerprints had developed. In the following months you continued to grow.

Section Review

1. How can Jesus understand the changes an adolescent goes through?

2. Briefly outline the development of an unborn child.

Where You Have Been

Birth, Infancy, and Childhood—After a nine-month period (about 280 days) of development, you were ready for one of the most traumatic experiences of life, your birth. Although your mother's uterus was a perfect place to grow during these critical months of development, you could not stay there forever. As you got larger and larger, there was soon no more room to grow. It was time for you to make your grand entrance into the world.

It was not easy for your mother to convince you to leave the secure environment of the womb. She had to go through an exhausting effort called **labor** to introduce you to the world. In labor, your mother experienced strong muscular contractions that moved you from her uterus, through the birth canal, and into the world. It was a traumatic experience for both you and your mother, but you obviously survived.

As a baby, you were still totally dependent on others to take care of you. You had to be fed, changed, and loved. Without the loving care of

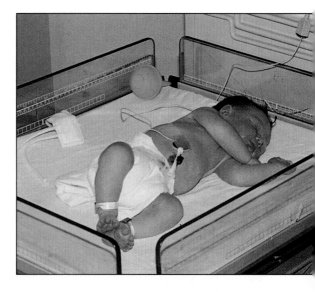

others, you could not have survived. Even as a helpless baby, you were developing your own personality, and your presence was able to influence the lives of those around you.

Abortion: More Than a Matter of Choice

By the time you were five months old, you were big enough and strong enough to let your mother know you were around when you moved. You weighed about a pound and were about ten inches long. You already had hair on your head. Although you continued to grow and develop until you were born, you were clearly "you."

A great tragedy is occurring daily around the world: **abortion.** Abortion is the ending of a pregnancy by death. If an embryo dies naturally, it is termed a **spontaneous abortion.** However, if a fetus (three months after conception) dies of natural causes, it is termed a miscarriage. Although natural abortions occur, the intentional killing of a human embryo or fetus is wrong.

In 1973, the United States Supreme Court ruled that abortion is legal. Since that time millions of babies have been killed. Some of these babies are cut to pieces by doctors' knives, others are torn to pieces by a machine that works like a strong vacuum cleaner, and some are shriveled in a strong salt solution. Abortion is a cruel and ugly procedure.

You may wonder how a country like the United States that does so much to protect the rights of its citizens can allow this tragedy to occur. Murder is obviously illegal in America, and the murder of innocent people is especially despised. How can this country tolerate the murder of the unborn?

As you now know, an unborn child is often called a fetus. Abortionists defend their actions by claiming that a fetus is not really a human. Many refer to the fetus as tissue or the product of human conception. In some people's thinking, the fetus is not human. Many do not view abortion as murder; it is just the termination of an unwanted pregnancy. ("I do not want a baby now. I will get rid of this tissue and be rid of the problem.")

However, the Bible clearly regards the unborn as people. In Psalm 139, the psalmist says God knew him and formed him in his mother's womb. Jacob and Esau struggled together and were referred to as two separate nations while they were in their mother's womb. Samson was called to be a Nazarite while he was still in his mother's womb. The Lord called Isaiah from his mother's womb, and John the Baptist leaped within his mother's womb when the unborn Christ came to visit.

Although he or she is unborn, the fetus in the womb is a human being. The fetus is even subject to mundane human traits such as hiccups, thumb sucking, and pain. The intentional killing of an unborn child is still the killing of a child; it is murder. Abortion is more than a matter of a mother's right to choose whether to have the baby; it is also a matter of a baby's right to live. It is more than what is convenient for the mother and her lifestyle; it is the decision of life and death for another human. It is the difference between survival and murder. Abortion is a matter of not taking responsibility for past actions and the irresponsible avoidance of consequences by killing an innocent party. Thus abortion is clearly a matter of what is right and wrong.

Unborn children must be protected. They cannot protect themselves. As a Christian you should stand against the killing of unborn children. Determine that, by God's grace, you will never consent to an abortion. Seek ways to encourage single girls who are pregnant to deliver their babies and not to abort their children. Support legislators who will vote against laws promoting abortion. The abortion issue is more than a matter of choice; it is a matter of life.

Toddlers actively explore and get to know the world that surrounds them.

During the first two years of your life you continued to grow rapidly (although not nearly as rapidly as you grew before you were born). By the time you were two years old, you had already grown about half as tall as you will be as an adult. Your mental, physical, and social development was also phenomenal. You could walk well and even run when you wanted. You had learned to talk and to feed yourself. You were learning to obey and also learning the consequences of disobedience. You were changing every day.

In the rest of your childhood, you continued to change, but these changes became more gradual. Your growth continued but at a slower rate. You were constantly learning, but most of the things you learned were not as dramatic as saying your first word or taking your first step. The most dramatic changes probably occurred in your spiritual life. During this time, you may have become aware that you were a sinner and accepted Christ as your Savior. If you have not made this decision yet, you cannot experience proper spiritual growth. You need a solid spiritual foundation to uphold you as you face the challenges, changes, and choices of this life.

Where You Are

Adolescence—Earlier you learned that the stage of transition between childhood and adulthood is called adolescence. You have already begun your journey into this stage. You will probably find every aspect of your person changing during this time. Mentally, emotionally, socially, physically, and even spiritually you are entering one of the most crucial stages of your life.

Although your journey through adolescence may be bewildering, confusing, and even scary, it is comforting to know that others have safely walked this path before you. The journey is not exactly the same for any two people, but it is similar for most. This section of the chapter looks at where you are in your development and some things that you can expect during this time.

Where You Are: Mentally—Your mental growth is often not as obvious as your growth in other areas. Nevertheless, you have grown mentally, just like you have grown physically. The achievement tests that you periodically take measure that learning. The fact that you have been promoted from elementary school to junior high and then high school also reflects mental progress.

Early appreciation of books and learning encourages mental development.

Childhood naiveté (lacking the ability to analyze information) should develop into healthy critical analysis during adolescence.

In elementary school, you generally believed and accepted everything you were told. However, because your mind has matured, you may now find yourself questioning information. You wonder how the facts given to you were attained. You may analyze the truths given to you to see if you can apply them to other phases of life. You are coming to the point where you can understand and intelligently discuss many of the issues that confront adults today.

It is important to keep learning, to continually add new information in a variety of areas to your mind. Although adolescence is usually a time of great physical changes, do not let it be a period of time where your mind grows stagnant. Ask questions if you do not fully understand an issue. Think things through. Pray for God's help to discern and to use information wisely.

Where You Are: Emotionally—Your emotional development is often not as smooth as your mental development. During adolescence emotions are often unstable. Young people frequently feel strongly about things. Emotions such as anger, fear, love, and hate are felt intensely but often change rapidly. One minute you may be so angry at someone that you feel as if

you could kill him, and thirty minutes later he is your best friend again.

These types of strong emotions are common and normal, but they must be controlled. Proverbs 16:32 says, "He that is slow to anger is better than the mighty; and he that ruleth his spirit than he that taketh a city." If you keep these strong emotions under godly control, you have disciplined a dangerous pitfall. If you fail to control your emotions, you are like "a city that is broken down, and without walls" (Prov. 25:28). A city without walls is a city without defenses. It is a city that can easily be defeated by any enemy. You must either conquer these emotions, or they will conquer you. Hiding God's Word in your heart can help you to control your reactions. Instead of trying for self-controlled reactions, strive for God-controlled reactions.

A problem that many adolescents face is insecurity. Insecurity is often thought of as a feeling of being unsure of yourself or lacking confidence in yourself. Actually, an insecure Christian lacks confidence in God's ability. Security and strength are found in God and not in you.

You may feel insecure about the way you look, about your popularity in school, about your future

Actual or perceived differences can lead to feelings of insecurity.

occupation, about the clothes you wear, or about a thousand other things. These feelings of insecurity probably will not kill you, but they can hurt you. One of the greatest dangers of insecurity is that it can make you more susceptible to peer pressure. If you are unsure of yourself, you are more likely to be influenced by others. Although feelings of insecurity will not kill you, the things your friends talk you into doing can.

As you mature, you should find it easier to trust in God's ways and His timing. You learn to depend on His leading rather than depending on your own resources and decisions. Although you may have occasional feelings of insecurity, these times should help you rely on God more completely. A Christian can be confident when his confidence depends on God and not on himself. Proverbs 29:25 states, "The fear of man bringeth a snare: but whoso putteth his trust in the Lord shall be safe."

Where You Are: Socially—Some of the greatest changes you face during adolescence are social changes. You may have entered a new school, been promoted into the youth group in your church, and joined various school clubs, athletic teams or musical organizations. You are probably away from your family more than you have ever been before. Your social circle may be dramatically different from what it was just a year ago.

A growing awareness—Not only has your social circle changed but also your interests within this circle have probably changed. If you are a girl, there was a time when you thought that boys were brats, but you now find that you think of these "brats" most of the time. If you are a boy, there was time that you thought that girls were boring, but you are now finding that girls are very interesting creatures indeed. Adolescence is often marked by a growing interest in the opposite sex.

Although this interest is not wrong, it can be dangerous if it is not controlled. The interest is not sin, but it can lead to life-ruining sin if it is not directed properly. Second Timothy 2:22 instructs you to "flee also youthful lusts." Lust is a strong, ungodly desire, and in James the Bible clearly indicates that lust leads to outward sin (James 1:15).

In America, sexual relationships outside of marriage have become common. They are so common that some teen-agers become convinced that "everyone is doing it." That is a satanic lie; everyone is not doing it. Those who choose not to follow godly principles by losing their purity often reap dreadful consequences such as sexually transmitted diseases, AIDS, pregnancy outside of marriage, guilt, and ruined lives. Sexual purity can protect you from these life-altering consequences. You should determine that by God's grace you will keep yourself pure.

Even if you have already determined to keep yourself sexually pure, you must remember that during adolescence your emotions are often difficult to control. If you spend much time alone with members of the opposite sex, you are putting yourself in a situation that even a strong Christian may not be able to handle. It is not wrong to have a strong interest in the opposite sex, but be careful that Satan is not allowed to use this interest to destroy your life or your testimony.

"Let no man despise thy youth; but be thou an example of the believers, in word, in conversation, in charity, in spirit, in faith, in purity" (I Tim. 4:12).

Also remember that you should develop friendships with people of both sexes. Not every boy or girl who is your friend has to be a boyfriend or girlfriend. You may find that you can develop many close friendships with those of the opposite sex without any romantic inclination.

A desire for independence—As you get older, you become more and more independent. When you were born, you were totally dependent on your parents for everything. They fed you, protected you, clothed you, and loved you. Now you can do many of these things yourself. You still need your parents (probably more than you realize), but you do not need them constantly.

The Bible clearly teaches that you are to honor and obey your parents (Exod. 20:12; Eph. 6:1; Col. 3:20). In fact, one of the evidences of a wicked society is a refusal to submit to the authority of parents (Rom. 1:30; II Tim. 3:2). Obeying your parents is a biblical command, not a personal option. Unless your parents ask you to do something that God forbids, when you disobey them you are disobeying God. Even though you are more independent than you used to be, God knows that you still need the loving guidance that your parents provide.

Soon your life will have undergone a complete change. As an adult you will earn your own living, take care of your own home, and make your own decisions. You will not be under the direct control of your parents any longer. However, independence is earned gradually. Because you are approaching adulthood, you may want to be more independent *right now.* You may resent some of the decisions that your parents make for you. You may even rebel against your parents' authority, especially when your parents refuse to allow you to do things that "all the other kids are doing." However, independence, like respect, must be earned. It is not a rite of passage so that when you become a teen-ager you automatically deserve to be trusted or given total freedom. It is a matter of proving not only to yourself but also to those in authority over you that you can make decisions in a godly and mature manner.

Although some conflict between you and your parents may be unavoidable, you can avoid major conflicts. It is just as natural for you to desire more independence as it is for your parents to try to protect you. If you willingly submit to the authority

A job may provide more than an opportunity to earn money. It may also be a way to earn respect, trust, and increased independence.

of your parents, you will usually find that they trust you more. The more they trust you, the more freedom they will allow you to have. Keep in mind that your parents are mainly motivated by their deep love and concern for you. Parents must also answer to God for their dealings with you. They have to adjust to your becoming independent just as much as you must adjust to preparing to leave. When handled in a loving, respectful manner, the entire experience can be rewarding.

It is important to remember that the parents that seem so difficult today have loved and cared for you from the day you were born. Remember that they were once teen-agers too. Take time to talk to them and not just to argue with them. You may be surprised at how reasonable they really are.

Where You Are: Physically—During adolescence you will experience a variety of physical changes that are different from any other stage of life; they are normal but distinct changes. This stage of development is called **puberty** (PYOO bur tee). Because the body changes that accompany puberty are special and personal, they should not be discussed in the vulgar and casual way that is common in society today. It is important to understand the changes that you are experiencing so that you can appreciate God's plan for your physical development. Since this information is personal and private, questions should not be directed to your friends (who may accidentally spread false information or promote wrong concepts), but to your parents (or another spiritual adult whom you have confidence in).

Even though puberty prepares you physically to become a parent, it does not prepare you spiritually, socially, financially, or emotionally to be a parent. It may be several years before you are ready in all these ways for parenthood. However, there are many changes involved with puberty that you may already be experiencing. Although many of the changes are different for boys than they are for girls, some are similar.

Puberty is a time when the differences between boys and girls become more pronounced; there are some changes that are common to both. One of these is a change in the rate of growth. Although you have experienced steady growth each year, during puberty your growth rate may almost double causing a growth spurt. You may grow faster than you have at any time since you were two years old.

Physical changes occur at different times for teen-agers.

It is important to remember that even though the changes are similar for most teen-agers, the time they occur can vary greatly. Most girls begin puberty before boys. In fact, girls tend to mature about two years before boys. Since the growth spurt usually comes sooner for girls than for boys, some girls are taller than their male classmates for a couple of years. If you are already a tall girl, this extra growth may be frustrating. Although boys begin to grow later, they often grow more than girls. In a couple of years, many of the boys who seem so short will be taller than the girls in their class.

Another change that is common to both sexes during adolescence is a change in the condition of the skin. In Chapter 10 you learned that acne is a common problem for teen-agers. In order to keep your skin clear, it is important to practice good hygiene and eat a balanced diet. Sweat glands complete development during puberty. This change causes body odor to be more of a problem than it was in childhood. A daily bath, deodorant or antiperspirant, and clean clothes are now necessities.

Other changes that occur during puberty are a little different for boys than they are for girls. Most of these changes are triggered by hormones. The hormones in boys are different from the ones in girls. The male hormones produce physical changes expected in the maturation of a boy into a man (angular build from broadened shoulders; deepening of the voice; etc.). The female hormones likewise promote the physical changes of a girl into a woman (curvature formation; widening of hips; etc.).

During this time of development, some people mature early and some people mature late. If you mature early or if you mature late, you may feel overly self-conscious. If you face this distinction, it may help you to remember that maturation is not a race. God has you on your own individual time table; you will physically mature at the right time. Although it is natural to be self-conscious about these differences, keep in mind that these changes are completely normal.

Secondary Sex Characteristics

Physical Changes in Boys	Physical Changes in Girls
• Growth spurt (long bones lengthen, ages 12–18)	• Growth spurt (long bones lengthen, ages 10–16)
• Increased secretion of oil in the skin	• Increased secretion of oil in the skin
• Increased secretion of perspiration	• Increased secretion of perspiration
• Enlargement of sex organs	• Enlargement of sex organs
• Increased body and facial hair	• Increased body hair
• Broadening of shoulders (ages 18–22)	• Widening of pelvic bones
• Thickening of skin	• Increased fat deposits
• Enlargement of larynx and vocal chords	

Where You Are: Spiritually—Your teen-age years may set the pattern for what you will be spiritually the rest of your life. This is because your teen-age years are often a time of re-evaluating your spiritual decisions. Many times teen-agers have questions: Is the Bible God's Word? Do I believe the Bible, or am I just going along with my parents? Was I ever saved? Do I really want to live a Christian life?

These questions are common because you are coming to a time when you will be governed by the things that *you* believe and not by the rules and beliefs of your parents or your school. If you come to the wrong answer to these questions, you could easily ruin the rest of your life or even face God's eternal judgment. According to II Corinthians 2:15-16, the message of the gospel is a message of life to those who accept it, but a message of death to those who reject it. The life of Pharaoh found in Exodus 5-14 shows that when truth is rejected it can result in a hardness of heart that rejects further truth. Many teen-agers who grew up in Christian homes and went to Christian schools have rejected their heritage and ruined their lives with drugs, immorality, or crime. Some of these were never saved and may never accept Christ because they have rejected God's truth for so long. Others are saved but are not living for God and must someday answer to Him.

If you are going through this time of questioning, there are two options that you may take. You can reaffirm your faith or you can reject it. Your parents and your school can control your actions (to some extent), but they cannot control your mind. This choice is yours, but you will answer to God for the decisions that you make.

What does it mean to reaffirm your faith? It means to settle in *your* mind your commitment to God and to God's will. It means that *you* choose to live a Christian life. It takes a personal and genuine faith to live a consistent Christian life.

Even if you choose to reaffirm your faith, you may have doubts about certain things. For instance, many teen-agers have doubts about their salvation. This is especially true for those who accepted Christ at a young age. If you are plagued by doubts about your salvation, you will not experience the peace and joy that God intends for you to have. You can settle these doubts by reaffirming your salvation. Get alone with God and confess that you are a sinner, repent of your sin, ask Christ to save you and to give you assurance that you are saved. When you come to God as He commanded in His Word, He *will* save you (John 6:37). Never be ashamed to admit you are having doubts or to ask others for help. Most Christians face doubts at certain times in their lives, and those who have overcome those doubts can help you to overcome them too.

Section Review

1. How does man rationalize abortion? How is this thinking wrong?

2. How much time usually elapses between human conception and birth?

3. What happens during labor?

4. What mental, emotional, social, physical, and spiritual changes occur during adolescence?

Where You Are Going

Adulthood—This chapter has examined where you have been and where you are; now it is time to look at where you are going. In this section an overview of what the future may hold for you is given. But before you look at the future, you must realize that the most universal characteristic of the future is uncertainty. Only God knows exactly what the future holds for you. Certainty is found only in what God has chosen to reveal.

In Luke 12, a rich fool had great plans for the future. He planned to tear down his barns and to build bigger barns. He planned to live in wealth and luxury. But God intervened in the midst of his plans and said, "Thou fool, this night thy soul shall be required of thee." No one, not even a young person, is promised tomorrow. If you live every day as though you may meet God that day, you will have nothing to fear about the future.

Where You Are Going: A Time of Decision—Late adolescence (ages 16-18) and entry into adulthood (ages 19-24) are times of life-changing decisions. You will decide on a **vocation** (work done to earn a living; a career; a profession). You will decide whether you are going to college and where to get your college education. You will decide whom to date and eventually whom to marry. Some may find it to be God's will to remain single. These decisions are among the most important choices that you will ever make.

Because these decisions are so important, you may worry about how you will know what the right decisions are for you. There is only one way to avoid mistakes in these important areas, and that is to seek God's will and surrender to it in each matter. Only God knows what is best for you, and you must place your future in His hands.

Godly young people who face these decisions will sometimes make a special decision to dedicate their future to the Lord. For some, this is a surrender for full-time service (pastor, missionary, Christian education). For others, it is a surrender to put God first in a secular occupation that God directs them to do. For many it is simply a surrender to do whatever God wants without knowing which vocation they should enter. God has a special place for you to serve Him, and you must find that place if you are to be happy and to know God's blessing. In God's will, there is no difference between the sacred and the secular. Whatever God calls you to do is sacred; anything else you do instead of what He calls you to do (even full-time service) is sinful.

There are primarily four ways that you can know God's will in these important matters.

1. **Direction from God's Word**

    One of the most important ways that God will lead you is through the instruction of His Word. God's Word gives specific directions for many of life's decisions. If you violate these, you are not doing God's will. For instance, God's Word clearly forbids lying. If you apply for a job and find that your employer expects you to lie to help sell a product, you can be sure that is not God's will. God's will never violates His Word.

Another example that often presents a problem to young people involves whom they should date or marry. Since God's Word clearly forbids an unequal yoke between believers and unbelievers, it is wrong to date and marry an unbeliever. If you violate this principle, you are violating God's will.

2. Deductions from God-given Wisdom

James 1:5 says, "If any of you lack wisdom, let him ask of God, that giveth to all men liberally, and upbraideth not; and it shall be given him." God gives the Christian who asks for it the wisdom to make right decisions. This wisdom can lead you to God's path for your future. For instance, you can use this wisdom to determine the talents and gifts that God has given you. This may help you understand what God has prepared you for. Remember, however, that God can overcome any weakness you may think you have and enable you to do anything He calls you to do (Exod. 4:11).

3. Dealing of God's Spirit

The Holy Spirit indwells all believers. Romans 8:14 says, "For as many as are led by the Spirit of God, they are the sons of God." God's Holy Spirit often guides a believer in the will of God by impressing a burden for a certain work on his heart. For instance, when your pastor was called to preach, he may have had a burden to read and preach God's Word for many months. He may have tried to relieve that burden by teaching Sunday school or being active in the church and found that the burden just became greater. Finally, he may have realized that the only solution for his burden was to surrender to the ministry. Although you may never be called to preach, God's Spirit will give you a burden for the work that He calls you to do.

"Expect great things from God, attempt great things for God." William Carey

4. Doors Opened or Closed by God's Providence

In Revelation 3, Christ is described as the one who opens and closes doors of opportunity. If you obey God's Word, ask God for wisdom, and are attentive to God's Spirit, God will open the doors of opportunity that He desires for you to go through. However, only a Christian who has followed the previous steps is in a position to understand what God is doing through circumstances.

Where You Are Going: A Time of Responsibility— The next category in adulthood is that of young adulthood (ages 25-39). This is a time of added responsibility. As a teen-ager, you understand what it is to handle a few responsibilities. Can you imagine having to provide the needs not only for yourself but also for your spouse and for each child that you have? When you reach young adulthood, you must purchase and prepare the food, pay the bills, keep the car(s) functional, and make sure that the children are kept clean (bathed, combed, teeth brushed, clothes washed and pressed), educated (school, extracurricular activities, music lessons), disciplined, and trained spiritually. You must also meet the responsibilities you have at work and at church.

As you know, physical needs such as food, clothing, and shelter are just a portion of providing a good home. These require money to buy them, a plan to obtain them, and work to prepare and keep them in good shape. As a young adult you must also add to your goals and schedule ways to increase spiritual growth, obtain mental stimulation, enjoy social stability, and continue to exhibit emotional equilibrium. Again, these are needs that must be met not only for yourself but also for the entire family. Decisions must be made every day.

You will find that in the adult world, it is not enough to merely provide for the daily needs of the family. Adults must also take positive actions to provide for their own futures (retirement funds,

Proper parenting includes provision for spiritual, physical, mental, emotional, and social needs of the child, but godly parenting is accomplished through biblical application in all these areas.

health care, life insurance), the futures of their children (college tuition, book costs, transportation or dormitory fees), and often the future or present care of their own parents (health care, housing, day care, or nursing home).

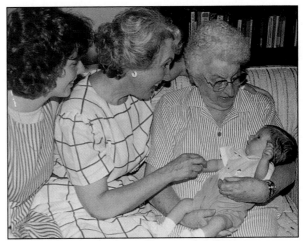

The decisions you make and how you handle responsibilities as a young adult will greatly affect your future income, relationships, and health.

Young adults who have elderly parents must often shoulder the responsibilities of caring for their own children as well as caring for their parents. Because of the dual role and responsibilities they must face, they are frequently referred to as the **sandwich generation.** Many have found that although there is added responsibility, there is also added blessing in this situation.

Your teen-age years are usually a time of few responsibilities. True, you must go to school, do your homework, and complete your chores, but these demands are not as tremendous as those your parents face. You still have time to play on a ball team, to sing in the chorus, and to do many other things that you want to do. You probably have more time now to do the things you want to do than you will ever have as an adult. But now is the time to develop time management, financial planning, and decision-making skills that will help you as an adult. When you consider all the responsibilities adults must meet, now is the time to support with your prayers and help those with whom you come into contact.

Where You Are Going: A Time of Transition—
When you reach this stage of life, you may be given an "over the hill" party. Black decorations, dead roses, and good-natured teasing often accompany this entry into middle adulthood (ages 40-59). You are beginning to face the adjustments of watching your grown children leave home. However, because many couples are marrying later in life, many middle-aged adults are still facing the responsibilities of young adults (having children in elementary, junior high, and high school). Like most people in this age group, though, you find this to be a period of transition in the home, a stage of physical changes, and a time of new roles.

In the home, your children are no longer the center of activity. You remember when your babies, toddlers, and young children required constant supervision and care. However, at this stage, your children are more independent. They are making their own plans, meeting their own schedules and obligations, and leaving home for school, marriage, or work. You may find it difficult to stand aside and to let God lead them. You pray that the godly principles that you consistently tried to instill in them have taken root in their minds and hearts. You must get used to playing a supportive role on the sidelines of their lives rather than being the center of their world. It may be difficult to let them go. For the millionth time, you commit them to God.

Physically you begin to notice changes. Although you may be exercising regularly, eating nutritiously, and getting plenty of rest, your body is beginning to show its age. You may notice a decrease in energy, in hair or hair color, in the ability to taste and smell, in your keenness of hearing and visual acuity, in skin elasticity, in bone mass, and in muscle mass. Those who have not followed a healthful lifestyle may also experience a decrease of lean muscle mass and an increase of body fat; flab sets in. Unfortunately, this is when many people become obese (20% above what they should weigh). Obesity in turn comes with its own set of

Maintaining an active rather than a sedentary lifestyle promotes healthful living now and later.

potential problems: coronary artery disease, hypertension, diabetes, varicose veins, gallstones, and osteoarthritis.

There are also new roles for you to play. You may have been a child, sibling, spouse, and parent. Middle adulthood may be the time to experience being an in-law and perhaps a grandparent. Both of these roles have new rules and responsibilities attached to them. Communication and respect are especially important at this time. Keep in mind that your role is supportive and not administrative. This is a transition that must be made in order to maintain peace and unity in your now expanded family.

Where You Are Going: A Time of Slowing Down—
What do you think of getting old? What do you think of the elderly? Is old age a horrible time of life that you do not want to think about? Do you picture geriatrics (the study of the physical problems of the

elderly) as only dealing with senile and useless people? Are the elderly always sick, feeble, and tottery?

If that is your attitude about old age, you have the wrong impression. The Bible views old age as a position of honor. It can be a time of respect and responsibility; it does not have to be a time of weakness and illness. The following information may help to prepare you for this time and change your attitude towards those who are elderly.

How old is old? When is a person elderly? In America, a person can apply for social security and retire at the age of sixty-five. However, many people continue to productively work well into their seventies. You cannot classify a person who is tired, suffers aches, has pains, and is forgetful as being old. Many teen-agers exhibit the same characteristics. Most people who are sixty-five do not think of themselves as being old. Many people who are seventy are just beginning to slow down but do not act, feel, or think old.

As one ages, he may find that if he does not continue using his physical, mental, and social skills, he risks losing the capacity to use them.

Old age is not something that suddenly pounces on a person when he turns sixty-five. It is a result of changes that have developed over a lifetime. Although you are still young, you age with every moment that passes. Many of the things that you do today will influence how you spend your days after you are seventy or eighty. If you develop a pattern of poor eating habits, a lack in exercising, and smoking cigarettes, you are almost guaranteeing yourself an old age of sickness and misery. What you do now will do much to determine what you will face later.

You should also realize that although you will become weaker as you get old, there is much variability in the rate that this occurs. Some people cannot get out of bed once they are sixty and other people still jog several miles every day when they are eighty. Much of the deterioration that occurs during old age is not caused just by getting older but rather by quitting the things that help to keep one young. Generally, the more active you are as you get older, the longer you will be able to stay active.

Many times sickness, accidental injuries, or genetic illnesses may cause elderly people to be set aside from the activities they want to do. Although they may not be able to get out and run errands or even walk, they still need and desire companionship, mental stimulation, and spiritual encouragement. There are an abundance of elderly people with fragile health but vibrant minds and spirits. If you suffered two broken legs, it does not mean that you would relish the opportunity to sit alone in the house and stare at your walls. Neither do they.

There is no reason to fear the aged. Although they usually look and act differently from young people, they are still people. They are often kind and godly people with many historical tidbits of information and wise insights. The elderly have many of the same desires, needs, and dreams that you have. If you take the opportunity to spend time with the elderly, you will often discover how much fun they are to be with. Many exhibit spunky or dry

HEALTH
JOURNAL

Geriatric Care

When you are with the elderly, it is good to be aware of physical problems that may be present. A crabby, old man may actually be a gentleman who is in pain or has suffered sleepless nights. Helping a grandmother to cross the street may be no help at all if you walk too fast or hold her elbow at an angle that could cause her anguish for the next week. Although many older Americans are not fragile, it does not hurt to anticipate potential health risks when dealing with the elderly.

There are many physical problems that can plague the aged. Some of these could have been avoided or at least postponed by healthful living when they were young, but other problems or diseases are bound to occur. The general rule is to be respectful and thoughtful. Help given with a loving attitude mirrors a spirit of compassion.

Being observant can be a key to tactfulness. Some people, no matter their age, do not like to discuss their health or disabilities. As you talk or interact with an elderly person, you may notice, for instance, that he may turn his head slightly toward the person speaking or that he has a hearing aid. It would not be polite to bring attention to the fact that he has trouble hearing, but you can speak distinctly. (Increase your volume only if you see it is necessary.) Careful listening to the conversation can sometimes supply you with information concerning health problems.

Being cautious may help to prevent injuries. Falls are the leading cause of injury to the elderly. Loose throw rugs, inadequate lighting, chairs that are too low or without armrests, high steps, and slippery floors provide added risks. Be extra careful and attentive to an elderly person if you notice any of these obstacles to safety. Offer assistance when you think it may be needed, but remember that not all elderly people require aid.

Being considerate is usually appreciated. Let the older person set the pace; the conversation; the agenda. You may have a game of chess in mind, but he may prefer to take a stroll. You may be in a rush, but he may need to take things at a more leisurely pace. Besides being patient, slow down; scurrying around may be frustrating or confusing for him. Be polite and thoughtful in your interactions.

Life expectancy has increased in America because of advances in sanitation, nutrition, medical technology, and beneficial changes in lifestyles.

humor. Most elderly people are filled with life and truly try to enjoy life to its fullest.

Finally, you should realize that old people are all different. Often young people tend to think that all old people are the same. Thinking of all members of a group as the same is called **stereotyping.** Stereotyping often hinders a proper view of individuals in that group, and this is often true with the elderly. For instance, your grandpa might decide to go hiking in the woods. He might be perfectly capable of doing this, and the hike might help him feel better. But your parents might try to talk him out of it because he is "too old to go traipsing through the woods like a teen-ager." A stereotype of what an old person should do may cause your parents to discourage your grandfather from trying an activity that could make him happier and healthier.

If you have had wrong ideas about the elderly, a good way to dispel them is to seek ways to be around older people. Get to know the elderly saints in your church. Volunteer to help them with some housework or some yard work. Go on visitation with an elderly person or have a devotional time with a shut-in. Another good way to become more familiar with elderly people is to take part in a ministry to a nursing home. If your church does not

Names Suggesting Age

Sexagenarian (SEK suh juh NAR ee un)—between 60 and 70 years of age

Septuagenarian (SEP too uh juh NAR ee un)—between 70 and 80 years of age

Octogenarian (OC tuh juh NAR ee un)—between 80 and 90 years of age

Nonagenarian (NON uh juh NAR ee un)—between 90 and 100 years of age

Centenarian (SEN tuh NAR ee un)—100 years of age or older

have this type of ministry, maybe God can use you to start one. These people can have a great influence on your life. Do not miss an opportunity to be a blessing and to be blessed.

Where You Are Going

Death—Dying can be a frightening thought. This is one reason that most young people do not like to think or talk about it. Yet death is an inevitable aspect of life. Until the rapture occurs, everyone you know will die. Your grandparents, your parents, your pastor, your brothers and sisters, and all your friends will die.

Not only will everyone you know die, but you will die someday too. It may be eighty years from now or it may be this afternoon, but you will die. The Bible clearly says that physical death will not end your existence. Your soul will live somewhere forever. The most important thing done in life is to make sure that you are prepared for your death; you must make sure that you are ready to face eternity.

Life After Death—Death is not the same for everyone. There are two possibilities that are as different as night and day. Death is a passageway to eternal life or to eternal torment. Physical death should not be feared, but the thought of eternal death (separation from God for eternity) should cause you to tremble. The only way to avoid eternal death is to receive eternal life. John 3:36 says, "He that believeth on the Son hath everlasting life: and he that believeth not the Son shall not see life; but the wrath of God abideth on him." You must choose eternal life or God's eternal wrath; that choice must be made before you die.

The choice you make will dramatically affect how you view death. Without Christ, death can be life's most fearful experience. It is an uncertain step into an unknown future. For a Christian, however, death is different. A Christian may fear dying, but does not fear death. He may fear the pain and separation from family and friends, but does not face death alone. Psalm 23:4 assures, "Yea, though I walk through the valley of the shadow of death, I will fear no evil: for thou art with me." For a

A grave marker tells only the identity of the deceased and usually gives no indication of the life it represents. Souls brought to Christ, people ministered to, and lives touched provide living monuments for a Christian.

Christian, death is gain. It is a passage to face-to-face fellowship with Christ. That is why many Christians face death with peace and calmness. Throughout history, historians have noted that Christians "die well." For Christians, death is more of a beginning than an ending.

Facing Death—How you will die, when you will die, and the certainty that you will die can be troubling if you meditate only on death and not on Christ's victory over death. Many people get upset when they face the fact that they are mortal; they will die. "Whereas ye know not what shall be on the morrow. For what is your life? It is even a vapour, that appeareth for a little time, and then vanisheth away" (James 4:14). Most people fear the unknown qualities of death. What is death anyway?

In the past, death was pronounced when a person's heartbeat and breathing stopped. When the heartbeat and respiration cease, it is termed **clinical death.** However, clinical death can often be reversed by the application of CPR or emergency life support procedures. Another determiner of death was needed. **Brain death** is pronounced when the brain ceases electrical activity. If the brain is deprived of oxygen for four minutes, brain damage can result; after fifteen minutes, the brain can die. This results in a straight line on the electroencephalograph (ih LEK troh en SEF uh luh GRAF; EEG), a machine which measures brain activity. Most physicians judge a person to be dead when the body indicates clinical death, brain death, and **cellular death** (the body tissues no longer function at the cellular level; rigor mortis [body rigidity] is present).

Because the advances of science have made it possible to keep the body living through life support machines, many moral questions have been raised. Is it moral to disconnect a life support machine from a person who is brain dead? Is it moral not to use a life support machine on a person who is not brain dead? Is euthanasia wrong? **Euthanasia** (YOO thuh NAY zhuh) is the intentional killing of a person as an act of mercy; it is also called mercy killing.

In order to address these questions, you must understand that there are two types of euthanasia. **Active euthanasia** refers to the termination of life by doing something to the patient (removal of a respirator or intravenous feeding tube; administration of a lethal substance or an overdose of medication). **Passive euthanasia** takes place if treatment which could sustain life is withheld and not begun.

Because some people do not desire the use of life support machines, they have written **living wills.** A living will is written by a person stating how he would like to be treated if unable to make decisions for himself. A living will may indicate the desire to use or not to use life support machines. Other considerations include whether to have intravenous feeding tubes inserted, whether food or water should be given if it will prolong the dying process, or whether medication should be administered at the risk of shortening life. Most people, including Christians, see a living will as a means of communicating their wishes and relieving their loved ones from having to make difficult decisions. Others, however, are uncomfortable with even the slightest tendency toward passive euthanasia.

The Death of Friends and Loved Ones—You will probably face the death of others long before you face death yourself. First Thessalonians 4:13 says, "But I would not have you to be ignorant, brethren, concerning them which are asleep, that ye sorrow not, even as others which have no hope." When someone you love dies, it is a time of sorrow, but the sorrow of Christians is different from those who have no hope. There is sorrow because you cannot talk to them or be with them anymore. You will feel lonely, and you will probably cry a lot. This sorrow is not wrong, nor does

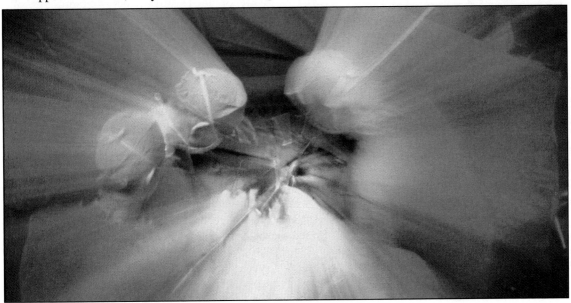

After a funeral, continue to uphold your friend in prayer. Continued support is especially helpful during holidays and special times throughout the year. It may help to note times on your own calendar (your friend's birthday, the anniversary of his loved one's death, etc.) so that you do not overlook your friend's needs.

you will not see them for a while but joy because you know that you will see them again. There is sorrow because you will not live with them anymore on earth but joy because one day you will live with them forever. At the funeral of a Christian, there are tears of sorrow mingled with peace and hope.

What can you do if a friend has lost a loved one? First, be there for him. Before you visit or call, pray. Let the Holy Spirit and not your own emotions control your words and actions. Let your friend know that you are praying. Be of service. There are many things that can be done: manage the phone, wash dishes, baby-sit if needed, help tidy the home for guests, fix food and meals, do laundry, help transport guests, or offer to stay at the home during the funeral (to discourage thieves who read the obituaries and plan to break in). Many people in grief are also in shock. Keep lists and important information noted for them (time to be at funeral home, who needs to be called, who is coming when).

If all of the details are taken care of, then just a card, a call, a hug, or your presence is all that may be needed for the moment. Many people hesitate to say or do anything because they do not know what to say or do. However, just your presence and compassion are often all that is needed. You do not necessarily need to say anything; just listen. It is often a help for some people to have the opportunity to talk about their loved one.

it make you less strong as a man or woman. God gave man the capacity to grieve.

The funeral of a Christian is both a time of sorrow and a time of joy. There is sorrow because

When Your Friend Is Dying

DO pray.
DO keep in touch.
DO visit if possible.
DO look at them.
DO act normally.
DO make their living as comfortable as possible.
DO offer your assistance.
DO listen.
DO be sensitive to their wishes and needs.
DO focus on Christ.

DON'T stay away or avoid them.
DON'T avoid a hug or loving pat.
DON'T stare.
DON'T give pious quotes and trite sayings.
DON'T guess at God's motives.
DON'T criticize the treatment.
DON'T promote home remedies or miracle cures.
DON'T focus on yourself.
DON'T visit too long.

Remember this simply stated truth: "Only one life 'Twill soon be past. Only what's done for Christ will last."

Remember that people respond differently to grief. That a person does not cry in public does not mean that he is not grieving. By the same token, because a person cries in abundance does not mean that he is not saved or trusting God. Do not be judgmental; be compassionate.

God knows best how to comfort the bereaved. If your friend has lost a loved one, keep pointing his thoughts toward Christ. God is the God of all comfort; He will be there for your friend long after all the other friends and family have gone home. Only God can fill the emptiness of the heart.

A LIFE FOR CHRIST

This chapter has examined life from its beginning to its ending. You have looked back on what you have been and forward to what you will be. You have also learned about the stage of life, adoles-

cence, that you are currently passing through. Only Christ knows what is actually in your future.

Some of you will have a full and fruitful life. Others of you may have a short and tragic one. Although God knows the future, He does not force you to do what is right or to do His will. He has given you the freedom to choose. He expects you to use discernment to make the right choices.

You can make choices that will change your life for the better or that will change your life for the worse. Many of the choices that affect health are made during adolescence. Your spiritual, physical, mental, emotional, and social health for the rest of your life are being determined today. Do not let peer pressure, emotional reactions, poor decisions, or ungodly choices ruin your future. Let Christ guide you each day, each step, each decision into the future. Choose to live a life for Christ.

Section Review

1. What are four guidelines for knowing God's will?

2. What is meant by the sandwich generation?

3. What are two general rules of conduct when dealing with the elderly?

4. What two things might a Christian fear about death?

5. List at least four things to remember when comforting the grief stricken.

CHAPTER REVIEW

Terms

adolescence

conception

zygote

embryo

uterus

placenta

labor

abortion

spontaneous abortion

puberty

growth spurt

vocation

sandwich generation

geriatrics

stereotyping

clinical death

brain death

cellular death

euthanasia

active euthanasia

passive euthanasia

living will

Content Questions

1. What four areas of development of Christ are mentioned in Luke 2:52?

2. What is conception?

3. Where in the mother's body does an unborn child develop?

4. In what ways are the physical changes different between boys and girls during puberty?

5. Why is independence usually earned gradually rather than given suddenly?

6. What is the difference between steady growth (increase in height) and a growth spurt?

7. At which age does puberty occur?

8. What are two things that can help to keep skin clear from blemishes during adolescence?

9. Why can body odor become a problem during adolescence? What personal hygiene practices should be incorporated to reduce body odor?

10. If a person is 84 years old, he is an octogenarian. What is the term used to denote a person who is 97 years old?

11. What is the difference between natural and eternal death?

12. If a person is brain dead and not placed on life support machines, is he clinically dead?

Application Questions

1. You may have wondered why many of the same doctors who fight to preserve the lives of premature and prenatal babies perform abortions on babies the same age (or in many cases older). What does God's Word have to say about being consistent in one's beliefs?

2. Is it possible to convince a person that abortion is wrong?

3. What personal spiritual habit do you now practice because you believe it to be important? How could this affect your physical health?

4. Based on the lives of elderly people in your family and on your present health habits and physical characteristics, what do you expect your life to be like when you reach 70?

Glossary

A

ABCs An acronym to remind the rescuer to check the victim's airway, breathing, and circulation.

abortion The ending of a pregnancy by death of the fetus.

abrasion A break on the surface of the skin; a scrape.

absorption Entry into the body through unbroken skin.

abstinence Choosing not to drink alcoholic beverages; denial of appetites or desires.

abuse Treating in an improper manner; to hurt or mistreat.

accessory organs Term often used to refer to the liver, pancreas, and gallbladder.

accident Unexpected event which causes injury or death.

acid rain (acid precipitation) The combination of gases with moisture in the air (rain, snow, sleet, fog) to form an acid.

acne Skin disorder in which the sebaceous glands are plugged with sebum or infection, causing the area to become inflamed.

active euthanasia Termination of life by doing something to the patient to hasten death.

addiction Physical dependence on a drug.

adolescence The period of time between childhood and adulthood.

adrenal glands Endocrine glands located on each kidney which secrete epinephrine.

aerobic exercise An exercise which requires large amounts of oxygen for an extended period of time.

aflatoxin A mycotoxin produced by the common mold *Aspergillus* found in nuts and grains.

albinism The inability of an organism to sufficiently produce melanin (a trait passed through a recessive gene).

alcoholic A person who has become dependent on alcohol in order to carry out normal duties; an alcohol addict.

alopecia The loss of hair.

alveoli (*sing.,* alveolus) Small bubblelike structures of the lung where gases are exchanged between the atmospheric air and the blood.

amphetamine A stimulant drug which causes an increase of activity, suppresses fatigue and hunger, and creates feelings of euphoria.

anabolic steroids Performance-enhancing drugs that are similar to male hormones; a group of synthetic derivatives of testosterone.

anabolism The building of necessary body compounds from simpler compounds.

anaerobic Environment with no oxygen present.

anaerobic exercise Intense exercise which causes the body's demand for oxygen to exceed its supply.

anaphylactic shock A life-threatening allergic reaction.

anemia Condition in which there are too few red blood cells, or the red blood cells are too immature, too small, or contain too little hemoglobin to transport sufficient oxygen to the body tissues.

aneurysm A weakened area of an artery that stretches like an inflated balloon.

angina pectoris Severe pain caused by the lack of oxygen to the heart muscle.

anorexia nervosa Eating disorder of self-imposed starvation.

antibodies Protein substances that provide immunity by neutralizing invading organisms or foreign substances in the body.

antiperspirant A substance which decreases the amount of perspiration where it is applied.

anxiety Fear of real or imagined threats.

appetite A desire for food.

aqueous humor A clear fluid which fills the area between the cornea and the lens of the eye.

arrhythmia An alteration of the normal heart rhythm.

arteries Blood vessels that carry blood away from the heart.

arteriosclerosis A cardiovascular disease in which the arterial walls thicken and harden.

asphyxiation Unconsciousness or death caused by lack of oxygen; suffocation.

assault A violent attack; an attempt at or threat of injury.

astigmatism Distortion of vision caused by a warped lens or cornea.

atherosclerosis A cardiovascular disease in which fat deposits build up on the interior walls of the blood vessels, hindering blood flow.

atmosphere The gaseous envelope which surrounds the earth.

audiologist A specialist who tests hearing.

avulsion A partial or complete separation of a portion of skin or other body tissue.

B

bacteria Unicellular (single-celled) microorganisms.

barbiturates Strong depressant drugs that can lead to both physical and psychological dependence.

basal metabolic rate The metabolic rate when resting; the rate at which the body uses just enough energy to keep vital maintenance activities functioning; energy output of a body at rest after a twelve-hour fast.

benign tumor A growth which is not in danger of spreading throughout the body (will not metastasize).

bile A greenish fluid produced by the liver and stored and concentrated in the gallbladder; necessary for the breakdown and absorption of fatty substances.

binocular vision The ability to focus on one object with two eyes.

biodegradable The trait of a material to be decomposed by living organisms.

blood-alcohol concentration (BAC) The relative amount of ethanol in a person's bloodstream.

blood pressure The force that blood exerts against the walls of the arteries.

blood vessels Passageways or ducts through which blood can be circulated.

body composition The proportion of body fat to lean body mass.

body system Organs that work together to perform a vital function in the body.

botulism Food poisoning from a toxin produced by the *Clostridium botulinum* bacteria.

brain death The cessation of electrical activity in the brain.

bronchi (*sing.,* bronchus) Two branches in the trachea which carry air to the lungs.

bronchitis A lung disease in which the tubes of the lungs (bronchi and bronchioles) become irritated and diseased.

bulimia Eating disorder of binge eating and self-induced purging or vomiting; also known as compulsive eating, bulimarexia, or bulimia nervosa.

C

caffeine A mild stimulant found in some beverages and foods.

calculus A hardened deposit that can form on teeth which can harbor bacteria and promote gum disease.

calisthenics Body-building exercises that develop muscular strength and muscle tone.

calorie A unit used to describe the amount of energy provided by a food; the amount of heat required to raise one gram of water one degree Centigrade.

cancer A group of diseases in which abnormal cells multiply and spread uncontrollably to other parts of the body.

capillaries Blood vessels with walls one cell thick where diffusion of nutrients and exchange of gases occur.

carbohydrates Compounds that are composed of sugars.

carcinogen A chemical, an organism, or type of radiation which causes normal cells to become cancerous.

cardiopulmonary resuscitation (CPR) A lifesaving technique used to treat cardiac arrest and respiratory failure.

cardiorespiratory fitness The ability of the heart, lungs, and blood vessels to efficiently supply oxygen to the muscle cells when under exertion.

cardiovascular disease A disease of the heart or blood vessels.

carriers Organisms that harbor a pathogen without exhibiting signs of illness.

catabolism The breaking down of large molecules into simple molecules and energy.

cataract Disorder of the eye in which the lens becomes cloudy and opaque.

cavities Holes in the enamel of the tooth produced by tooth decay which expose the dentin or pulp cavity.

cell The most basic living part of the body; a structural unit of all living things.

cellular death The body tissues no longer function at the cellular level; rigor mortis is present.

cerebral aneurysm Stroke caused by an aneurysm which bursts.

cerebral hemorrhage Stroke caused by rupturing brittle or damaged arteries in the brain.

cerumin Ear wax.

cholesterol A fat-related substance found in foods from animal sources and manufactured by the human body.

chyme The semiliquid mixture of partly digested food and digestive juices in the stomach and small intestine.

cilia Hairlike structures (i.e., lining the respiratory tract in humans to move mucus containing trapped pathogens toward the stomach).

cirrhosis Disease in which the liver cells harden, turn orange, and die.

clinical death Cessation of the heartbeat and respiration.

clique A closed or exclusive group of friends that tend to ignore others and share a private interest.

closed fracture A crack or break in a bone which does not puncture the skin.

cocaine A stimulant drug extracted from the leaves of the coca plant.

collagen A fibrous protein characterized by strength and flexibility.

colorblind Unable to discern or distinguish between certain colors.

communication The exchange of information, messages, or thoughts.

complete fracture A break that passes completely through the bone.

complete protein A protein with all the amino acids essential in human nutrition.

conception (fertilization) The union of a sperm cell with an ovum resulting in a fertilized cell.

concussion Injury to the brain which may result in an abrupt and temporary loss of consciousness.

cones Photoreceptors which can distinguish color.

congenital heart disease A cardiovascular disease that occurs due to a malformation or structural damage that occurred prior to birth.

conserve To use less of a resource.

contract To shorten or pull together; to reduce in length.

convalescence Period of time between outbreak of the disease and renewed health.

convulsions Intense, involuntary muscular contractions.

core temperature The temperature of the heart, lungs, brain, and vital organs.

cosmetic Any article that is put on the body to cleanse, beautify, promote attractiveness, or alter the appearance without changing the body structure or function.

crash diets Diets with drastic changes which promise rapid (but not necessarily healthful or lasting) results.

cut An even or jagged break through the skin and underlying tissues.

D

Daily Values Levels of nutrients (usually the highest RDA for any age and sex group for each nutrient) shown on labels to indicate amounts of the recommended dietary intakes; replaced the U.S. RDA (United States Recommended Daily Allowances) labels used between 1972 and 1993.

dandruff A condition of the scalp in which flakes of dead skin are shed.

deafness Total loss of hearing.

deciduous teeth The first or primary set of teeth; baby teeth.

deforestation The removal of trees, forests, jungles, and rain forests.

dehydration Excessive loss of water from the body.

dental caries Tooth decay.

deodorant A substance which reduces odor by killing odor-causing bacteria.

dependability Responsibility; trait of being reliable.

depressants A category of drugs which slow the action of the central nervous system.

depression A condition of sadness and discouragement that can result in insomnia and the inability to concentrate.

dermis The thick inner layer of skin just beneath the epidermis.

diabetes A group of potentially fatal, non-infectious diseases caused by the inability of the body to produce or respond properly to the hormone insulin; a group of disorders of abnormal sugar usage.

diagnose To identify or distinguish (such as a disease) through an examination.

diastole Pressure in the arteries when the ventricles of the heart are in a state of rest between beats.

dieting The practice of changing the amount or the type of food eaten.

digestion The process of breaking food down into its component parts.

discernment The ability to make a judgment, to perceive differences, or to separate into distinct parts.

disease A condition which causes the body to function improperly.

dislocation A bone moved out of its normal position.

diuretic A chemical which increases the excretion of urine.

drownproofing Method of staying afloat which requires little effort and expends little energy.

drug Any chemical substance (except for food) that changes bodily functions when it is taken into the body.

drug abuse Repeatedly misusing medicines or using drugs for a purpose or in a manner which can damage a person's health or ability to function.

drug misuse Taking a drug for the medically intended purpose, but not using the amount, frequency, or manner that is prescribed.

duration The length of time that one exercises in order to obtain a training effect.

E

electrolytes Substances that dissociate into ions with an electrical charge when dissolved.

embolus A blood clot, air bubble, cholesterol particle, or other foreign mass which moves through the circulatory system and lodges in a smaller vessel, obstructing blood flow.

embryo Term for a zygote during the first two months of pregnancy that has implanted in the mother's womb.

emphysema A chronic lung disease in which the alveoli (air sacs) are damaged.

environment The combinations of the area and surrounding conditions.

Environmental Protection Agency (EPA) A governmental agency set up by the United States to set and enforce standards for proper care of the environment.

environmental tobacco smoke (ETS) Smoke that remains in an area of air.

epidermis The outermost layer of skin.

epilepsy Disorder resulting from abnormal electrical activity in the brain causing seizures, which may vary in intensity and type.

erythrocytes Red blood cells.

esophagus The tube that connects the pharynx and the stomach.

etiquette Rules of common courtesy and conduct.

euphoria A feeling of well-being.

euthanasia The intentional killing of a person as an act of mercy; mercy killing.

evacuate To remove from, empty, or vacate an area.

exposure Stage of infection when the pathogen is transmitted to the host.

extrovert A person who tends to direct his attention outside of himself to people and things.

F

fad Temporary trend in dress, language, or action.

farsightedness Visual acuity problem where close objects appear out of focus.

fat The most abundant type of lipids (composed of glycerol and fatty acids); a compound which provides a concentrated source of energy.

fat-soluble vitamins Hydrophobic (water-fearing) vitamins that can be carried by fats to the various cells in the body; vitamins A, D, E, and K are fat-soluble.

fetal alcohol syndrome Mental retardation, physical deformities, and retarded growth patterns in a child caused by the mother's drinking alcohol while the child was a fetus.

fetus An unborn child; the term for an embryo after two months of development.

fever Increase of body temperature.

fiber Part of the rigid structure that surrounds plant cells; cellulose; also referred to as roughage.

fibrillation Irregular and uncoordinated twitching of the cardiac muscle fibers as opposed to a distinct contraction of the heart muscle.

fibrosis Scarring of liver tissue.

first aid Immediate and practical treatment given for injury or illness.

first-degree burns Burns that injure only the top layer of the skin (epidermis) and usually heal without leaving a scar.

flammable Of or pertaining to a substance which can catch fire easily.

flashbacks Recurrences of a drug's effects although the drug has not been used for a long time.

flash point The lowest temperature at which a substance will produce a vapor that can ignite.

flexibility The ability to move the joints and to stretch the muscles easily through a full range of motion.

flossing Procedure used to clean between teeth and gums in order to remove plaque.

food additive Substances which are added to food either intentionally, such as nutrients or colors, or by accident.

fracture A break or crack in a bone.

frequency The number of times one exercises in order to obtain a training effect.

frostbite Destruction of skin and other tissues due to freezing; formation of ice crystals in the body tissue.

G

gallbladder A small sac on the underside of the liver which concentrates and stores bile.

generic drug A drug with the same active ingredients as name brands but which may have different inactive ingredients.

geriatrics The study of the physical problems of the elderly.

gland A structure that makes and secretes substances.

glaucoma Disease of the eye which results in increased pressure within the eye.

gluttony The overconsumption of food.

goals Objectives; things one endeavors to accomplish.

greenhouse effect The process of the earth's surface absorbing the sun's radiation and re-emitting it as infrared radiation; the process of greenhouse gases trapping this heat in the earth's atmosphere.

greenhouse gases Gases such as carbon dioxide, methane, and nitrous oxides which are purported to trap heat in the earth's atmosphere.

H

halitosis Bad breath or breath that is displeasing.

hallucinogens A category of drugs which alter the senses so that users see, hear, feel, or smell things that do not exist.

hangover The effects of alcohol on the body following intoxication.

hashish A hallucinogenic drug made from resins from the flowering tops of marijuana.

hazardous waste Dangerous waste products that can be in solid, liquid, or gas form.

hazards Potential dangers; situations or things that can be sources of injury.

health The process of attaining spiritual, physical, mental, emotional, and social well-being.

health risks Factors (habits, traits, or conditions) which increase the possibility of having health problems.

health screening A program to test large groups of people for health problems.

hearing impairment The partial loss of hearing.

heart attack (myocardial infarction) A malfunctioning of the heart muscle; death of an area of the heart muscle due to an obstruction of a coronary artery.

heart failure The inability of the heart to pump a normal amount of blood.

heart rate The number of times the heart beats each minute.

heat cramps Muscle cramps and spasms caused by overexertion and heat exhaustion.

heat exhaustion Condition which occurs from excessive heat causing one to sweat profusely to the point of mild shock and lowered blood pressure; symptoms include heavy sweating, pale skin, dilated pupils, nausea, and dizziness.

heat stroke A potentially life-threatening condition in which the body is unable to cool itself as the body temperature rises; symptoms include dry skin, constricted pupils, rapid pulse, and unconsciousness.

Heimlich maneuver (abdominal thrusts) A potentially life-saving technique which forces air out of the lungs to dislodge an obstruction in the airway.

hepatitis One of several diseases that cause an inflammation of the liver.

heredity The passing of genetic traits from parents to their children.

hormone A chemical regulator that is produced in ductless glands and carried in the blood, affecting metabolism.

humanism A religion which promotes and glorifies man.

hunger The body's response to a need for food.

hygiene Practices that help to prevent disease.

hypertension High blood pressure.

hypodermis The innermost layer of skin; subcutaneous layer.

hypothermia A condition of lowered body temperature.

I

immunity Resistance to a specific pathogen or other foreign substance.

incineration Burning solid waste at high temperatures.

incision An even cut through the skin and underlying tissues.

incomplete protein A protein that does not contain all the amino acids essential in human nutrition.

incubation Period of time between exposure and appearance of disease symptoms.

industrial smog Particulates combining with sulfur dioxide and sulfuric acid in the air.

infectious disease Any disease caused by organisms or particles that can be spread from one person or animal to another, either directly or indirectly.

inflammation Localized heat, swelling, and redness produced as the body reacts to infection, injury, or irritation.

ingestion Oral entry into the body; to swallow a substance.

inhalants Substances breathed into the body in order to obtain a euphoric feeling.

inhalation Entry into the body through respiration; to breathe a substance.

inhibition The ability of the mind to make judgments and to promote correct actions; an inward caution.

injection Entry into the body through punctured skin.

insulin Hormone secreted by the islets of Langerhans in the pancreas which regulates blood sugar levels.

intensity The level of effort put into an activity.

intoxication A point at which one who has consumed alcoholic beverages loses the ability to function normally.

introvert A person who tends to be more introspective and direct his attention to more private matters.

involuntary muscles Muscles not controlled by conscious thinking.

isokinetic Of or involving training muscles for strength by using equipment which provides resistance equal to the force applied.

isometric Of or involving training muscles for strength by pushing or pulling against an object that does not move.

isotonic Of or involving training muscles for strength by involving muscle contraction through a complete range of motion.

J

jaundice The yellowish discoloration of body tissues.

jaywalking A pedestrian's illegally or recklessly crossing a street.

joint Location where two or more bones meet or a point of connection between cartilage and bones.

junk foods Foods in the limited extras group that have little or no nutritional value.

K

keratin A strong fibrous protein that fills epidermal cells.

kidneys Organs of the excretory system that remove waste products from the blood.

L

labor Strong muscular contractions which move the unborn from the uterus, through the birth canal, and out of the mother.

laceration A jagged tear or rip in the skin.

large intestine Organ in the digestive system that extends from the small intestine to the anus.

larynx A passageway from the pharynx to the trachea that also produces sound; the voice box.

leaching The removal of soluable substances such as minerals or chemicals as water seeps or filters through the soil.

leukocytes White blood cells.

leukoplakia A white, thickened area of irritation in the mouth that is caused by direct contact of mouth tissues with tobacco juice.

lifestyle A way of living which reflects one's values, attitudes, and habits.

living will A legal statement presenting how a person desires to be treated if he is unable to make decisions for himself.

loyalty Faithfulness or allegiance to a person or a cause.

M

macrominerals Minerals needed by the body in relatively large amounts; calcium, phosphorus, magnesium, sulfur, potassium, sodium, and chloride.

mainstream smoke Smoke that is inhaled and then exhaled by a smoker.

malignant tumor A tissue mass that can threaten to spread to other parts of the body (is cancerous; can metastasize).

malnutrition A state of poor nutrition and imbalance of nutrient amounts which may be caused by inadequate food intake or an overconsumption of nutrients.

malocclusion A condition in which the upper and lower teeth do not fit together properly.

manicure The procedure used in caring for the hands and fingernails.

marijuana A hallucinogen made from the Indian hemp plant.

maturity The state of being fully grown or exhibiting qualities of full growth.

medicines Drugs used to fight disease or to relieve pain.

meditation Concentration on a specific content that leads to reflective inner conversation and (for the Christian) positive biblical change in action.

megadoses Nutrients obtained in quantities that far exceed the RDA.

metabolic rate The speed at which the body uses energy.

metabolism Processes through which nutrients are broken down into energy and used by the body; the sum of all the chemical reactions occurring throughout the body.

metastasis The spread of cancerous cells to another part of the body.

minerals Non-organic atoms or molecules, some of which are essential for use in minute amounts by the body.

miscarriage When a fetus dies of natural causes prior to birth.

mucous membranes Layers of cells that secrete mucus.

muscular endurance The ability of muscles to exert force many times or for a sustained period of time.

muscular strength The ability of muscles to exert force.

mycotoxins Poisons produced by molds.

N

narcotics (opiates) Depressant drugs which are made from the sap of the opium poppy.

natural foods Foods that have not been processed, do not contain artificial ingredients, and are usually grown without pesticides.

nearsightedness Visual acuity problem where distant objects appear out of focus.

negative self-concept A self-concept in which a person has a low opinion or view of himself.

neuron A nerve cell; a cell in the nervous system that receives and distributes nerve impulses.

neuroses Group of disorders in which individuals experience anxiety, phobia, or other abnormal behavioral changes.

nicotine A colorless, oily poison that is found in tobacco leaves.

noninfectious disease Any disease that is caused by internal changes in a person's body that cannot be spread from one person to another.

nonprescription drugs Medication legally sold to the consumer without a written prescription from a doctor (commonly known as over-the counter drugs).

nonverbal communication The exchange of information without the use of words (usually through gestures or facial expressions).

nutrients Substances obtained from food and used for growth, repair, and maintenance of the body.

nutrition The study of the nutrients in food and how they affect health.

O

occlusion The way the upper and lower teeth fit together.

open dump A form of disposing of solid waste by depositing it in a pile.

open fracture A break or crack in a bone that actually protrudes through the skin.

optimist Person who tends to see the positive sides of a situation or expects a favorable outcome.

organs Tissues that work together to perform a specific function.

orthodontist A dentist trained in methods used to straighten teeth.

osteomalacia Softening of the bones; adult rickets.

osteoporosis Reduced density of the bones.

outbreak Stage of infection during which the symptoms of the disease appear.

ovaries Female reproductive organs which produce ova and secrete hormones.

overload principle Training concept that to develop a component of fitness, one must increase the resistance.

ozone Gas composed of three oxygen atoms; O_3.

P

pancreas An organ that secretes enzymes into the duodenum to aid in digestion and secretes the hormone insulin, which regulates the amount of sugar in the blood.

paralysis Inability to move or have sensation in a portion of the body due to injury or disease of the nervous system.

partial fracture A crack in a bone; a break which does not pass completely through the bone.

particulates Minute pieces of liquids or solids suspended in the air.

passive euthanasia Termination of life due to withholding treatment which would sustain life.

passive smoke Cigarette smoke produced by others that is inhaled by a nonsmoker.

pathogens Organisms or particles that can cause disease.

pedestrian An individual who travels on foot.

pedicure The procedure used in caring for the feet and toenails.

peer pressure The influence of friends on one's life, actions, and attitudes.

peers People of equal standing in age, class, or rank.

periodontal disease Gum disease.

peripheral vision The ability to see objects in the outer limits of the visual field; the temporal or outer visual field.

permanent teeth The second set of teeth, which replace deciduous teeth.

personality Distinctive qualities and traits that influence one's attitudes and behavior.

pessimist Person who tends to see the negative sides of a situation.

pharynx A passageway for air from the nose to the larynx and a portion of the digestive tract from the mouth to the esophagus.

photochemical smog A secondary air pollutant produced from primary air pollutants in a reaction requiring energy input from sunlight.

photoreceptors Specialized cells which change chemically when stimulated by light rays and send electrochemical messages to the brain.

physical dependence The desire for a drug resulting from a physical need by the body for the drug; repeated drug use making the body unable to function without that drug.

physical examination A thorough medical exam to determine a person's physical condition.

physical fitness The ability to complete each day's activity with energy and alertness, to participate in the things one enjoys with vigor, and to respond to strenuous activities or emergencies without undue stress.

pitch The frequency of sound waves; how high or low a tone sounds.

pituitary gland (hypophysis) An endocrine gland attached to the lower part of the brain; often referred to as the master gland.

placenta A special structure which transports nutrients, waste materials, and oxygen between the mother and the fetus.

plaque An almost invisible, sticky film formed by bacteria colonies on teeth.

plasma Clear, yellowish liquid portion of the blood.

platelet A small, colorless body in the blood that lacks hemoglobin and a nucleus and is involved in blood clot formation.

pollutants Potentially harmful substances.

pollution The introduction of pollutants into the environment.

positive self-concept A self-concept in which a person accepts himself and feels at ease with others.

predisposition A tendency or inclination toward a particular trait.

prejudice The formation of an opinion before knowing all the facts; literally, prejudging.

prescribe To recommend a treatment or medicine as a remedy.

prescription drugs Medication obtained with the written permission of a doctor.

presumption Bold arrogance; to take for granted or to take undue advantage.

primary air pollutants Air pollutants that result from natural or human actions.

processed foods Foods that are manufactured.

procrastination Putting off doing something; to postpone or delay until a later time.

protein A compound composed of amino acids chemically bonded in a chain.

psychoactive A drug that can produce changes in the activity of the central nervous system and affects a person's behavior, perceptions, and moods.

psychological dependence Drug dependence that does not result from a physical need for a drug; a drug habit.

psychoses Group of disorders in which individuals experience partial or complete loss of contact with reality.

psychosomatic illness Illness that is caused by one's state of mind; mental or emotional conflict which causes a physical illness or disorder.

puberty A stage of physical development and maturation that occurs during adolescence.

puncture A penetrating wound that causes a hole in the body tissue.

R

radon A colorless, odorless, tasteless, radioactive gas that results from the disintegration of radium.

reason To think logically; to come to a conclusion through a step by step process.

Recommended Dietary Allowances (RDA) Recommended daily intakes of nutrients for normal, healthy individuals in the United States.

recycle To process waste materials so they can be reused.

reflex An automatic, involuntary response to a stimulus.

rescue breathing Technique used to administer air to a victim who is not breathing.

resting heart rate The number of times the heart beats when one is at rest (the lowest heart rate).

risks Dangers; hazards.

rods Photoreceptors which can distinguish light from dark.

S

saliva Fluid produced by the salivary glands that breaks down starches and moistens food for easier transport through the digestive system.

Salmonella Genus of bacteria which produce toxins that can cause food poisoning.

sandwich generation Adults who have the responsibility of caring for their elderly parents as well as their own children.

sanitary landfill A method of disposing solid waste by depositing it in an area and daily covering it with soil.

saturated fats Fats in which all the fatty acids are filled with the maximum number of hydrogen atoms; fats which are usually solid at room temperature and found primarily in animal products.

sebaceous glands Oil glands.

sebum A mixture of fats, cholesterol, proteins, and salts secreted by the sebaceous glands.

secondary air pollutants Air pollutants that result from a chemical reaction between components found in air and various primary pollutants.

second-degree burns Burns that injure the top layer and second layer of skin (epidermis and dermis); scars may result.

second opinion To seek the assent of another physician's diagnosis and prescription for treatment.

sedatives Depressant drugs which slow the body's systems (heart, brain, nervous system).

sediments Earthy materials suspended in or deposited in water.

self-concept What one thinks about himself; the result of perceptions of oneself and how one thinks others perceive him.

self-discipline Training and controlling one's conduct.

sewage Water that is polluted with waste products from bathrooms and kitchens.

sexually transmitted diseases (STDs) Diseases which are transmitted through sexual contact; venereal diseases.

shock A potentially life-threatening condition caused by the collapse and failure of the cardiovascular system; slowing of blood circulation in the body which can lead to death.

sibling rivalry Competition and fighting between brothers and sisters.

siblings Brothers and sisters; offspring of the same parent(s).

side effects A different, unknown, or undesirable reaction to a drug or medicine.

sidestream smoke Smoke that comes directly from the end of a lighted cigarette.

small intestine Organ in the digestive system where most of the digestion and absorption of food occurs.

smokeless tobacco Tobacco products that are not smoked, such as snuff and chewing tobacco.

social skills Characteristics that enable a person to interact with others more easily.

solid waste The solid portion of waste products.

specificity Training concept that to develop a component of fitness, one must work on that particular component.

sphygmomanometer Equipment that measures blood pressure.

spinal cord The nervous tissue that conducts messages between the brain and the peripheral body parts.

splint Any device or bandage used to keep an area from moving.

spontaneous abortion The natural death of an embryo; miscarriage.

sprain A joint that is pulled to the point that surrounding tendons and ligaments are stretched or torn.

standards Levels of attainment or degree of requirement; limits of acceptability.

stereoscopic vision The ability of using binocular vision to perceive depth as well as length and width; to see three-dimensional images.

stereotyping Thinking of all members of a group as being the same.

sterility The inability to reproduce.

stewardship Management of another's property.

stillbirth The death of a fetus or child at birth.

stimulants A category of drugs which speed up the action of the central nervous system.

stimuli Something that causes a response in an organism.

strain The twisting or pulling of a muscle.

stress The body's reaction to any demand placed on it.

stressors Things that cause stress; pressures of living.

stroke An interruption of blood flow to the brain which causes brain damage.

suicide The intentional killing of oneself; voluntarily taking one's life.

sun protection factor (SPF) The rated ability of a sunscreen to protect from the rays of the sun.

sunscreen A substance which protects from the effects of the sun.

symptom Any change in appearance, feeling, or function from normal which may indicate the presence of a disorder or disease; evidence or a sign of a condition.

systole Pressure in the arteries when the ventricles of the heart contract.

T

tact Responsiveness to people's feelings in word and deed; diplomatic, kind, compassionate, or considerate behavior.

tar Particles other than nicotine and moisture that are present in cigarette smoke.

target heart rate The number of times per minute that the heart must beat in order to produce improved fitness.

temple A place dedicated to worship a deity; a place where God chooses to dwell.

testes Male reproductive organs which produce sperm and secrete hormones.

thermal inversion Situation in which cool air and pollutants are trapped beneath a warm layer of air.

thermal pollution The release of heated water into the environment.

third-degree burns Burns which destroy all the layers of skin, nerve endings, and blood vessels.

thrombus A blood clot formed in the heart or artery which blocks blood flow.

thyroid gland An endocrine gland located in front of the trachea that affects growth and metabolism in the body.

tissues Groups of similar cells that work together to perform a specific function.

tolerance The physical resistance of the body to drugs, resulting in the need to take more of the drug to obtain the same effect.

trace minerals Minerals needed by the body in relatively small amounts; iron, iodine, zinc, chromium, selenium, fluoride, molybdenum, copper, and manganese.

trachea A tube extending from the larynx to the bronchi.

tumor A tissue mass formed from the multiplication of abnormal cells.

U

undernutrition A lack of essential nutrients due to insufficient food intake.

unsaturated fats Fats in which all the fatty acids are not filled with the maximum number of hydrogen atoms (includes monounsaturated fats with only one double bond and polyunsaturated fats with two or more double bonds between carbons); fats in liquid form from plants.

urinary bladder An organ designed as a reservoir for urine.

uterus An organ in the female in which the fetus develops; the womb.

V

vaccination The process of introducing weakened or dead organisms into the body to cause antibody production in order to produce immunity.

values Things of importance and merit, or considered worthwhile; principles.

vectors Animals which transport pathogens from one host to another.

vegetarian A person who omits meat, poultry, fish, or other animal-derived foods from his diet.

veins Blood vessels that carry blood toward the heart.

viruses A pathogen that is composed of a nucleic acid wrapped in a protein sheath which can multiply only inside a living cell.

vitamins Essential organic nutrients required by the body in small amounts.

vitamin supplements Non-food preparations (pill, powder, or liquid forms) which contain vitamins.

vitreous humor A clear, jellylike substance which fills the eyeball.

vocation Work done to earn a living; a career or profession.

volume The intensity of sound waves causing sounds to be quiet or loud.

voluntary muscles Muscles under conscious control; muscles controlled by thinking.

W

water-soluble vitamins Hydrophilic (water-loving) vitamins that can be carried by water in the blood to various cells in the body; B vitamins and vitamin C are water-soluble.

withdrawal Illness and a variety of symptoms resulting from ceasing the use of an addictive drug.

wound A break in the skin or mucous membrane.

Z

zygote A fertilized cell that under normal conditions can survive and mature.

Index

Diastole 260

Diet (balanced) 95, 112, 114, 122, 266, 272, 276, 278, 283

Dietary guidelines 127-29

Dieting 9, 101, 125-27, 197

Dietitian 132

Digestion 50, 98, 152, 287

Digestive system 26-29, 113, 128

Diphtheria 247, 250-51, 323

Disaccharide 101

Discernment 43, 54, 69, 379, 395

Discipline 5, 43, 52, 72

Disease 84, 99, 106, 112, 239-67, 297

defined 245

infectious 245-56

noninfectious 245, 257-66

transmission of 248-49, 322, 326

Dislocation 221-22

Disorders 54, 126

Diuretic 99

Divorce 48

Doctors 155, 240-42, 254, 276. See also specific titles

Drinking. See Alcohol

Driving 38, 170, 184-91, 196, 345-46

Drowning 193, 227, 346, 350, 352

Drownproofing 194

Drugs 38, 48, 58-59, 82, 99, 116, 174, 191, 202, 332, 333-67, 384

abuse 336-40, 366

misuse 335-36

Duration 136, 144, 153

Dust 26, 310-11

Dysentery

amoebic 247, 249, 323

bacillary 249

Ear 253, 298-302

care 300-301

parts of 298-99

problems 301-2, 362

Eardrum. See Tympanic membrane

Earth 43, 308

Earthquakes 198-99

Eating 38, 48, 59, 388

Ectomorph 148

Elderly 8, 88, 388-91

Electrical safety 181-83, 195-96, 199

Electrolytes 116

Elephantiasis 249

Embolus 258

Embryo 375, 377

Emergency 88, 166, 196, 199, 205-9, 235

Emergency medical services (EMS) 206-8, 210, 218, 221, 227, 234

Emergency medical technicians (EMT) 202

Emotional health 5, 38, 47, 50, 54, 60, 65

Emotions 38-39, 49, 51, 61, 379-80

Emphysema 361, 365

Enamel 286-87

Encephalitis 249, 301

Endocrine glands (ductless) 32-33

Endocrine system 32-33

Endocrinologist 8

Endomorph 148

Endosperm 102

Energy 4, 61, 104, 108, 110, 128, 136

Engaged (engagement) 48, 50

Environment 7, 66, 132, 257, 307-30

Environmental Protection Agency (EPA) 312, 315, 326

Enzymes 104, 115

Epidemic 240

Epidermis 273-74

Epiglottis 27

Epilepsy 206, 226-27

Epinephrine 33, 50

Epithelial tissue 16

Erythrocytes 23

Esophagus 27

Etiquette 73-75

Eustachian tube 298-99

Euthanasia 393

Evacuation 170

Evaluate 5, 43-46, 61, 164

Excretory system 29-30

Exercise 7, 9, 11, 21-22, 52, 58, 100, 109, 116, 126, 133-56, 221, 252, 261, 265-66, 272, 278, 388

Exhaustion. See Heat exhaustion

External oblique 20

Photograph Credits

The following agencies and individuals have furnished materials to meet the photographic needs of this textbook. We wish to express our gratitude to them for their important contribution.

Advanced Water Systems
Allied Pix
Suzanne R. Altizer
American Cancer Society
Armed Forces Institute of Pathology
Susan Biddle, The White House
Bob Jones University Collection of Religious Art
Bureau of Reclamation
Carolina Biological Supply
Center for Disease Control (CDC)
Circus World Museum
George R. Collins
Tom Coss
Department of Defense
Department of Energy
Eastman Chemicals Division
Environmental Protection Agency
Exxon Corporation
General Motors
Paul Gillette
The Greenville News
Steve Hicklin

Hubbard Scientific Company
Iowa State University
Brian Johnson
Ellyson Kalagayan
Library of Congress
Chuck Luttrell
Ben Mathes
National Aeronautics and Space Administration (NASA)
National Cancer Institute (NCI)
National Geophysical Data Center (NGDC)
National Heart, Lung, and Blood Institute (NHLBI)
National Institute on Aging (NIA)
National Institute of Health (NIH)
National Library of Medicine (NLM)
National Oceanic and Atmospheric Administration (NOAA)
Ginny Nutz
Parke-Davis
City of Philadelphia, Department of Records
St. Louis Science Center

Michael Slattery
The Wallace Smith Family
South Carolina Lung Association
Chimene Speer
Kimberly Stegall
STEM Labs
Sandra Stock
Anna Turner
United States Department of Agriculture
United States Department of the Army
United States Department of the Navy
United States Geological Survey (USGS)
University of Utah
Unusual Films
Westfälisches Amt für Denkmalpflege
World Bank
Gail Yost
William Yost
Doug Young

Cover

Unusual Films (all except clouds); George R. Collins (clouds)

Title Pages

Unusual Films (all) i-iii

Introduction

Unusual Films vii

Unit 1 Opener

Unusual Films xiv-1

Chapter 1

Unusual Films 3, 4, 11,14; Suzanne R. Altizer 8, 12; St. Louis Science Center 10

Chapter 2

STEM Labs 15; Armed Forces Institute of Pathology 16 (l); Tom Coss 16 (connective, epithelial), 28; Suzanne R. Altizer 16 (muscular), 20 (cardiac); Unusual Films 16 (nervous), 20 (striated), 26; Carolina Biological 20 (smooth); NIH 23 (t), 36; NLM 23 (b); STEM Labs 24, 25; University of Utah 29; George R. Collins 30; Circus World Museum 32

Chapter 3

Unusual Films 37, 42 (l), 49 (tm, tr, ml, mr, bl), 53, 54, 56, 60, 64; Bob Jones University Collection of Religious Art 40, 42 (r); Department of Defense 47 (both); Ben Mathes 49 (tl); Ellyson Kalagayan 49 (br); Suzanne R. Altizer 49 (b); NLM 59 (both); Courtesy of Chuck Luttrell 61

Chapter 4

Unusual Films 65, 66 (both), 68, 70, 72 (both), 73 (l), 76, 77, 78 (l), 79, 80, 83 (both), 86 (both), 90 (both); Susan Biddle, The White House 67; Library of Congress 73 (r), 84; William Yost 78 (r); Kimberly Stegall 81; Courtesy of Doug Young 87

Chapter 5

Unusual Films 91, 96, 99, 108, 123 (both), 126, 128 (both), 132 (both); U.S. Navy 92; William Yost 104; Suzanne R. Altizer 105, 114; CDC 106; Eastman Chemicals Division 112

Chapter 6

Unusual Films 133, 134, 135, 136, 137, 141 (l), 143, 145, 146, 147, 148 (both), 149, 151, 152, 159; NIH/NIA 138; Kimberly Stegall 141 (r); Eastman Chemicals Division 142; George R. Collins 154; Ginny Nutz 155

Unit 2 Opener

Unusual Films 160-161

Chapter 7

George R. Collins 163, 170, 197 (t), 202; Bob Jones University Collection of Religious Art 164; U.S. Army 165 (l); Sandra Stock 165; Unusual Films 166, 173, 177, 185, 186, 191, 192; Eastman Chemicals Division 167; Hubbard Scientific Company 180 (l); CDC 180 (r); NOAA 182, 195 (t); Ginny Nutz 187; *The Greenville News* 188, 189; General Motors 190; Suzanne R. Altizer 193; Bob Jones University Press Photo Collection 195 (b); Bureau of Reclamation 196; Joe Golden, NOAA 197 (b); Library of Congress 198 (t); USGS 198 (m, b, background)

Chapter 8

George R. Collins 203, 205; Unusual Films 204, 210, 214 (both), 215, 217 (both), 218 (both), 220, 223, 224, 232; NCI 225; NIH 228, 238; CDC 231, 234

Chapter 9

NIH/NHLBI 239; Iowa State University/University Archives 240; NIH/NIA 241; NLM 242; CDC 246 (l), 247 (polio, ringworm, tapeworm), 248, 249, 256; STEM Labs 246 (r), 247 (rickettsia, cocci); Tom Coss 247 (plasmodia); City of Philadelphia, Department of Records 249; NIH 250 (l), 258 (l), 259, 270; Parke-Davis 250 (r); Unusual Films 252, 253 (both), 254, 260, 261, 265 (both); Gail Yost 257; Advanced Water Systems 258 (r); NCI 262, 263 (both), 264

Chapter 10

Unusual Films 271, 272 (t), 279, 280 (all), 284, 285, 288 (l, b) 289 (all), 292, 298, 300, 301 (both), 306; Courtesy of Brian Johnson 272 (b–all); Suzanne R. Altizer 274; NCI 275 (both), 288 (r); George R. Collins 277; STEM Labs 281; NLM 296 (inset), 302; Library of Congress 297

Chapter 11

George R. Collins 307, 312 (t), 318; Suzanne R. Altizer 308, 310 (t), 315 (b), 326, 327 (t); Courtesy of Paul Gillette 309; U.S. Department of Agriculture 310 (b), 323, 327 (b), 332; NIH 311; NOAA/NGDC 312 (b); Allied Pix 313; NASA 315 (t); Eastman Chemicals Division 316 (b); Exxon Corporation 316 (t); World Bank 321; Westfälisches Amt für Denkmalpflege 322 (both); Department of Energy 325; Environmental Protection Agency 328

Chapter 12

Unusual Films 333, 336 (both), 340, 341, 343, 344, 355, 364 (r), 366, 370; Kimberly Stegall 339, 363, 364 (l); Steve Hicklin 342; George R. Collins 347, 348; Brian Johnson 349 (t); Suzanne R. Altizer 349 (b); S.C. Lung Association 360 (l, m); Armed Forces Institute of Pathology 360 (r); American Cancer Society 361 (both); Michael Slattery 365

Chapter 13

Unusual Films 371, 372, 374 (t), 379, 380, 381 (both), 382, 383, 384, 385, 386, 387 (l), 388, 390, 391, 394; Bob Jones University Collection of Religious Art 373; NIH 374 (b); Armed Forces Institute of Pathology 375; Kimberly Stegall 376, 392; Chimene Speer 378 (t); Anna Turner 378 (b); William Yost 387 (r); Brian Johnson 389; NHLBI 393

Pronunciation Key

The pronunciations given in this text are designed to be self-evident and should give the average reader an acceptable pronunciation of the word as he reads it from the page. For accurate pronunciations, consult a good dictionary. This sample pronunciation key may help those who have difficulty with the symbols used.

Stressed syllables appear in large capital letters. Syllables with secondary stress and one-syllable words appear in small capital letters. Unstressed syllables are in lowercase letters. Most consonants and combinations of consonants (ng, sh) make the sounds normally associated with them.

Some Symbol Key Words and Examples

a	cat KAT, laugh LAF	ih	pity PIH tee
a-e	cape KAPE, reign RANE	o	potion POH shun
ah	father FAH thur	o-e	groan GRONE
ar	car KAR	oh	own OHN
aw	all AWL, caught KAWT	oo	tune TOON
ay	neigh NAY, paint PAYNT	oy	toil TOYL
e	jet JET	th	thin THIN, nothing NUH thing
ee	fiend FEEND	th	then THEN
eh	rebel REH bul, care KEHR	u or uh	above uh BUV
eye	ivory EYE vuh ree	ur	person PUR suhn
i	women WIM un	wh	where WHEHR